StoneSoup

Annual 2019

Edited by Sarah Ainsworth (Blog),
Jane Levi (Annual) & Emma Wood (Print)
Cover design by Joe Ewart
Production by Sarah Ainsworth
Director: William Rubel

Published by Children's Art Foundation
--Stone Soup Inc.
126 Otis Street, Santa Cruz, CA 95060 USA

Stone Soup, founded in 1973, is a magazine
available as a print subscription, a single user
digital subscription, or as an institutional site
license. Visit www.Stonesoup.com for full details

Cover Art

"The Chase" by Avery Multer, 12, Chicago, IL.

Interior Art

Contents (facing page): Detail from "Contrast" by
Delaney Slote. 13, Missoula, MT. Published in
Stone Soup November 2019.

Preface (facing page): Detail from "Shadow in the
Sun" by Isha Narang, 13, Austin, TX. Published in
Stone Soup May 2019.

CHILDREN'S ART FOUNDATION

StoneSoup

Annual 2019

A Year of the Magazine
by and for
Creative Young People

Contents

Preface

This has been a great year for *Stone Soup*. We've explored themes of change, belonging, relationships, nature, and home; and new forms like concrete poetry and flash fiction. We've published paintings, iPhone photographs, collages, computer art, and sculpture, as well as music and video on our blog. We partnered with a podcast series to run a contest for stories that were eventually produced in audio format. We published an issue composed entirely of thoughtful reviews of classic books and poems. We ran our first annual book contest (and cannot wait to share the books with you in 2020—stay tuned!). By the time this is published, we will have just closed our first personal narrative contest, run with our partner, Society of Young Inklings. Finally, we have been working all year to create connections with refugee organizations worldwide, in order to collect art and writing from children who have been displaced. Our short-term goal is to create a special issue of this work, and in the long term, to become a resource and space for refugee children everywhere.

It is my second full year as editor, and I feel as if I really found my feet in the role this year. I am so proud of the work we have done as a team to run these contests and more importantly, produce the 11 extraordinary issues of the magazine in 2019. But I am even prouder of all of you who have been writing amazing stories and poems and creating incredible art and sending it to *Stone Soup*. Without you, we would have no magazine, no blog, no community. You are the reason we are all doing this: we want to foster and encourage your creativity—both by publishing the best work by your peers for you to read and by being a venue for you to submit your own work when you're ready. So: thank you. Thank you for your minds, your imaginations, your time, and your eyes. We are so grateful you have made a place for *Stone Soup* in your life.

StoneSoup

Issues

Stone Soup

JANUARY 2019

VOLUME 47/ ISSUE 1

StoneSoup

*The magazine supporting
creative kids around the world*

Editor:
Emma Wood

Director
William Rubel

Operations
Jane Levi

Education & Production
Sarah Ainsworth

Design
Joe Ewart

Stone Soup (ISSN 0094 579X) is published
online 11 times per year—monthly, with
a combined July/August summer issue.
Copyright © 2019 by the Children's
Art Foundation, a 501(c)(3) nonprofit
organization, located in Santa Cruz,
California. All rights reserved.

Thirty-five percent of our subscription
price is tax-deductible. Make a donation at
Stonesoup.com/donate, and support us by
choosing Children's Art Foundation as your
Amazon Smile charity.

POSTMASTER: Send address changes to
Stone Soup, 126 Otis Street, Santa Cruz, CA
95060. Periodicals postage paid at Santa
Cruz, California, and additional offices.

Stone Soup is available in different formats
to persons who have trouble seeing or
reading the print or online editions. To
request the Braille edition from the National
Library of Congress, call +1 800-424-8567.
To request access to the audio edition via
the National Federation of the Blind's NFB-
NEWSLINE®, call +1 866-504-7300 or
visit www.nfbnewsline.org.

Check us out on Social Media:

Editor's Note

In January, the days are already
getting longer but it doesn't feel that
way! This issue has some short short
fiction—the winners of our 2018
contest—to match the season's short
short days, as well as wintry, dark
landscapes in both art and poetry.
It also has three longer stories that
matched the seasonal mood in a
different way; their "darkness" is
more metaphorical, but each one still
leaves you with a feeling of hope and
the presentiment of longer, lighter
days ahead.

Here's to some fireside reading!

Emma Wood

Letters: Do you have something to say
about something you've read or seen in
Stone Soup? If you do, we'd love to hear from
you, and we might print your letter on our
Letters to the Editor page! Post a comment
on our website, or write to us at
editor@stonesoup.com.

Submissions: Our guidelines are on the
Submit page at Stonesoup.com, where you
will also find a link to our Submittable online
submissions portal.

Subscriptions: To subscribe to *Stone Soup*,
please press the Subscribe button on our
webpage, Stonesoup.com.

On the cover:
"Fox on a Snowy
Night"

**by Sloka Ganne, 9
Overland Park, KS**

StoneSoup
Contents

Silence/Ages

by Eleonore Lecue, 6
Asheville, NC

Silence shine

When the silence goes over the mountains
And when it goes down into the sea
We never know how far it's going to go
In the sea or in the trees
And the silence spreads so far away
That no one can say
When you look over and around
You'll see a rainbow that shines with silence
And you'll see everywhere this thing wherever you go
Then think about it in your mind
If you look at the sky in your silence
Why does the silence shine all over
'Cause silence is so beautiful and fun
And silence goes all over the world where you can see

Silence trees

Trees have silence in them
Trees spread the silence and the wind all over
In perfect silence
Of the leaves in the trees
You know why
Well, you'll see
How cool is this world with these trees
These trees bring everything to you
These trees shed you from the sun
If it's so sunny
That's right
Do you want to see more with me?

Shining rainbow

Rainbows spread across the world
Even with a bit of silence
And you know that already
'Cause silence is everywhere
'Cause everybody sings songs of silence

You already know that
Yes, that's true
Would you like to come with me
To see a bit more?
You would?
Then just come with me to see more
And more and more and more

The leaves and the trees

When the leaves go in the trees
They make a cradle
They make a sound like a lullaby
They make the cool wind
And the air for us to breathe
And they make you sing a song
That's what everybody says
And so that's true
While they whisper in the breeze
And while they sing songs
That's the truth
Oh yes, you say

The ages

While you grow and grow and grow
While you continue growing forever
But one day you'll die
Yes, that's true
All of that is true
Yes, yes, yes
Okay, okay
Let's continue
This fabulous day
Let's continue traveling past this song
Quietly
Like silence
You know that already
Now that is true
Oh yes, oh yes
Yes, yes, yes
Okay, okay
That's the song
That we are done with today

Tick Tock, *colored pencil*

by Marco Lu, 12
Champaign, IL

The Pendulum

1st Place in the Short Short Fiction Contest

by Sabrina Guo, 12
Oyster Bay, NY

Prompted by her cat, a writer meditates on time

Most nights, my cat stares at the grandfather clock in the living room. She is a grey tabby with splotches of black and white. Her eyes are golden and edged in greenish blue, like a miniature painting of the sun over a forest, or a mood ring, because you never know when the colors will change.

When she is calm, you see more of the gold, flickering. But when she is scared, her pupils are large and black, and you notice more of the green, which is the way she looks before the clock at night—her back arched, her fur raised like small tufts of grass. She stares at the oval shape of the clock as if it is the moon revolving around the earth and the earth around the sun. When the clock sounds on the hour, her ears twitch, but she doesn't move. She simply resets her eyes, refastening them to the pendulum's sway.

Unlike my cat, I think this time might have been better spent outside in the fresh air like my mother always wants me to do. But for my cat, no second is wasted; she merely sees and does: when she is hungry, she eats, when she is tired, she sleeps, and when she is frisky, she scratches the furniture, no matter how much we scold her.

When she is happy, she purrs, or she brushes her side against my leg, nudging her head and nose into my wrist when I reach down to pet her as if she is pleading, but for what I am never sure: more food, a toy, my lap? I never know exactly what she wants except that when I am with her, I am warm and calm, certain there is still enough time for everything.

The Greater Good

by Valentine Wulf, 12
Seattle, WA

Miss Plum's company starts as a tiny, innocent store, but soon grows into a massive, destructive corporation

Lizard Corporation started as a tiny, innocent store in Miss Angelica Plum's basement when she was only 18 years old.

"Want an invention of your very own? A novelty item to show off to your friends? Come on in!" she shouted, in her loud voice with an accent nobody could identify. Those were the first words she mentioned about her company, back when she was young and innocent and didn't know the horrible things she would go on to do. She stood outside, twirling a bright, colorful sign advertising her products. With her dark hair in a ponytail tied off with a pink ribbon, too much lipstick, and a skirt so short it would earn her a very long lecture from an old lady, she didn't look like someone who could turn the world into a wasteland in just seven years. Not at all. This was back when the world was sunny and pure. When the world was full of light and hope. When the sun shone bright in the sky and cast black shadows across the ground. When she was just a kid with an impossible dream.

"This is never going to happen," "It's impossible," "You're just a kid," people said, sometimes with a condescending laugh or a wink. But she didn't listen. Her first customer was an old man by the name of Frederick Lizardworth. He bought a device she had nicknamed "voiceover." It was practical, it was useful, it was amusing. He was impressed with her. He told her that when you have a dream, you don't let anyone stand in your way. Mr. Lizardworth told everyone he knew about the remarkable young lady over on the corner of Starling and 34th, and soon, people were coming in great crowds to get a genuine hoverboard or the 100 percent authentic "glove phone." She made enough money in just one week to open up a real store in an old garage. People came from miles and miles to see her and buy her products. She hired workers, got clients, and sponsored sports teams. She was a local celebrity. Until one day, she wasn't just local anymore.

Word went overseas, and gossip spread like wildfire. Pretty soon, people were flocking in from other countries just to see her, and soon she opened her first factory and named it "Lizard Corporation," in honor of Mr. Frederick Lizardworth, the man who got her started. Her dream of a world-wide company was now a reality, and bright-red Lizard Corporation logos began appearing everywhere, plastered across billboards, airplanes, and buses.

After a while, other people sponsored Lizard Corporation and made new stores all over the world, and Miss Plum made more and more money. The factories began spewing smoke into the air, and though some people complained, Miss Plum just said it was "for the greater good."

The demand for Lizard products grew so high that they began making factory workers go faster and faster, and paid them less and less, the lowest wages they could get away with. There were casualties, there was pollution. In only a few weeks, the complaints began. They came in the mail, pouring out of mailboxes like flocks of birds. In white envelopes with colorful stamps and *Angelica Plum, 9924 Lobster Way, Yellowseed, NX, lot 511* scrawled across all of them in a myriad of different handwritings. They looked like pretty white snow as they were dumped into the recycling bin. And the ones that came in person, from the workers themselves, were not treated with any more thought. When an enraged worker, overworked and underpaid, came up to her and demanded a change, Miss Plum just laughed and told them, "It's for the greater good!" before tossing them a buck or so, then walking away to go count her money.

That's when billboards started popping up, with the brand-new Lizard Corp slogan: "For the greater good"

and Miss Plum's face showed up in magazines, in newspapers, on TV with the words next to it, reassuring people.

The factories went up everywhere, lining every cityscape in the world. The sky turned black, and the oceans turned brown. Sometimes people worried about it. Sometimes they said it was dangerous. Sometimes they questioned it. But then they saw Miss Plum's face up on a billboard, or in a news report, with her accent, her warm smile, and her eyes sparkling and full of dreams, they reminded themselves that it was for the greater good. After all, nobody that sweet and innocent could cause something so horrible. So people ignored it. After all, she was just a kid. A kid with a dream that maybe wasn't so impossible anymore.

And now, only seven years later, Miss Plum has the world under her illusion. She's smart. She's rich. She's powerful. She's admired. People want to meet her. People want to *be* her.

People will do anything to defend Lizard Corporation, because without Lizard Corporation,we wouldn't have glovephones or hoverboards or all these magnificent things. We like to say we're just buying these things to support Miss Plum, and sometimes it really seems like we've even convinced *ourselves* of that.

In fact, every month Lizard Corporation comes out with a new and improved version of an old product and people just *have* to buy it. Because buying things is fun. Thrilling. *Trendy.*

Every time they launch a shiny new product, the blue plastic trash cans lining every alley in the city are piled high with the old, "inferior" products as the looming Lizard Corporation factories start up for the day, spewing their smoke into the already black sky. Cardboard boxes roll out with the new device, and they're loaded into trucks and distributed all over the world.

Huge mobs of screaming people pour through the gleaming glass doors into the immaculate Lizard Corporation shops, and the telephones in each shop ring furiously with excited consumers on the other side, ordering the new trend. Customers scream, employees scream, and telephones scream, till the whole city echoes with the cacophonous din.

Sometimes people complain of the noise. Of the screaming. But then Miss Plum comes on the news and reminds us of the Lizard Corporation slogan. Reminds us that what we're doing is okay. Reminds us that a few people suffering is *for the greater good.*

The Lizard Corporation trucks pollute the streets with their signature red logo, standing out against the gray city. Even at night they run, under the bright nighttime sky, stained with the light of a thousand glowing cities. The trucks swarm through the streets all day every day, rushing to deliver to greedy and impatient customers.

Sometimes the trucks crash because they're going so fast. Sometimes workers die. Sometimes innocent people die. Either way, nobody tells them to slow down. They can't. We buy so much. We buy so fast.

Because we don't really want the products after all; it's the buying them that's so thrilling. So we do. We buy and we buy and we buy as the sky

gets smokier and the air gets colder and the world gets greedier as Miss Plum and Lizard Corporation continue their sugar-coated reign of terror. And nobody even so much as tries to stop her. Because she's doing all this *for the greater good.*

In the Mirror

by Anna Calegari, 12
Chicago, IL

It's not surprising
I look like a monochrome:
The only colors are pink laces on my shoes
And purple bags beneath my eyes.

Like an old-fashioned photograph—
"Subject stares beyond the camera.
Subject seems so sad."
The people in the pictures never smile.

Their faces stay stony and unreadable
Even though they see everything,
Forever watching, like me.

Smiling is hard when it looks so wrong.
My best face is my frown.
So I wear my frown as I walk away
And the monochrome behind the mirror disappears.

The Lonely Tree, *iPad*

by Tessa Papastergiou, 11
Ontario, Canada

The Sycamore Tree

2nd Place in the Short Short Fiction Contest

by Mira Johnson, 8
New Braunfels, TX

A sycamore tree protects a bunny from a baying dog

Once upon a time, there lived a bright and cheerful sycamore tree named Triffle. Triffle was bewildered by the rapid riffles at the edge of the clear blue river. She was very astonished at how rapidly the river was moving.

She spotted a baying dog and a squalling bunny running away, trying to resist from getting caught. With lots of sympathy, Triffle waved her ancient branches to try and coax the frightened bunny in a safe domain under her broad roots. Triffle noticed a wound on the bunny and used her special soap as a liniment to heal the injury.

The eager dog was full-fledged on catching his prey but he'll have to hunt another day.

The Power of Nature

by Adam Smith, 10
London, UK

A boy finds happiness in a magical spot in the forest

The water gushed from the waterfall that I could just about see and it formed a sapphire river feeding life itself. Dark green shrubs poked their beautiful heads out of the ground pleading with the smiling sun to grow and live. Just by looking at this beautiful jewel, a feeling of pure happiness washed over me. Birds sang an orchestral song and they fluttered over me while the wind blew a gentle gust of wind as I slept, not to wake for eons to come. The bridge's planks were strong and sturdy like bodybuilders. Small fish gently swam and talked in an indecipherable language. Reeds waved to the wind, sang from sleep, and smiled a green leafy smile. The flowers all radiated beauty and life. Ants skittered to and from their anthill, all serving their queen, while a pretty butterfly alighted on my finger. All evil fled into the dark pits of hell to meet the devil while God in his heavenly throne granted the hope, wishes, and prayers of all. This was a nearly sacred idyll, undisturbed by tourists and their noisy cameras. Smoke floated up from the chimneys of the nearby village and the forest replenished the air while creatures squeaked as they ran in and out of trees. Cows mooed and talked and played with their calves. Flicks of migrating swallows showed their skill on the wing and their tails directed them home. I trotted home only to in the night dream about going to that ball of magic again.

The Deadly Storm

by Madesyn Fogg, 10
Thorndale, PA

Elizabeth and her mother struggle to survive in the years after Elizabeth's father dies—until a terrible storm changes everything...

"It's so dark tonight," said Elizabeth to her mother. Elizabeth is an only child. She's 12 years old. Her dad died from a heart attack when she was only four years old. They were on the way to the hospital because her dad was having severe chest pains. Two years before he died, the doctors told him he needed a pacemaker, but he refused. But, to this day, they still didn't know why he hadn't wanted a pacemaker.

When her dad died, they had to move from their massive house in Thorndale to a little broken-down house in New Jersey. Their new house was on a tilted, cracked cliff. They lost all their money when the father died. He was a scientist; he created things like computers, phones, and more. He got paid about a million dollars a month. He created something new almost every day. Also, when Elizabeth's dad died, her mom didn't remember their bank account number, and that was the only way to get into your bank account in 1866. Elizabeth and her mom, Sally, barely had any money.

Since the night her dad died, eight years ago, Elizabeth didn't talk to her mom at all. They were both so de-

pressed. It just made Sally even more depressed when her own daughter didn't talk to her. Elizabeth had just started talking to her mom a few days ago. The first words Elizabeth said to her mom were "Why do the good people have to die?" Now, Elizabeth was mad about how she treated her mom those past years. To make up for all of those years, she now cares about her, is respectful, and is a big help.

That night, in 1874, Elizabeth went outside to get the snow and ice from the gigantic river they live near. When she brings it home, they put it on the counter until it turns into water. They're poor, so they need some water to drink. She had her one foot in the rim of the river, which was freezing water. Then, out of nowhere, she slipped on the rock that her foot was on. She fell into the water. She could barely see the water around her, but she did see that it was dark—a deadly bloody red. The tide was pulling her under. She couldn't swim. Elizabeth felt herself getting weaker and weaker. Then, she couldn't move; she was sinking.

Elizabeth's mom was sitting on a

The Cuts of the Blade, *Nikon D3400*

by Delaney Slote, 12
Missoula, MT

wooden chair, drinking river water and looking at a picture next to the chair. The picture was of Elizabeth and her nine years before. After about 30 minutes, Elizabeth's mom started to get worried. She put on her faded coat and gloves and stepped her foot outside the door.

There were big streaks of lightning and loud roars of thunder. It was sunny out, but sleeting. When she was about to go down the stairs, she saw Elizabeth in the river, and the rest of her body was going under. There was blood surrounding her. Elizabeth's mom started screaming. Then the house started shaking rapidly, and there was blood surrounding the river now. Elizabeth's mom ran over to the river and jumped in. She twisted her ankle, but as bad as it hurt her, her daughter was still more important to her. She dragged Elizabeth out.

After she dragged Elizabeth out, she realized that her head had a horrible, bloody gash in it. Elizabeth's mom was determined to get her inside. Elizabeth just got inside and was on the kitchen floor when Sally heard the thunder and got struck by lightning. Then, she fell and passed out.

It started to hail, snow, rain, thunder, sleet, lightning, and was windy all at once. Do you know what happens when they all come at once? A hurricane! All of the sudden the house started to rumble, the house started to shake when BOOM! The house went off the edge of the cliff, and BAM went into pieces. Elizabeth went off the edge first, then right after Elizabeth, went her mother.

The weather stopped, everything stopped. After about 30 seconds, it was pretty and sunny. A horse-and-buggy was driving by the house when he saw the last bit of the house go off the edge. The guy, whose name was Matthew, ran out of his horse-and-buggy over to the edge, looked down, and right away saw two bodies lying on the ground. Right away, he got in the horse-and-buggy and went off to get help. But right after the horses started to run, something flew through the cloth on the buggy. What was it? It was a huge piece of sleet. Luckily it didn't hit him, but it was so large and sharp, it went through his seat.

He started driving faster and faster. The weather got worse and worse. Now there was sleet, snow, rain, hail, every different kind of weather. Right after he got off their property, it was sunny out. Matthew looked behind him at the property and heard thunder and saw lightning. That's when it came. The tornado! He smacked the reins on the horses as hard as he could, and they ran the fastest he has ever seen them run. He needed to get someone, and it needed to be quick.

He drove to the police station and talked to Officer Tom. Matthew said, "There's a giant storm about 16 miles west, and two bodies lying on the ground."

The police officer asked, "Where are their bodies?"

"Their house fell off a ginormous cliff, and so did they," Matthew replied.

Immediately, Tom asked Matthew if he could borrow his horse-and-buggy because the other policemen were using the other ones. There were other horses, but they don't go so fast any more. Matthew allowed Tom to borrow his horse-and-buggy. As Matthew was riding, Tom was asking him questions about the house, the bodies, and the weather. When they finally arrived he looked off the edge of the cliff, and there were the two bodies and the little broken down house in little pieces.

Then it happened again. The lightning, thunder, hail, rain, snow, and that caused a tornado. It started off little. They sprinted back to Matthew's horse-and-buggy. That wasn't it for Tom. He got back out of the buggy and said, "This is my job. Stay in the horse-and-buggy, and don't come to find me if I don't come back."

Tom got out of the horse-and-buggy and saw that the tornado had gotten bigger. Tom was determined to save the two girls at the bottom of the cliff. Tom climbed as carefully as he could, but as quick as he could down the cliff. It took him about 15 minutes to finally get down. Tom grabbed Elizabeth in one arm and her mom in the other, and he climbed up the cliff. It took him 20 minutes to climb back up because of how determined he was.

When he got up the cliff, the tornado was giant. He had to resist it, though. It took Tom so long to get back, but he did get back. Tom did have scars on him, though. When he got the two girls back in the buggy, they rushed to the hospital. It took about a half hour to get to the hospital.

Right away, they came in with Elizabeth in Tom's arms and her mom in Matthew's arms. Immediately, the doctors got them to a room and asked Tom and Matthew many questions about what happened. They answered the questions the best they could. After that, they told Tom and Matthew to go into the waiting room. They did some type of surgery on both girls, but Tom and Matthew didn't understand what the surgeons were talking about, but apparently it helped them.

When their scars healed up a little bit, one of the doctors, named Chelcy, said that she knew Elizabeth's mom and that her husband was the person who invented all of the different medical supplies, but then had passed away. The first question she asked Chelcy was if she knew their bank account number. Chelcy thought and thought, but didn't remember it. But, she did remember one thing. She remembered that Elizabeth's dad trusted her with all his heart, and he let her take $2,000 out of the account because she saved him from his first heart attack. Chelcy knew three of the numbers but forgot the other two.

She went under a wooden chair and grabbed her purse. It was a mess. She dumped it out on a table and found a little scrap piece of paper. She looked at the numbers and gave her the paper. The numbers were 34679. Elizabeth's mom gave her a hug and thanked her so many times.

When they got to the bank, Eliz-

When they got to the chairs, they both started to cry. It wasn't a bad cry; it was tears of joy!

abeth's mom said that the numbers were 34679, and a girl named Linda told her that her total in the bank was $300,000,000! Elizabeth and her mom's jaws dropped!

Linda asked if there was a problem, but Linda didn't believe how much money that was herself. Elizabeth's mom said that there wasn't a problem; she just didn't know that she had that much money in her bank. Linda asked, "How much money would you like out of your bank?"

"Ten million dollars," she replied. Linda asked for a minute.

Elizabeth and her mom went to sit on a couple of wooden chairs lined up in the corner. When they got to the chairs, they both started to cry. It wasn't a bad cry; it was tears of joy! About 15 minutes later, Linda said in her crackly voice, "Your money's ready." They both ran up, Elizabeth's mom grabbed the money, thanked Linda, then left.

Elizabeth and her mom got a new, gorgeous, three-floor house. Also, they donated $2,000 to charity. They got new outfits, toys, and everything they wanted. Still, they had to be careful not to use their money on unnecessary things. Elizabeth and her mom kept trying, not to forget, but to keep their minds not always on her dad. Although he passed away, Elizabeth and her mom were thankful for every moment he had been with them.

Two years later, about 35 minutes after they went to bed, Elizabeth felt the house shake. She looked out of her window, and it all started over again...

A Dinner Party

3rd Place in the Short Short Fiction Contest

by Anyi Sharma, 10
Greenwich, CT

An old man, recently released from prison, decides to throw a party for his old friends

The old man tidied his home for his dinner party. Slowly, the guests trickled in, and a subtle murmur burbled across the room. He stepped across his woven carpet, antique and intricate like moss burnishing a forest floor.

The guests seemed uneasy, whispering amongst themselves around the oaken table. The old man pulled in his ragged coat, concealing its tattered holes.

"Are you adjusting well?" He turned around and saw an old classmate.

"To tell you the truth, they're taking away my house and car soon to cover attorney costs," he replied quietly. "I'm really glad you guys came out here."

"Must have been hard . . . 25 years locked up in p-prison . . ." His friend smiled nervously, glancing down at his cell phone.

"I mean—"

"Sorry, I have to run. Family emergency, you understand," his friend stuttered. They stared at each other for a brief moment before he vanished, the door creaking in his wake.

Suddenly, the old man realized that all the other guests were glancing at him. He padded around the room unsteadily. Somehow he felt their stares following him, cold and cautious, betraying the veneer of their smiles.

"Sorry to leave early, something last-minute came up," someone abruptly exclaimed.

"I need to babysit for a friend," his co-worker apologized.

"My wife has something she needs help with." The chairs scraped against the ground.

Confused, the old man gulped in the heady, wet-soil air as everyone began to vanish. The chandelier creaked with every slight breeze, bathing the dinner table in warm moonlight.

The chairs, rocks, gazed at him with hollow expressions. The walls of his house, towering trees, enveloped him, trapping him with their tall, spectral frames. The plants whispered, glanced, stared endlessly.

The hermit was alone in the forest. He had always been alone.

Silent Stalker, *iPhone 7*

by Elizabeth Hedge, 12
Alberta, Canada

Snow

by Eliza Wagner, 8
West Hartford, CT

drifting

falling

a small
voice calling

through the wind
through the
clouds

snowman
made
on the ground

a snowball
fight
begins

a cold ball
hits
me on the chin

Night

by Mae Gesser, 9
Brooklyn, NY

The stars stood gleaming
Like sequins
On a black cloth

The moon came to rest
On the surface
Of a pond

The grass swayed
From side to side
Like a rocking horse

The night was as quiet
As an empty page.

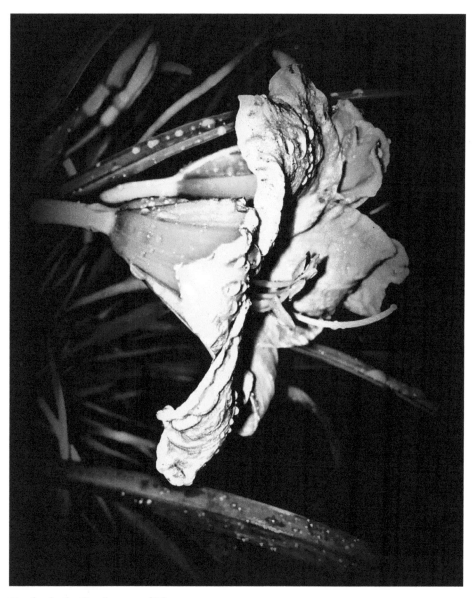

Optimistic Darkness, *iPhone 5*

by Daania Sharifi, 13
Gainesville, VA

The Hummingbird

4th Place in the Short Short Fiction Contest

by Clare McDermott, 12
Madison, WI

A hummingbird brings its light, joyful presence to the forest

As I walked along the trail, the wind rustled the deep-green leaves in the tall trees. I could sense everything in the forest that day; the soft whispers of the tall grass, the chipmunks that silently skittered across the trail, the lullaby of the creek as clear water trickled over smooth stones.

But there was something else. A light, joyful presence, a presence that made the whole forest stop to look. It made me stop and look too. I stood in place, still as a statue, looking for whatever creature created this magical atmosphere.

And then I saw it. Quick as a flash, a burst of color in the green leaves above. It zipped past me, and towards the small patch of flowers on the edge of the trail. Only then was I able to get a good look at it.

A hummingbird, each feather meticulously crafted by Mother Nature herself, shimmered in the dappled green-gold light of the forest. Miniscule bright eyes glinted mischievously as iridescent wings moved back and forth so fast that they were merely a blur. Its tiny body shimmered in the sunlight, capturing all the colors of the rainbow.

It perched gracefully on in a nearby bush, and that bush seemed to quiver with delight at this pint-sized miracle. The hummingbird chirped sweetly and fluffed itself out.

And just like that, the hummingbird spread its miniature wings and was gone as quickly as it had come.

Hide-And-Seek

by Eva Juette, 11
Singapore

*It's 1943 in Denmark, and Freja's best friend,
Madeline, a Jewish girl, is in danger*

For my Opa

"Faster, faster, faster!" Carlotta squealed, her eyes shining with excitement. Freja Larsen and Madeline Aaron, best friends since birth, laughed at the silliness of Freja's younger sister. Giggling and talking, they rode home on Farmer John's hay cart every day after school. "Three, two, one and . . . jump!" All three of them, Freja holding her little sister's hand, jumped off the hay cart as they reached their home. Running with the hay cart to give Lily the cow a little pat, they finally waved goodbye to the cart that moved into the distance, dust trailing behind it.

As they walked to the door, Carlotta blabbed on about what they were going to play once they got home. "We can play dolls!" she exclaimed.

"Lotta, no, nobody wants to play dolls."

"I do." Carlotta stuck out her tongue, held her nose in the air, and walked toward the house, her arms crossed stubbornly across her chest.

"Lotta, c'mon, can't we play anything else?"

Slowly, Carlotta turned on her heel and eyed Freja suspiciously.

"Like what?" she asked, squinting at her older sister.

"What about hide-and-seek?" Freja suggested. Carlotta's face fell then lit up.

"I know where I'm going to hide! In our closet upstairs! The latch right at the back of the closet opens up and a hundred people can fit in!"

"Lotta, you're not supposed to tell the seeker where you're going to hide. And anyway, it's barely big enough for two!"

"I bet you still can't find me. It's so . . . hidden!"

Freja's mother, Marie, was waiting for the girls at home and greeted them warmly as they came in. They walked straight into the kitchen, their mouths watering as the smell of freshly baked *wienerbrød* filled their noses.

"Oh girls, what have you done?" Marie said, trying to suppress a smile. "Not one day goes by without you getting yourselves dirty. Now, who's going to help me cook tonight?"

"And . . . done!" Freja had been helping Madeline get ready for Rosh Hashanah, the Jewish new year. This year, 1943, it was on the 29th of September.

Freja had helped prepare the apples, pouring honey into a pretty jar big enough to dip the apples in. Madeline's mother, Grace, had baked honey cake, which Carlotta was trying to nibble. Grace had also baked fresh, round challahs, and the girls couldn't wait to eat the sweet cinnamon treats. The girls also laid out the head of a fish and some pomegranate and many other goodies. Madeline looked stunning in a beautiful but modest dress, and so did Grace. Now everything was finally set. Grace had invited the Larsens to share the first, special evening of Rosh Hashanah with them, and the best friends were excited for the first time celebrating together.

Ring, Ring, Ring. The doorbell rang and everyone froze. Slowly, her heels clacking, Marie walked to the door and peeked through the keyhole, holding Carlotta by the hand. It was so silent you could hear a pin drop. Marie let out a sigh of relief and mouthed "Kasper." Freja's mother was in the *modstandsbevægelsen*, the Danish resistance, a group of people who fought secretly to protect the lives of Danish Jews. She opened the door a crack and then swiftly let the young man in.

"*God aften, Kasper*," she bade him good evening in Danish. Even though he was not who she had feared, Marie didn't look very pleased. Her face showed no concern, but her eyes were filled with worry.

Kasper talked quickly and secretly to Marie, not taking off his coat or hat or coming any farther than the hallway. He whispered something, and Marie's face turned pale and her lips dry. She bade him goodbye and moved quickly back into the living room.

"We cannot stay here. You must come with us to our home."

———————————————————

Marie drove everyone back to the Larsens' home—the car was the family's only piece of luxury—as it was faster than walking. She told Carlotta to stop fussing about wanting to hide in the closet and ordered the girls to go to bed straight away. Madeline and her mother squeezed into the secret back closet that was Lotta's favorite hiding spot. Freja and Carlotta went straight to bed, as it was late anyway. In their room, Lotta cuddled up to her sister and fell asleep soon, but despite the fact that Freja's eyes felt like lead, she could not bring herself to sleep.

There was a firm knock on the door about an hour later, and Freja still lay awake. She could hear her mother's footsteps move across the tiled kitchen floor, out into the furnished living room, down the hallway, and to the door. Muffled sounds of voices and then boots scraping against the burnished wood floorboards. Freja imagined what Carlotta would have thought about this. In her mind, she could hear Carlotta's young voice stubbornly refusing to let them in without taking off their shoes and throwing a tantrum when she saw how they were treating the beautiful house.

The footsteps came closer, and Carlotta started to fuss. Knowing it would be dangerous if Lotta were to wake, Freja held her close, and Lotta's breath slowed once more. Freja shut her eyes tight and turned the oppo site way of the door. The door opened loudly and light flooded into the room. Two uniformed officers, one stout, one lanky, closed the door and shone their torches on the bed.

"Please, my children are sleeping, don't wake them." Marie gripped the lanky soldier's wrist and moved the torch's glare away from the bed. Only now did Freja dare to open her eyes.

"We have nothing to hide. Now please—leave my children to sleep."

The soldiers started to back out but then suddenly walked towards the closet. The uniformed officers opened Lotta's beloved closet doors with a bang.

Freja's body tightened against her sister's as the tall Nazi felt around the closet. She could faintly see his fingers streaking the outline of the secret opening where the Jewish mother and her daughter were hiding. Freja's body tensed and her heart pounded. She thought: *It's funny: when you play hide-and-seek, the fun in it is being found, but in real life, you hide and pray that they don't find you.* If the officers found Freja's friend, they would be torn apart forever, but even Freja knew that that would not be the worst part. The lanky Nazi reached toward the dresses that covered the tiny wooden knob, and Freja felt that her heart was going to jump out of her chest. Closer and closer his hand moved, now touching the fine silk embroidery of Carlotta's favorite princess gown.

As quickly as his partner had opened it, the stout soldier slammed the closet doors shut, and a wave of relief came over Freja. She closed her eyes and heaved a silent sigh of relief.

The Nazi shone his torch on the bed once more and then led the way out. The taller one followed behind, still looking suspicious. Mama glanced at the bed and then shut the door, enclosing the room in darkness once more.

In the morning Freja woke up to find the room exposed to light. Sleepily, she walked into the living room to find Mama and Carlotta sitting at the dining table.

"They are in the basement and have eaten. They will stay with us for a couple of weeks," Mama explained, without having to be asked. Smiling bleakly, Freja asked her sister: "Do you want to play hide-and-seek?"

Honor Roll

Welcome to the *Stone Soup* Honor Roll. Every month we receive submissions from hundreds of kids from around the world. Unfortunately, we don't have space to publish all the great work we receive. We want to commend some of these talented writers and artists and encourage them to keep creating.

Visit the *Stone Soup* store at Stonesoupstore.com to buy:

- Magazines: Individual issues of *Stone Soup*, past and present.

- Books: Our collection of themed anthologies (Fantasy, Sport, Poetry and more), and the Stone Soup Annual (all the year's issues, plus a flavor of the year online, in one volume).

- Art prints—high quality prints from our collection of children's art

- Journals and sketchbooks for writing and drawing

...and more!

Don't forget to visit Stonesoup.com to browse our bonus materials. There you will find:

- 20 years of back issues—around 5,000 stories, poems, and reviews

- Blog posts from our Young Bloggers on subjects from sports to sewing—plus ecology, reading, and book reviews

- Video interviews with *Stone Soup* authors

- Music, spoken word, and performances

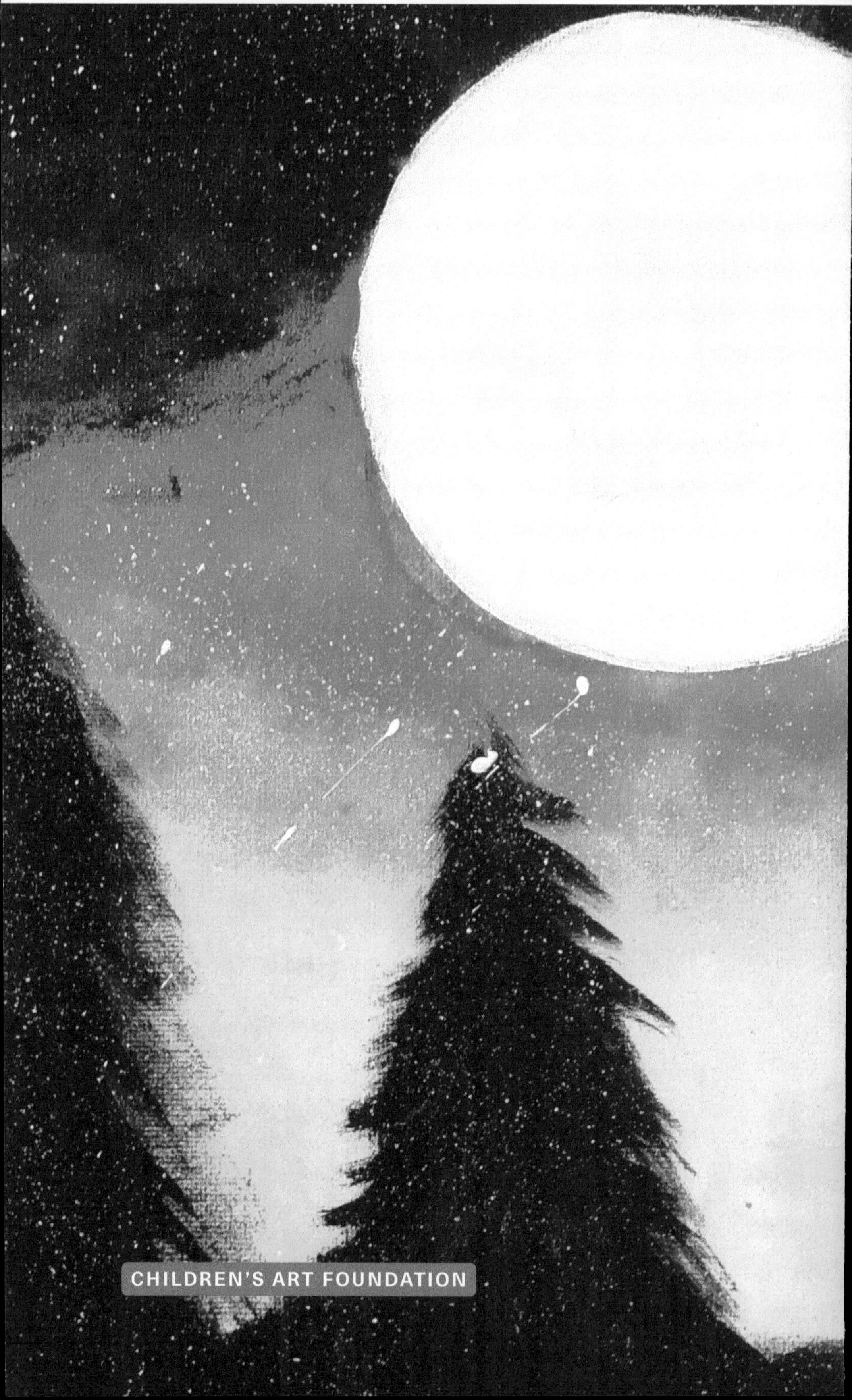
CHILDREN'S ART FOUNDATION

StoneSoup

FEBRUARY 2019

VOLUME 47 / ISSUE 2

StoneSoup

The literary magazine by and for kids up to age 14

Editor:
Emma Wood

Director
William Rubel

Operations
Jane Levi

Education & Production
Sarah Ainsworth

Design
Joe Ewart

Editor's Note

This issue is unusual: it is made up of a novella (a short novel) and a cycle of poems. When I came across the novella *Dancing in the Rain*, I immediately sat up. I loved the clarity and simplicity with which Harper Miller, the author, set up scenes, not only creating a picture in my mind but evoking a mood. As you read her book, you will notice that, though she is tracing a single central plot—the drought—Miller is not afraid to let her story meander a bit.

A cycle of poems is simply a group of poems on a single subject or in a single form. Vidhat Kartik's cycle is about the four seasons. I loved the playfulness and inventiveness of his rhyme and the way certain motifs (like the "hose") resurfaced throughout the pieces.

There is so much incredible artwork in this issue, as well—from the incredibly detailed "Four Seasons" drawing to the mysterious rock formations framed so beautifully in the photograph, "Canadian Beach."

Happy reading and looking!

Letters: Do you have something to say about something you've read or seen in *Stone Soup*? If you do, we'd love to hear from you, and we might print your letter on our Letters to the Editor page! Post a comment on our website, or write to us at editor@stonesoup.com.

Submissions: Our guidelines are on the Submit page at Stonesoup.com, where you will also find a link to our Submittable online submissions portal.

Subscriptions: To subscribe to *Stone Soup*, please press the Subscribe button on our webpage, Stonesoup.com.

On the cover:
'Umbrellas'

by Marlena Rohde, 12
San Francisco, CA

StoneSoup
Contents

DANCING IN THE RAIN (A NOVELLA)

by Harper Miller

When a drought comes to her hometown, Ayita is determined to help

Dear Reader,

Hi! My name is Harper Miller, and I want to be an author when I grow up. I live with my very old dog, Oscar, my Mom and Dad, and my little brother, Theo (with me in the picture above), who is three years younger than me. I started my book on May 11, 2017, when I was 10 and finished on November 27, 2017, and now I am 11. I worked a lot on this book, and I want to say thank you to my Mom and Dad, who helped make this possible. Also, thank you to my editor (and close friend), Mackenzie. You might wonder why I wrote about a girl going through a drought. Here is my answer. I wrote this book to show that a child can make a difference in the world, even when things might be looking pretty bad. Writing this book was one of the many highlights of my life so far. I hope you enjoy it as much as I did.

Sincerely,
Harper

Dancing in the Rain

by Harper Miller, 11
Northfield, MN

*This book is dedicated to
my little brother, Theo,
for encouraging me to try.*

Canadian Beach, *iPad*

by Tessa Papastergiou, 11
Kitchener, Ontario, Canada

CHAPTER 1
The Beginning

I let the curtains wrap me in their warm embrace. I was watching the rain. I mean, who wasn't? The time was around midnight, and I was shivering from the air conditioning that was cranked up all the way. It was late June, and I would turn 12 this summer. Next year, I would be going into the big sixth grade. First year of middle school.

All of a sudden I felt the urge I had been having these last few hot, rainy nights. Not bothering to pull on my raincoat or rain boots, I ran straight out of the curtains and burst out the front door. I ran out into the front yard. I let the cool rain melt down my body, and let the hot, misted air mix with it. I collapsed, and let all my worries, pain, and grief be washed away.

And then, the joy came. I leapt up and jumped for joy. I let myself forget the things that had been on my mind for the last couple of days. I danced, and danced, and danced until the sun began to rise just the slightest bit. Then I crept back inside, and back up the stairs. I stepped into my bedroom, and I stood there shivering, until my senses jolted back to me, and I crept back into my bed.

The next morning when I walked down the steps and into the kitchen, the first thing I heard was, "Ayita, were you dancing again!? I can tell because your hair and nightgown are soaked,

and you are covered in mud!"

"Papa, you know I like to dance. My name means *first to dance*," I replied in my best-little-girl-in-the-world voice.

My father sighed. "What am I going to do with you, Ayita?" he said softly. "Please go take a shower and wash your nightgown."

"Okay Papa," I said, equally softly. I turned around and headed back upstairs. An hour later, I was back downstairs. I walked back into the kitchen, and sat down at the table. A bowl of cold gray mush sat at my spot. A little note was slipped underneath it. It read: "I have decided to work in my study for the rest of the day, so please leave after breakfast and don't return until dinner time. Don't get into any trouble or you're grounded."

I sighed, picked up the bowl of gray mush, carried it over to the sink, and dumped it out. Next, I got down one of my mother's old cookbooks and began to flip through it. Just a few minutes later, I had decided on a good breakfast meal. Soon, I had a hot, steaming bowl of apple-cinnamon oatmeal.

Just 10 minutes later, I was walking down the sidewalk all the way on the other side of town. I was heading to what was (in my opinion) the best place ever. When I reached my little hideaway, I began to have some fun. The place I liked to hang out was a big clearing of grass that was set back from the road and hidden by a thick blanket of trees. There was even a swimming hole. But what I liked the most was the big, wire fence that surrounded the place. It was not made of barbed wire, so it was safe to climb up. It made me feel as though it was just my place. It made me feel like home.

CHAPTER 2
I Go to a Forbidden Restaurant

If someone were to go to my secret place right now, they would see a girl in jean shorts and a tank top, and that girl would have dark skin and long, straight, black hair. She would have bright-green eyes, just like her mother. That girl would be me.

I thought about this for a moment, and then jumped up and raced over to the basket that I had brought along. I had already devoured my picnic lunch, and I was now looking for my kite. When I pulled out the kite, I felt a pang of sadness go through my body, because as I looked at the kite, a rush of memories flooded my mind. And I saw in my mind a little scene playing out.

I saw a little girl sitting on the floor of our kitchen. Sitting next to her was a young woman who looked exactly like me. We were decorating a bright-red kite, and on the kite we had written my name in multicolor sparkle glue and markers. I knew that little girl was me, and that young woman was my mother.

I sighed, picked up the kite, and began to unspool the thread. When the kite was as spread out as it could be, I began to run.

As I walked home, I began to listen to the other conversations people were having inside their homes. Their voices drifted out the open windows, and I listened. There were a bunch of different topics: the weather, work, school, bills, phone calls, parties, and friends. I wondered what it was like to have a meal with at least one other person. I **always** ate alone.

My father worked in his study during the day and in a taco truck at night. He would drive around in a brightly colored van, selling tacos till around 10 o'clock at night. There were no seats in the taco truck, and even if there had been, my father would never have a long enough break to have a meal with me. So, I usually went somewhere else to eat dinner. By myself. Even when my father was off from work, he would always grab his food, and then head up to his study. Anyway, when I got home, my father was already getting ready for work.

"Ayita, I trust you didn't get into any trouble?" my father asked, eyebrows raised.

"Yes, Papa," I replied.

"Then here are some pesos to spend down at the bar. They should be enough to treat you to a *tamales* combo and some *champurrado*," my father said as he handed over a handful of coins and pulled on his coat as he did.

"*Gracias*, Papa," I replied, trying to sound happy and grateful, even though I wasn't.

I try really hard not to complain,

but every night my father either has
the neighbor come over to feed me
the same cold, gray mush my father
makes, or I am given money to go
"treat" myself to some *champurrado*
and *tamales* at the bar.

So, tonight, I was going to do
something else. Ten minutes later, I
was climbing off the bus. Then I looked
up and saw the little restaurant I had
picked out. It was a perfect restaurant
for this occasion. I paid the bus driver,
who tipped his hat at me.

"Have a good evening, miss," he
said.

"You too," I told him.

And then the bus doors closed
and it rumbled off, back to the town of
Austin, Texas, and I was left walking
towards the restaurant.

CHAPTER 3
My Story

The restaurant was in the middle of nowhere, but the bright lights coming from inside were very comforting. I walked up the steps and through the front door. I took a seat at a table and ordered up. As soon as I had ordered, I took out a small pocket notebook I had been given when I was very little, from my mother. I wrote down lists, ideas, quotes, stories, poems, songs, notes, or sometime just little thoughts or memories I wanted to capture on paper. I flipped to a blank page and began to write a little story.

My Story
Once there was a girl. She lived with just her father. Her mother was gone. It was raining when she was born. She loved to dance and loved the rain too. But the girl had a problem. Her world was turning upside down. And even the bravest of souls was scared.

That seemed like a good start to a story. If only something dramatic would happen to me. That was all I could think of at the moment, which was perfect timing because just as I put the little book down, my food arrived.

As I began to eat, I looked around. The restaurant was called Diego's Acogedor Cafe (Diego's Cozy Cafe), and it *was* cozy, with its glowing lamps, comfortable chairs, and slightly dusty curtains. There was even a wild boar's head mounted on the wall! I loved it. I ate as much as I could, and then tipped the waiter with the little extra money I had. I had used all of the money I had been saving up the last few months combined with the money my father had given me that day.

When I climbed off the bus and crept inside my house, my father wasn't home from work. So I went straight to sleep, and I dreamed about Diego's Acogedor Cafe.

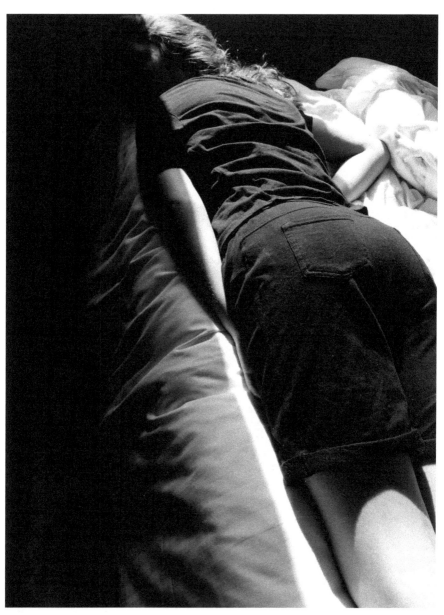

Girl in the Shadows, *Nikon D3400*

by Delaney Slote, 12
Missoula, MT

CHAPTER 4
The Drought

Something weird happened today. I was taking a walk when I saw an old tree, which had been there as long as I could remember, dying. Or at least I think it was dying. The leaves were singed, and the grass around the tree was brown. In fact, I saw many trees like that on the rest of my walk. And the rest of the week, and the following weeks after, there was not a lot of rain, and a lot of hot weather. The plants began to wilt and then die. And the days seemed to grow hotter every day.

But the main thing was this: the sink had a knob that you could twist so you could get either hot or cold water. Well, only a trickle came out. And all through the town of Austin, Texas, the same thing was happening to everyone. I knew something was up with the weather. And I knew exactly how to find out what.

I stood in a T-shirt and shorts, sweating in the hot summer sun. My plan was ready to go, and I was excited. I pulled out a tiny scrap of paper on which I had written down:

1. While Papa is getting recorded, I will sneak into the school.
2. Find janitor's closet and get changed into outfit.
3. Pretend to be cleaning and get into trailer.
4. Find notecards, read them, and put them back.

That's right. My papa was getting recorded to go on TV. But actually that was quite normal. My papa had a show called "Taco Tips." It was exactly what it sounded like. Since he worked at a taco truck, my papa took advantage of that. He got recorded once a month. And usually I stayed out of the way, but today I wanted to be part of it all.

So, I put my plan in action: I waited until my papa had started being recorded, and then I crept into the school doors. The filming was always done right outside of the elementary school. And the director's trailer was behind the school. The director always had his trailer cleaned, so I was going to sneak into the school, dress up as a janitor, and get inside his trailer.

I set off on my journey. I snuck around the entire school until I reached the janitor's closet. Then I dressed up and set on my way to the back of the school. I sauntered up to the director's trailer and tried the doorknob. It was locked. I looked around. A muscular man was standing a few feet away.

"Sir, could you please give me the code to the director's trailer?"

"Um . . . no," he said uncertainly.

"But I'm the janitor. Have you ever heard that the director has his trailer cleaned every time he visits?" I asked slyly.

"Yes, I have heard that, but every time the janitor comes, they know the code!" he told me.

I had to think fast.

"Um . . . I am the janitor's daughter. My dad is sick today," I told him.

He eyed me suspiciously.

"You do kind of look like him."

I gave him my best-little-girl-in-the-world face, the face that I gave to my father.

"Fine," he grumbled. I smiled as he told me the code: "1694, that's the code."

"Thank you!" I chirped happily.

Once I was in the trailer, I pretended to clean until the muscular man went away. Then I began searching. When I finally found the notecards, I sat down to read them. These were the radio weatherman's notecards. He always forgot where he put them, so the director just kept them in his trailer until it was time for him to go on. I began to read. The notecards said: "The weather forecast is a severe chance of drought this summer. Plants are suffering and water supplies are running short. We will update you as we have more news."

I set the notecards down, and stared out the window. If the drought persisted, it would mean no rain. Or water. Or dancing. And there would be a lot of hot weather. And sun. And dying plants, animals, and trees. And hard, hot, cracked ground. I was terrified.

Desert Abyss, *Panasonic Lumix TS2*

by Kendall Vanderwouw, 13
Nevada City, CA

CHAPTER 5
I Babysit a Demon

My father thinks I'm old enough to babysit. I agree, but that doesn't make me want to babysit anymore than I usually do. I **HATE** babysitting. But it's been a month since the day I crept into the director's trailer. The drought has gotten worse, and everyone is worried. Tonight, the usually quiet houses scattered through the neighborhood are ablaze with light. The grown-ups are hosting a big meeting, and my father is invited. And he is going. And since I'm the oldest child out of all the people attending, I'm the sitter for the night.

Luckily for me, there was only one child I had to take care of. And her name was London. I had never met her before, but I had heard about her. The things I had heard were all different. My old teacher told me that she was a darling, beautiful child. That was the same teacher who had given me a D on my report card, so I paid no heed to her. I instead thought about what the kids had said. The kids who had London in their class. "She's a monster. A real teacher's pet. Horrible! Just horrible!" they said. But I decided to take my chances.

I walked over to London's house. I gulped when I saw it. It was more of a mansion then a house. I bet they still had completely clean water. (Most houses had not-so-great water.) I walked up the front path and knocked on the door. The door swung open at once. A girl with blonde hair put into pigtails and light blue eyes stood there. She wore a flowered dress and a pair of pink, sparkly party shoes. And to complete the look, she had a skull-and-crossbones-patterned Band-Aid on her right cheek. She scowled up at me. "Are you Ayipa? The babysitter?" she asked skeptically.

"My name is Ayita, not Ayipa. And, yes, I am the babysitter." I told her. "Are you London?"

"Yes. And we're going to play dollies until my mommy and daddy get home."

Her parents left in a hurry, and I was left with the little monster. I sighed. "So where are your dollies?" I asked.

"In my room. Come on, slowpoke!" she said, already climbing up a spiral staircase.

I followed her, and she led me down what seemed like a never-ending hallway. Finally, we reached a set of double doors, which led into the biggest bedroom I had ever seen. It was like a dining hall, and everything was entirely sparkly pink and black. Striped walls, polka-dot covers, and plaid furniture. All in pink and black. The biggest chandelier I had ever seen hung above the enormous bed.

London pointed to a dollhouse the size of me. Barbies and other dolls were set up inside. I gulped. We spent

Appealing Balloons, *Prismacolor*

by Cathy Tu, 11
Shanghai, China

the next two hours playing dolls. We were about to do something else, when London shouted "TAG! YOU'RE IT!!!!" She tore out of the house and into the dark night.

"LONDON!!!" I screamed.

I ran around searching for her until I finally heard some shuffling coming from the playground at Ms. Friar's house. I peeked around the corner of the house and saw a shape moving. It was London. I carried her kicking and screaming back to the house.

After that, I sat through the movie *Animal Friends Rescue*. Finally, London had some milk and cookies and got ready for bed. I tiptoed out of London's dark room and read my book until London came down stairs.

"Can't sleep?" I said, smiling slightly. No reply. "London?" I asked. That's when I saw her eyes were wide open. It looked really freaky. I asked again, "London?" Nothing.

My natural instinct was to tap her on the shoulder, so I did just that. Suddenly, she thrust her arm at me and punched me in the stomach. That was when I realized she was sleepwalking. I carefully carried her upstairs, to her bed. Then, her parents came home. And even though they paid me well, I know I will never sit for London again.

CHAPTER 6
Breaking out the Books

I was having an okay week until Papa told me some pretty horrible news.

"So, Ayita," my papa said, taking his favorite seat in our living room.

"Yes . . . " I said, sucking in my breath.

"I got a call from your teacher. She said you didn't do so well in science this year. Care to explain?"

I couldn't pretend I didn't know what he was talking about. My science grades had been horrible all last year. "I'm not so good at science." That was all I could say.

"Clearly," my father said, sighing. "Your teacher said she's signed you up for science tutoring. It starts tomorrow." And with that, he left.

I slumped down in my chair. Science tutoring! What was I thinking! Well, there goes the rest of my summer . . .

The fan was blowing, but it wasn't doing much. I was positive we were baking. By we, I mean me and the six other kids who were being tutored.

"Now turn to page 312, to learn about, um . . . I forgot," the teacher said. The other kids and I groaned and turned to page 312.

I sighed, and looked outside. Despite the hot weather, it was still a good day to play outside. The air smelled kinda weird, though, like a storm was brewing.

Something happened right after our water break. Something I would never forget. The ground began to tremble and was jumping up and down. The desks were thrown from one side of the room to the other. Children scrambled around. And then it was calm and quiet. It had ended just as soon as it had begun. Kids were crying, but no one was hurt. The teacher hurried from kid to kid, making sure we were okay.

We switched on the TV. A news reporter was standing in the town square. "Scientist believe that the earthquake was caused by the effects of the drought. Luckily, no major damage was done, and only a few injuries. We have just witnessed a small earthquake, folks," the man was saying.

While the other kids kept watching, I crept into the back of the classroom to the phone. I dialed my father's phone number and prayed he would answer.

"Ayita?" my father asked.

"Papa . . . " I whispered. I began to cry. I hugged the phone tight.

"Come home right now. I want to make sure you aren't hurt." I didn't argue.

"OK, Papa." I hung up. Every story has a problem. And this drought was mine.

I burst through the door. My father swept me up in his arms. I had missed this. Then my father went to go find the first-aid kit, while I made a batch of *crema catalana* (a popular Spanish dessert). We went around the neighborhood, making sure people were okay, and giving out *crema catalana*.

We passed through the town square, and I gasped when I saw a house that had been wrecked. I wasn't sure what I expected with an earthquake, but I was startled. It was a nice house, too, with architecture beyond compare.

An old woman was talking with some firefighters.

"Ma'am, are you okay?" my father asked.

"Oh, yes, I'm fine. But the house my husband built is ruined," she replied, hanging her head. My father had a thoughtful look on his face.

"Now, I am not a great architect, but I do like building," my father said.

"Oh, I would pay you a lot to come fix it!" the woman said happily.

"I will come here tomorrow at 10:00 am. Because I must first walk my daughter to her tutoring class," my father said.

"Oh, Papa!" I cried, and hugged him tight.

We walked home, and I then watched my papa call the taco truck and told them he would be quitting. Then he called the newspaper to tell them he would no longer be doing the taco tips. I smiled because it seemed all my little problems were solved.

STONE SOUP

Dandelion in Black and White, *Nikon Coolpix L830*

by Hannah Parker, 13
South Burlington, VT

CHAPTER 7
A Sign of Hope

It was now August, and my tutoring was done. My father was still working on the old lady's house, whose name was Ms. Kemp. Everything seemed to be alright. So I was back at my special place.

I admit, it wasn't the same, but I was still determined to have fun. I was going to camp out here, just like I had before the drought. I first took a walk in the woods that surrounded my special place. When I got back to camp, it was time for some dinner. I glanced down at the watering hole. Normally, I would catch a fish and cook it, but it was still all dried up. Luckily, I had packed my own dinner tonight.

I was just about to start a fire, when I saw something in the base of the watering hole. I scrambled down, cutting my knees as I went. I squatted down, and fingered the small treasure. It was a small, green seedling, growing out of the hard, cracked ground. I scrambled up the bank and grabbed my water bottle. I carefully trickled water on the seedling. Maybe it was my imagination, but it seemed to brighten.

I ate my dinner and roasted marshmallows. I even went on a star walk. And as I snuggled into my sleeping bag, I realized what I could do. I could help stop this drought.

"Hey, you're back!" my father said when I walked in the door.

"Hello, Papa," I said.

"Want to maybe go out for some dinner?" my father asked. He had been trying to spend more time with me lately.

"Sorry, Papa, but I have to work on something," I said apologetically. He nodded. I headed into the study and sat down at the computer. I first googled my question. Then I started writing. I was writing a song. A simple chant, in Spanish:

Los problemas que enfrentamos son grandes, pero seguiremos luchando!

I know some people do not speak Spanish, so I will translate. "The problems we face are big, but we will keep fighting!" That was the plan. It was a good plan. And I was ready to put it into action. Soon.

CHAPTER 8
Saving the World

"*Los problemas que enfrentamos son grandes, pero seguiremos luchando!*" I chanted. I was standing outside of one of the most popular restaurants in the city. I had started out with nothing except a foldout table, a handmade sign, a chant, gallons of water, and a sign that read:

HELP SAVE THE WORLD!
Water for the earth!
Water your plants, so they can survive
PS: Do not drink the water!

My first visitor was a mom and her son. They stopped to read the sign.

"We will take two gallons," the lady said.

"Thank you!" I called after her as she walked away with her two gallons of water.

An old couple came out of the restaurant. They heard my chant and took a gallon. I was just starting to have a lot of business when a man asked, "Hey kid, where are you getting all this water?"

"There is a watering hole, but it is not super clean water, so it is for the plants, not to drink," I replied. It was all true, too. I had dug with my father's shovel and had made a crack in the surface, and water had spurted out! Now the watering hole was full. Or at least it used to be. I had filled every last gallon with the water, and now the hole was empty again. If people watered their plants, they could all make it through the drought! Maybe.

The line was getting long now. More people kept joining the line. When the sun began to set, I packed up my table. As we pulled into the driveway, I saw my neighbor watering her plants. With a gallon of water she had taken. I smiled and waved. She waved back. Maybe doing my part wasn't too hard after all.

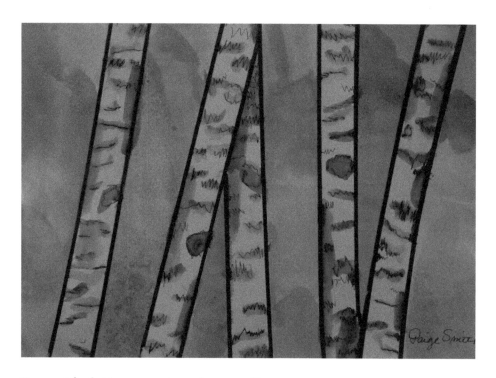

Paper Birch Trees, *watercolor acrylic*

by Paige Smith, 7
Bryant, AR

CHAPTER 9
The End

It is late August, and it is still hot, but that's no surprise. I woke up this morning and realized that it was my birthday. I am 12. I slipped into shorts and a T-shirt. I cook our breakfasts now, and I don't mean to brag, but they are all super delicious. Today was no exception. I searched through the cookbook, and my eye landed on the apple-cinnamon oatmeal recipe. I prepared it, but this time when I ate it, I wasn't alone.

After that, my father headed off to work, and I took a walk. I headed down the streets and to the old woods. I wove through the blanket of trees, and I ended up in my special place. I stood in the grass and let the sun beat down on me. I looked down at the worn-out flipflops on my feet and wondered if maybe my father would take me shoe shopping. Yep, this summer had changed me. Maybe I would take some sort of dance class this fall.

I stepped into the cool canopy of the trees and kept walking until I reached the dried-up creek. I walked along the bed and stared up at the sky. I wished I could fly. But I can fly, I realized. I can dance with all my heart, and if that doesn't feel like flying, then my name isn't Ayita. Or something like that.

I finished my loop, and found myself back at my special place. I fished around in my backpack and pulled out a chocolate cupcake made by my father. Truthfully, it looked more like a chocolate brick with chocolate frosting as the cement. There was a candle on top. *Make a wish.* I thought.

"I wish for my Mama," I whispered.

I sniffled and wiped away the tears as I ate my cupcake. As soon as I finished, I felt a tear plop on my arm. I looked down. I wiped my tears away again, but after that I felt another drop. And another. It was raining.

The Seasons (A Poetry Cycle)

by Vidhat Kartik, 9
Saratoga, CA

The Four Seasons (Illustration)

(Copic markers and pen)

by Avery Multer, 12
Chicago, IL

Winter

Birch trees so brown and white

Glowing in the moonlight

Shaking trees

In the howling breeze

The tall trees

Have falling leaves

There is a bird's nest

Where it will rest

It is so tall

So do not fall

Sleds sliding the snow

Santa comes with a ho

Frozen ice starts melting into water

As it gets hotter

The ski

Was near the tree

From the top of the tree

You can see the sea

The beautiful stream

Is like a dream

Frozen toes

Are standing in the winter snows

The snowman so tall

He may fall

The horse trudging through the snow

Farmers do not need the hoe

While bears go into hibernation

The beautiful carnation blooms

Santa's hat

Fell on a cat

Rudolph's nose

Lit a hose

That is how winter goes

Spring

In the months of spring flowers bloom

No more cold winter doom

The melted ice turns into water

Because it got hotter

Blossoming trees

In the cool breeze

No more ice and snow

So farmers need their hoe

Birds are back

Don't say ack

No more heavy rain for flowers

Only April showers

Baby animals are born

Some have horns

While bears wake from hibernation

The beautiful carnation has bloomed

Growing leaves

On trees

You need to use a hose

Even when the spring wind blows

That is how spring goes

Summer

In the season of summer

There is almost no bummer

It is bright and sunny

It is nice and funny

Whisper in others' ears

Summer is here

The holidays make everyone happy

Don't be snappy

The summer breeze goes here and there

It does not give a blast of air

On July 4 it is Independence Day

So watch the beautiful fireworks and say hey

The leaves

Stay on trees

Everything is ripe

People type

Watch the beautiful sunset

As you eat baguette

Water the seeds with a hose

And put the fertilizer that I chose

This is how summer goes

Autumn

Falling leaves

In the howling breeze

Trees are so tall

Leaves still fall

Birds flying south

Turkey in your mouth

Cold weather here and there

Running and jumping mare

Yellow, red, and orange falling leaves

While the farmer heaves

Piles of leaves on the road

Being a heavy load

Everyone is jumping

Nobody is bumping

Thanksgiving and Halloween are there

Families having fun here and there

The harvest is coming

Farmers are humming

The icy wind blows

Mighty fine big boughs

That is how autumn goes

Honor Roll

Welcome to the *Stone Soup* Honor Roll. Every month we receive submissions from hundreds of kids from around the world. Unfortunately, we don't have space to publish all the great work we receive. We want to commend some of these talented writers and artists and encourage them to keep creating.

Fiction
Kathryn Glover, 13
Ava Horton, 13
Makenzie Kelley, 12
Luna Castro Mojica, 12
Emily Xu, 12

Poetry
Justine Freis, 9
Arielle Kouyoumdjian, 12
Isabella Posel, 12
Aashni Shah, 11

Art
Enoch Farnham, 11
Joshua Garza, 9

Don't forget to visit Stonesoup.com to browse our bonus materials. There you will find:

- Magazines: Individual issues of *Stone Soup*, past and present

- Books: Our collection of themed anthologies (fantasy, sport, poetry and more), and the *Stone Soup Annual* (all the year's issues, plus a flavor of the year online, in one volume).

- Art prints: high quality prints from our collection of children's art

- Journals and sketchbooks for writing and drawing
  . . . and more!

Visit the *Stone Soup* store at Stonesoupstore.com to buy:

- 20 years of back issues—around 5,000 stories, poems, and reviews

- Blog posts from our Young Bloggers on subjects from sports to sewing—plus ecology, reading, and book reviews
- Video interviews with *Stone Soup* authors
- Music, spoken word, and performances

Stone

MARCH 2019   VOLUME 47 / ISSUE 3

StoneSoup

The magazine supporting creative kids around the world

Editor
Emma Wood

Director
William Rubel

Operations
Jane Levi

Education & Production
Sarah Ainsworth

Design
Joe Ewart

Stone Soup (ISSN 0094 579X) is published 11 times per year—monthly, with a combined July/August summer issue. Copyright © 2019 by the Children's Art Foundation, a 501(c)(3) nonprofit organization, located in Santa Cruz, California. All rights reserved.

Thirty-five percent of our subscription price is tax-deductible. Make a donation at Stonesoup.com/donate, and support us by choosing Children's Art Foundation as your Amazon Smile charity.

POSTMASTER: Send address changes to Stone Soup, 126 Otis Street, Santa Cruz, CA 95060. Periodicals postage paid at Santa Cruz, California, and additional offices.

Stone Soup is available in different formats to persons who have trouble seeing or reading the print or online editions. To request the Braille edition from the National Library of Congress, call +1 800-424-8567. To request access to the audio edition via the National Federation of the Blind's NFB-NEWSLINE®, call +1 866-504-7300 or visit www.nfbnewsline.org.

Check us out on social media:

Editor's Note

This issue includes the winners of our concrete poetry contest; the winning poems are both beautiful visual works in their own right and inventive, singular texts. However, it is the combination of both shape (the form) and text (the content) that made these poems stand out. I hope when you sit down to write any work, but especially a poem, that you think about its form: Will it have stanzas? Will the lines be short or long? Will you use any rhyme or other sonic devices? These decisions are as important as what you end up writing. In addition to the concrete poems, there are many incredible photographs that I hope will encourage you to pick up a camera (or a phone), as well as stories and poems engaging with the theme of selfhood and belonging.

Happy reading!

Emma Wood

Letters: We love to hear from our readers. Please post a comment on our website or write to us via Submittable or editor@stonesoup.com. Your letter might be published on our occasional Letters to the Editor page.

Submissions: Our guidelines are on the Submit page at Stonesoup.com, where you will also find a link to our Submittable online submissions portal.

Subscriptions: To subscribe to *Stone Soup*, please press the Subscribe button on our webpage, Stonesoup.com.

On the cover:
"London"

**by Keira Callahan, 10
San Francisco, CA**

StoneSoup
Contents

Steam

First place in the Concrete Poetry Contest

by Sabrina Guo, 13
Oyster Bay, NY

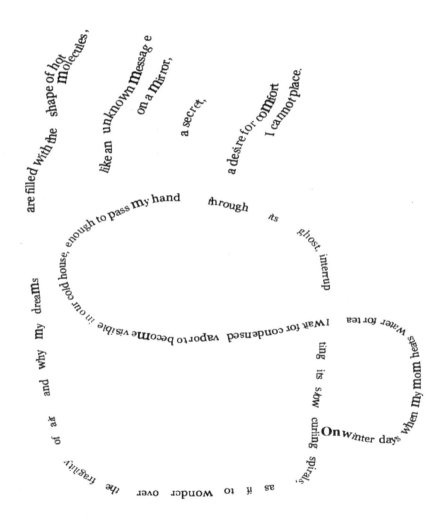

are filled with the shape of hot molecules, like an unknown message on a mirror, a secret, a desire for comfort I cannot place.

enough to pass my hand through its ghost, interrup

in our cold house, vapor to become visible I wait for condensed Water for tea when my mom heats

On winter days curling spirals ting its slow

and why my dreams of air the fragility the wonder over to if as

The Bridge, *Canon EOS30D*

by Marlena Rohde, 12
San Francisco, CA

Unmasked: A Collection of Short Stories

by Aditya Singh, 12
Bellevue, WA

Sun Blotches and Angelic Smiles

Everybody in my family has different hands. Mine are light brown with weaving veins, like rivers flowing through a desert. Curvy lines streak across the surface of my palm, bards silently singing the story of my life.

My sister's hands are smooth and innocent, round knuckles jutting out when she curls them into a fist, the nostrils of her nose flaring with adorable anger.

Dad's are rough with hardship, his palms jeweled with callouses. He has broad fingers and nails thick and ridged, like clam shells. His sinewy tendons bulge when he flexes his hand, strong and supporting, always ready to help.

Grandpa's hands are like sandpaper. The skin on his hands is wrinkled and blotched with sunspots. His fingers are like the gnarled limbs of an ancient oak, weathered and wise.

Grandma's are small and pudgy, the fat from the hams of her hand gently creasing as she grasps her cup of ginger chai.

Uncle's hands are light as feathers, his long and slender fingers gracefully sweeping across the keys of the piano, like a casual wind fluttering across the surface of a sandy beach. Knotted joints curl around the tips of his metacarpals and phalange bones. I want hands like Uncle, a musician's hands.

Auntie's are always gleaming with eloquence, her designer acrylic nails sparkling like shining stars. Her hands are a smooth tan, their oily surface engulfing me in a warm, comforting hug.

But Mom's hands—Mom's hands are the summer sun, soft, welcoming, and always warm, like when her eyes wrinkle with joy and her mouth peels into an angelic smile.

Everybody in my family has different hands, some lighter, some darker. Some smoother, some rougher. Some are warm, but they'll eventually become cold as old Time washes over them. Hands. They hold the marks of our past and will soon tell the story of our future.

Clocks in Tuxedos

Thick sheets of tension drape over the room as trembling fingers reach across the boards. Beams of intense concentration emanate from players' eyes, lines of focus creasing their foreheads. Shiny raindrops slip down cheeks, the result of many conceding defeat. Faces flush with a despaired red, their egregious mistakes abruptly annihilating all hopes of a trophy.

Then, the horn bellows its long, sonorous sound, announcing the time has come. The judges, dressed in their neon-green and orange vests, place down the Chronos timers. Wavering sighs of anxiety escape from many mouths at the sight of the timers. Dressed in a tight black tuxedo, my timer begins to drone in its monotonous *tick-tock tick-tock*. With each passing second, an ounce of apprehension grows, sticky sweat coating the back of my neck. My opponent is an older teenager, wearing a red-and-blue-striped shirt. Burgundy freckles are splattered across his face, and he has curly maroon hair. Behind his pair of claret spectacles, his eyes suddenly light up with joy. As his mouth peels into a beaming smile, he confidently brings his hand forth and moves his queen across the board, placing her next to my king and says the words of a chess player's nightmare: "Checkmate!"

The Tree of Salmon Berries

The tree of salmon berries is an unarmed merchant, constantly being harassed by malicious robbers. They reach in their selfish fingers and pull off its jewelry as the tree screams a silent plea. The tree's green neighbors remain in stupid oblivion, frivolously fluttering in the July breeze as they revel in the company of heaven's water. The wavering limbs of the tree shake with anger, futilely attempting to slap the thief.

But it is a tough tree. Always coming back fuller than ever, only to repeat the vicious cycle. The tree of salmon berries is the man in the maze, constantly navigating through and overcoming obstacles, only to find the next corner and hurdle. The tree sees me as yet another monster of greed. And the tree is right. I am very greedy, but I need to be. The greediest are the most successful, for without greed there is no motivation. Caesar, the indomitable emperor of insatiable greed, led the ancient Roman Empire to power and might. Without greed, one is weak and will find oneself bending to others' wills, becoming more servile with each passing day. I will continue to steal from the tree, ripping its children from their home and devouring them like a cannibalistic demon. The tree of salmon berries will remain the subject of torture, forever ruled by the great lord by the name of Greed.

Conquering Ghosts

Dear Young Aditya,

I know what you're thinking. You think that if you confess and admit you stole Maya's phone, everyone will hate you for the rest of the year. You'll lose all your friends and your repute will be that of a malicious, untrustworthy boy. Sure, there will be some hard feelings, but it's about doing the right thing.

So stop. Don't get on the bus and go home. Turn around and tell the truth. Don't let the ghosts of your actions haunt you, weaving their threads of guilt and shame into your brain. Confront and conquer them, so you don't wage an endless war with the demons of your past. What's the worst that can happen? Mom and Dad find out and yell at you.

But, in the matter of a week or two everyone will forget about it. The burden will be lifted from your shoulders, no longer plaguing you. On the other hand, if you internalize your crime, little straws of hay will be sprinkled upon the pile of guilt every day. As time passes, and your shameful secret gnaws at your insides, that pile of hay will become a stack, which in turn will become a heap. A heap of guilt and shame so heavy that it will be too late to turn back and tell the truth. You will have to live hampered down by your impulsive, rash decision, always present and ominous, like a painful scar seared across your skin. Please don't do what I did. Don't walk away.

Your older self,
Aditya

Chalky Powder and Salty Breezes

Aditya. In Hindi, it means the sun. Although I've always felt my name was more triangular than circular. Circles don't change. It's the same repetitive cycle, and if you flipped a circle upside down, it would still stay the same. But when you flip a triangle, it becomes something different. A new perspective, a fresh idea. In my religion, a triangle represents creation, destruction, and preservation. I'd prefer to create things. I think my name is a creator name. It's like the number 6. In control, with power, on top.

Aditya. To others, I believe my name is like a gray piece of grass. Unusual, yet dull. Most people I meet think it's an interesting name, although they usually say that out of politeness. My name is not flashy or exciting. Just like my personality. I'm a quieter person, who likes to observe and listen.

Aditya. My name has its ups and downs. Slide down the A only to meet the vertical face of the d, impossible to climb over. But I will persevere, turning trials into triumphs. Eventually I will get over the d and onto the dot of the i. And all the way over to the cliff of the a, with a frightening drop. In these moments of apprehension and anxiety, I will methodically weave my way past the obstacle, scaling down the spine of the a onto the welcoming ground.

Aditya. It tastes like the salty breeze near the sea. It is the stunning decorations bursting with explosions of vibrant colors, celebrating love and unity. The thick-yet-comforting smell of chalky powder. Sometimes the feel of cracked lips and cold handshakes. My name is the strums of the sitar on the radio as my father cooks lunch. Each note an expression, winged emotions, from one artist to listeners across the world. That's what I want to do. Send my emotions and ideas across the world, inspiring and motivating.

Aditya. A name that will ignite passion, drive innovation, a symbol of humanity's desire to succeed and progress. Yes. That's the legacy my name shall leave.

Trapped in Glass, *iPhone 5*

by Ava Horton, 13
Gresham, OR

Octopus

Second place in the Concrete Poetry Contest

by Marco Lu, 12
Champaign, IL

```
                    SMOOTHLY,
                SWIFTLY, SILENTLY
               SLIDING    OVER      THE
               ROUGH,   RUST   RED   ROCK,
              ITS TENDER, TWISTING TENTACLES
              GRASPING  THE  SHELLED,  SHARP
              SHRIMP. ITS   MOIST    MOTTLED
              MANTLE MORPHING INTO A CRUSTY,
              CRACKED CORAL, AS IT LURKS LOW,
              LONE  FOR   ITS    NEXT    PREY.
              SUDDENLY SENSING DANGER, IT
               SLOWLY SQUEEZES THROUGH
                THE GRITTY, GRIMY GRAVEL
                  TO   DEFTLY  DISGUISE
                    ITSELF   INTO
          A        CHISELED,   CHAPPED
       CHUNK. THE  DARK,  DAUNTING  DOLPHIN
      SWIMS       SILENTLY PAST, VAINLY VYING TO SPOT
    ITS           POLYMORPHOUS   PREY.              THE
             OCTOPUS   QUIVERS  QUIETLY              IN
       THE      DOLPHIN'S SHAKY, SHIFTING,            SHA-
       DOW.     THE OCTOPUS    DREARILY   DROWSILY
    DRIFTS    BACK            IN-          TO-
     ITS      SMALL             SAFE      SNUG
     SINK     HOLE,             TO        REST
      UNTIL    IT               IS        READY
       FOR     ITS             NE-        XT
       H-      U-       .       N-         T.
```

Profile of a Guardian, *Nikon Coolpix L830*

by Hannah Parker, 13
South Burlington, VT

Behind

by Christine Chang, 10
San Carlos, CA

Can a missing dog bring two estranged friends back together?

The fluorescent light of the classroom made it even harder to concentrate on the fine, black print that consisted of nothing but endless boredom. My mind tried to make sense of it. The book was written long ago; the 1800s? It reminded me of when a good friend of mine pretended to travel back in time with me. My nose wrinkled at the thought of her. I remembered Alice being fierce and stubborn. Just like I didn't pay any mind to the words of this book, Alice never listened to me. I groaned just thinking about it. She was like a pestering bee. Going away but always returning. Alice had the eyes of an eagle and the ears of an owl. And, apparently, the instincts of a bee. She had those funny front teeth that jutted out at anything that didn't seem right.

Against my will, my eyes scanned the pages: "Meg, being oldest, seemed to think she could order us about . . . "

Those words hit me like the harsh wind outside, and, as the realization slowly sank in, I felt the air sucked out of me. But why had she let me boss her around? It may have given me pleasure at first, but in the long run, it definitely drove us both out of our minds! I felt lightheaded. Gears seemed to turn in my mind, contemplating this theory. A broken piano key seemed to finally strike the string it had missed up until now and echo through my body. My ears rang. My hands trembled. The whole world spun around me, blurring my vision and clouding my head. If you looked inside my body, you would see a fogged-up window with many attempts to rub the mist off. My eyes skimmed a whole page in my book, but the echo of that dissonant piano chord in my ears was so loud, it diverted my attention so I couldn't hear the words in my mind.

For a moment, I wished I could really travel back in time and fix my mistakes. *When had I started to boss her around? One year ago? Two? Since we'd met?* No. It didn't matter. The only thing that mattered was that I had done it, and now I'd have to fix it—without time travel. I racked my brain for ideas. I didn't want to straight out say, "Did you notice I boss you around a lot?"

I came to my senses. I'd just have to stop bossing her around. Plus, now I´d have to reread a whole page in my book that I had missed, but it was too late. My teacher clapped her hands, and I was behind on my book—and my friendship.

The recess bell rang its piercing song, decimating my ears. I snapped my head up and stepped outside. A

A shiver ran down my spine and pooled on the ground in puddles of trepidation

blast of air almost blew me down. I let the door close in front of me and stood back.

"Did you hear that Linda has . . . "

"What did you get on your test? I got a . . . "

The loud sounds of the hall barely receded every time a cluster of kids exited the building and came back saying it was too cold or windy or this or that. Did I really want to go outside? I shoved the door again, willing it to open. The wind, rougher this time, whipped my face. Even so, I pushed myself through the wind tunnel and stumbled outside, tripping over my feet and using my arm to shield my face. I wished my arm were bigger. The light outdoors was bright, yet the sky was clouded and overcast. The wet dew made my feet cold, and the grass crunched beneath my shoes. The sun was low in the sky making my shadow long. My friends chit chatted as if it were a normal day. But it wasn't.

My friend, Bella, approached me. "We've been looking for you!"

"Not now. I need to find something. And no, I do not need help right now." My tense body relaxed a little on a rickety bench that looked as if it would topple over. I stayed completely still as my eyes darted around the school. *Where was she?* I studied the school. On my right, a bush covered in geraniums lined the grass. The sun was just up behind the bush. A dirt path traversed

by a stream from the recent rain led to a cluster of trees. The trees stood tall and blocked most of my view of the benches that surrounded the school. I sensed movement beyond the trees.

There.

I inched toward Alice ever so slowly, and she, of course, with her uncannily keen senses, noticed me immediately. I continued toward her, the leaves crunching beneath my boots. My arms tensed. My stomach churned, and my legs pulled at me to back up. A shiver ran down my spine and pooled on the ground in puddles of trepidation. The world spiraled about. I couldn't think straight. I uneasily twirled a strand of my hair.

"Hey Alice," I stammered. She turned her back on me. I looked down. "I'm so sorry."

Alice glared. "I can't believe I didn't stand up to you before! Why did I let you make a toy out of me?! Buzz off."

Ha! She really is a bee. I stiffened. "I *said*, I'M SORRY!!" Whoops. Now she'll never forgive me.

"Leave me alone!" Alice's mouth was a big, gaping hole. Tears formed in her eyes.

Hmm. . . I thought. Nice comeback. What else did you learn on the playground? My cheeks turned bright red. I attempted to hide my face and darted back toward the rickety bench. I could feel Alice staring after me, her eyes boring a hole in my gut. I had just lost a friendship that was so hard to keep. A friendship that was just within reach, close enough to pull back to me; but I had let it slip away, or rather, pushed it away.

I could barely live through the next two periods. I didn't hear a word my teacher said. I probably flunked the math test I'd been studying for all week. I tuned out my friends' conversation at lunch period. I just made it through my last two classes before darting home.

"How was your day, honey?" my mom asks as I slump down in the front seat of the car.

"Shut up," I whisper. Mom glares at me, but she doesn't say anything. She's good at being quiet when I want her to. She'll scold me later. I watch out the window as the world flies by in a blur. Faster than the speed of sound. It seems slow, still, compared to how quickly I lost a friend. Slow, compared to how fast my temper slips through my fingers until it is no longer mine to control; the moment when I release it, and it is just out of reach.

The car crunches up the gravel driveway. I leap out. Before I dart off, something catches my eye on the sidewalk, haphazardly tossed under an ivy bush. I bend down to look closer. It's a dog biscuit someone must've dropped. I adore finding little "treasures" around town while I'm out exploring: buttons, coins, acorns—you never know when you might need them. I curl my fingers gently around it, though in my current state, I wish I could smash it—or any-

thing else for that matter—to pieces. I race down the street, tripping over my own feet in my desperation to burn off my frustration.

As I near the end of the block, empowered and exhilarated from my run, with only a trace left of my frustration, I slow down and begin to notice "Lost Dog" signs posted on nearby telephone poles. *Wait*, I think, a knot forming in my gut, *isn't that Alice's dog?*

Alice and her family are standing outside their house, yelling, "Roger! Roger! Come here, puppy!" As I get closer, Mr. Weston climbs into the car with Alice, setting out to look for Roger. Alice sees me out of the corner of her eye. I can tell. She clenches her jaw.

"Isn't that your friend?" Mr. Weston glances my way. The wind whips my face. I wish he would stop the car so I could have a moment with Alice.

I barely hear her reply as she murmurs under her breath: "Not anymore."

"Daddy, let's just go," Alice grabs his arm firmly.

Just then, my mom rounds the corner to Alice's block. *Ugh. She worries too much about me, always wondering where I am and if I'm okay.* She spies Mrs. Weston and begins waving. "Jennifer!" she calls.

Mr. Weston stops the car.

Alice groans.

Mrs. Weston calls back, "Susan!"

I stare. I wasn't expecting my day to turn out like this. I went to school ready to have a normal day and then go to my piano lesson at 4:30.

I watch Mom, Mrs. Weston and Mr.

Weston have their boring little adult talk about losing a dog while Alice tentatively steps out of the car's back seat.

"... Alice might ..."

"... go easy ..."

"... Roger was special to her ... "

"... miss him too ..."

I can only make out a few whispers. That leaves me to talk to Alice. We're silent. I won't look at her. After a few minutes, though, I feel her eyes on me. I look up hesitantly. Her shoulders are drooped.

For some reason, I feel the beginnings of anger boiling again in the pit of my stomach. *Is she just standing there feeling sorry for herself?* This time, my temper is close enough to snatch back. I can barely get myself to reach out and grab it. "I ... I ... uh ... " I can't think of what to say first. S*hould I ask about Roger or talk about what happened at recess? I mean, recess is more recent, right? How long had Roger been missing anyway? A day? A week? A whole month, maybe?* I glance again at the signs. "*Lost dog!*" they read. *Had I been so self absorbed that I hadn't even noticed that Alice had lost her dog? Was that why she had been so upset at recess or was she truly angry at me?*

Suddenly, a rustling sound. Roger darts out of the bushes. His paws pat the ground, spraying up mud and clearing out the overcast sky. He wags his tail and flops his golden retriever ears. His collar jingles in the strained silence. The adults cease talking. Alice whirls around. "Roger!" Roger sticks his wet, sloppy nose into Alice's hand. "He came back!" She looks up at everyone else. Her eyes linger on me. I pat his head. Alice's parents pet him too and hug Alice.

"I wonder how he got home?" Mr. Weston asks no one in particular.

Mom and I stand back. Mom is teary-eyed. I stand by her side, feeling the comforting warmth of her arm around my shoulder. Roger struggles to break free of the Weston family hug and looks up at me expectantly.

"Oh, Roger!" Alice pulls him back. "What're *you* so interested in?"

At first I'm confused, but then I chuckle and slide the dog biscuit out of my pocket. Alice looks longingly at me before breaking into a smile. I guess she still remembers what we used to do when Roger was a puppy.

I laugh. "Fetch!" I toss the treat into the air. Roger pounds the ground and jumps up on his hind legs.

"Wow! Mid-air!" Alice rejoices, waving her hands in the air and jumping up and down.

Our parents enter her house, while Alice and I stand together. I gently put my arm around her, and together we watch Roger chase his tail. A slight breeze blows my hair into my face. The skies have cleared, revealing a bright sun. Just out of reach, though it seems I could brush it with my fingertips. A feeling washes over me, and I know right then, that this moment doesn't need words. Recess didn't need words. We share our warmth, and Alice smiles. Her smile is sweet and spreads across her face, bringing out her vibrant red hair, glistening in the light of the day with an air of peace. I couldn't remember seeing this smile before. This was her real smile.

School

by Julia Li, 12
Mason, OH

What if everyone wants to be your friend ... but for all the wrong reasons?

There is an alien among us.

She has built a wall across her heart, one made of sheets so thick others do not see her. Until they realize—

An alien is here, an alien is here—there is the alien.

She tries to walk the halls in silence, tries to creep up to classrooms.

It works, and the alien is not noticed.

Homework.

"Damn it," I mutter to myself quietly.

But everyone hears, and they crowd around me.

"Are you hurt?"

"Is there anything I can do?"

"If you need anything, just tell!"

I force a smile upon my face. "I'm okay—I just forgot my homework."

A girl whom I have never once noticed in my life walks up to me. In her hand is her homework.

This alien—she is an experiment.

She is a fake, she is different. And she knows that nobody will try to break down that wall around her. Who can see her first behind those green paper walls?

Maybe it's because I'm rich, because my dad is a millionaire.

I know nobody wants to be friends with a nobody. I know that nobody would willingly give their own homework away ...

To a nobody.

Who will like me once I grow up?

Once I am not different from the rest of them?

This alien, she knows that everyone loves that wall. They probe and push and talk. They do not care.

She is an experiment, a test to see who can take away that wall first.

I walk these halls alone.

Nobody comes to me until they realize that it's her, the girl with the money!

Soon enough, I might forget who

I am. I might just be the girl with the money.

This experiment is gone. This experiment is a nothing.

Blurred Love, *iPhone 6S*

by Daania Sharifi, 13
Gainesville, VA

Some Days

by Olivia Cadham, 11
Ontario, Canada

Some days I am a girl.

On these days I like to giggle and play with toys. I wear bright blue clothes and shirts with cats on them. When I feel like a girl, my feelings change. I feel kind and happy. I like being a girl.

But . . .

There is a downside.

My heart is bigger than on other days. It becomes too big for my body. This causes my feelings to mix together, and that results in emotional drama. This doesn't make me want to be a girl.

So . . .

Some days I am a boy.

On these days I like to be silly and play rough. I wear darker clothes, like blue, black, or red. When I'm a boy, I feel like my body fits me better. Sometimes it's as if God intended me to physically be a boy, but changed his mind at the last second. I like being a boy.

But . . .

Sometimes I feel like I'm too awkward to be a boy. I'm not a very sporty person, and I don't like jokes. This causes me to appear abnormal and too "sensitive." This doesn't make me want to be a boy.

So . . .

Some days I am a dragon.

On these days I like to stomp through the hallways and growl under my breath. I wear light clothing on these days so, being a Dutch Angel Dragon, my fur doesn't overheat. When I'm a dragon, I like to use pronouns like it, they, them, and their.

But . . .

Dragging around invisible wings, horns, and a tail all day gets exhausting really fast. I get agitated, and sometimes chirp swears (or something rude) in my language. Even though no one can understand, it is not a good feeling to be cursing, even if it's an accident. This doesn't make me want to be a dragon.

So . . . It's really quite simple. I make another choice . . . to be Olivia, who is currently a dragon (roar!!!).

Encased in Ice, *Nikon Coolpix L830*

by Hannah Parker, 13
South Burlington, VT

Moonlight

Third place in the Concrete Poetry Contest

by Ashley Xu, 13
Lexington, MA

Moonlight paints
the water white, rippling
like autumn frost on a window
pane, the texture of lace, or the
thin lines of froth spitting from a

creek searching for stillness in a midnight

storm, leaving the taste of wet
pavement, a pre-dawn driveway
lined by grass, milky drops
of petrichor clinging
to every green

blade in iridian teardrops of dew, light

lingering   dusty lilac,

reminiscent of a

photograph drenched

in silver halide

fading into being,   as if to say that

no image is static,

but always shifting,

shimmering

evanescence.

Figadindi

by Dennis Losett, 11
Philadelphia, PA

A stray dog begins to follow a boy and his family during their hike

I began to notice a collarless brown dog that seemed to be following us as the shadows of stucco houses became the shadows of trees and the narrow cobblestone street faded into a packed dirt path. It wasn't stray: it had a well-groomed coat of hair and was rather clean and friendly, but it wasn't quite a house dog either. I asked my mother about it, and she told me that I should ignore it—she didn't want a dog following us thinking we were its owners. My dad agreed. It seemed to run away, but then further up the trail, it sprang from the shaded understory of mulberry trees saplings and grass onto the trail with us.

I was trying to obey my mother, but it was impossible to ignore. I found that I shared many similarities with the dog. We both had boundless energy that inevitably made us centers of attention, we both ran ahead of my parents, and we both eventually brought smiles to my parents' faces.

When we passed the last human settlements, an entirely new terrain lay before us: van-sized cacti lay on bare earth scoured by drought and sunshine, semi-lifeless grass reached up from the ground like hair, and occasionally a daring tree stood beside the trail, soaking up the cloudless sky and providing much wanted shade. Another dog, even darker than the first one, began to follow us. His hair was very well trimmed, and he kept a pace equal to that of my parents. He was a house dog, for he had a collar, but he was as dark as good dark chocolate, while the dog we had met earlier was more of a milk chocolate hue. Throughout the course of the trail so far, my father and I had been scouring the area, looking for cactus pears. We had become enthusiasts of the odd fruit since we had found them on a walk. The sweet red-violet orbs hung off cacti by the half dozen or so, and in the local Neapolitan dialect of Italian they were called "figadindis." We had taken it upon ourselves to name the first dog this, and my parents seemed to be warming up to the idea of letting him stay.

Slowly but surely, the life was seeping back into the field, in optical form. At first, the grass became greener and taller, but then flowers and plants of every kind began to carpet the sides of the trail—brooms, tulips, poppies, sea thistles, daisies. As the verdant growth closed in from all sides, the trail narrowed our group down to single file. By this point, Figadindi was our only canine companion, for the collared dog had left. Small lizards scuttled in the fields and sunbathed on rocks, which Figadindi chased for entertainment. My dad now had a plastic shopping bag for holding cactus pears. A few wispy clouds floated on the horizon, shading faraway mountain peaks. From this altitude, the whole of the Amalfi Coast was visible. I was amazed at the beauty of the vista, though I did not show it.

We rounded a hilltop, and the trail fell into shrubbery and forest. I was intrigued by the contiguity of such drastic microclimates. Somehow, amazingly, evergreen pines had colonized the sides of the trail, and now the trail was separated from the surrounding thicket by wooden poles that lay parallel to the ground. I could sense that we were getting closer to Sorrento—a highway roared in the distance, and the sounds of wildlife grew ever fainter. We had not even so much as petted Figadindi, yet he almost felt like a family member to me. My parents implied that they felt the same way. About 50 meters from the fringe of the thicket, I heard a large rustle in a tree. Figadindi, crouching, was intimidating a large fowl sitting somewhere near the top of an evergreen. With a few barks, he sent the fowl on its way, breaking a number of branches as it scampered away. My family was awed. Figadindi, unfazed, simply returned to trotting down the path, and we soon followed.

We brushed through some bushes and branches, and a single two-lane road lay before us. Over the course of the trip, I had noticed that Italian roads were remarkably narrow, so we deduced that it was a highway. We crossed it and followed it downhill. We then came upon an urban labyrinth of streets, upon which my parents pulled out several maps and navigated us through a winding path of narrow alleys, shady streets, and mossy stairs. In fact, another dog had joined, this one a spotted, short-haired pitbull I named Motley. Relations between Motley and Figadindi were remarkably intriguing—sometimes the dogs were indifferent to each other, sometimes they were friendly, and at some point Motley even tried to mount Figadindi, which made me reconsider the genders of both. After a walk of about a mile, we arrived at a park, where we settled down for some hard-boiled eggs and pickles.

The park was only a temporary resting place, for after lunch, it was back to a fun exploration of the streets. For the rest of the walk, we did not return to the wild hills we had been in earlier. Some areas had more plants, some had less, but the two recurring themes were stucco houses and dogs. Frightening canine guards, perched on high walls, made sure that their masters' gardens were well protected. This area was famous for its lemons and oranges that grew to great sizes thanks to the fertile ash of Vesuvius, and local gardeners made sure no one intruded. Ironically, Figadindi was nothing more than annoyed by the guard dogs and fiercely stood his ground when intimidated. Motley was indifferent to them.

We soon came across a large boulevard leading down to the sea.

We followed it down a bit and then decided to roost at a restaurant. Motley had left, and Figadindi decided to lie down in the shade of our table. I began a conversation and became happily engrossed in food and dialogue. When I looked down, I saw that the spot where Figadindi had lain was empty. He had gone quickly, silently, and unnoticed, just like he had come.

Photo supplied by the author

STONE SOUP

Honor Roll

Welcome to the *Stone Soup* Honor Roll. Every month we receive submissions from hundreds of kids from around the world. Unfortunately, we don't have space to publish all the great work we receive. We want to commend some of these talented writers and artists and encourage them to keep creating.

Fiction
Leah Barrentine, 13
Claire Jiang, 12
Madeline Sornson, 11
Cathy Tu, 11
Sasha B. Wang, 12

Poetry
Shirin Gohil, 12

Art
MacKenzie Reese, 11

Honorable Mention in the Concrete Poetry Contest
"Snowflake" by Emma Almaguer, 13
"A Tree" by Andrew Lin, 8
"The Cloud" by Madeline Nelson, 12
"Seeing the Sea" by Maya Viswanathan, 12

Visit the *Stone Soup* store at Stonesoupstore.com to buy:

- Magazines: Individual issues of *Stone Soup*, past and present.

- Books: Our collection of themed anthologies (Fantasy, Sport, Poetry, and more), and the *Stone Soup Annual* (all the year's issues, plus a flavor of the year online, in one volume).

- Art prints—high quality prints from our collection of children's art

- Journals and sketchbooks for writing and drawing

... and more!

Don't forget to visit Stonesoup.com to browse our bonus materials. There you will find:

- 20 years of back issues—around 5,000 stories, poems, and reviews

- Blog posts from our young bloggers on subjects from sports to sewing—plus ecology, reading, and book reviews

- Video interviews with *Stone Soup* authors

- Music, spoken word, and performances

StoneSoup

APRIL 2019   VOLUME 47 / ISSUE 4

StoneSoup

*The magazine supporting
creative kids around the world*

Editor
Emma Wood

Director
William Rubel

Operations
Jane Levi

Education & Production
Sarah Ainsworth

Design
Joe Ewart

Stone Soup (ISSN 0094 579X) is published
11 times per year—monthly, with a
combined July/August summer issue.
Copyright © 2019 by the Children's
Art Foundation, a 501(c)(3) nonprofit
organization located in Santa Cruz,
California. All rights reserved.

Thirty-five percent of our subscription
price is tax-deductible. Make a donation at
Stonesoup.com/donate, and support us by
choosing Children's Art Foundation as your
Amazon Smile charity.

POSTMASTER: Send address changes to
Stone Soup, 126 Otis Street, Santa Cruz, CA
95060. Periodicals postage paid at Santa
Cruz, California, and additional offices.

Stone Soup is available in different formats
to persons who have trouble seeing or
reading the print or online editions. To
request the Braille edition from the National
Library of Congress, call +1 800-424-8567.
To request access to the audio edition via
the National Federation of the Blind's NFB-
NEWSLINE®, call +1 866-504-7300 or
visit www.nfbnewsline.org.

Check us out on social media:

Editor's Note

It's spring! The season of blooming flowers,
blue skies, and baby birds cheeping in their
nests. So, in this issue, in honor of spring,
I wanted to celebrate the visual in all of its
mediums. In addition to the romantic Parisian
painting, with its dreamy golds, pinks,
and blues, that graces our cover, this issue
features: a painting with a paper boat literally
pulling the piece into three dimensions; a
painted figurine that includes an ancient
Chinese poem about spring; a portfolio of
stylistically bold, bright landscapes; and
a traditional paper collage with a dark
twist. The quality and variety of the art
submissions we receive and publish in *Stone
Soup* never ceases to amaze me; I hope you
will leave this issue inspired not only by the
writing but by the visual art—in all of its
forms.

Enjoy the April showers!

Letters: We love to hear from our readers.
Please post a comment on our website or write
to us via Submittable or editor@stonesoup.
com. Your letter might be published on our
occasional Letters to the Editor page.

Submissions: Our guidelines are on the Submit
page at Stonesoup.com, where you will also find
a link to our Submittable online submissions
portal.

Subscriptions: To subscribe to *Stone Soup*,
please press the Subscribe button on our web
page, Stonesoup.com.

On the cover:
"Eiffel Tower"

**by Divya Narne, 12
Overland Park, KS**

StoneSoup
Contents

A Hardship, *mixed media*

by Alice Guo, 12
Austin, TX

A Trip to Paris?

by Claire Rinterknecht, 13
Strasbourg, France

Matthew, a travel writer with a dark past, prepares for his next trip

I visited the Shugakuin Imperial Villa on the last day of my trip. The garden is situated in the hills of the eastern suburbs of Kyoto.

Tangerine, magenta, and gold maple leaves glided down and settled on calm water like peaceful raindrops. The smudged greens and oranges of the foliage and the shadow of the rounded stone bridge merged on the pond to create a rainbow. The harmonic gong of a bell brought my gaze to a little scarlet and white pagoda. Its up-turned roof corners and nine-tiered tower made it easily recognizable. For Buddhists, each tier on the pagoda's tower represents one of nine levels of heaven. The scent of pond weed and lilies drifted up on the damp breeze. Camera snaps and elevated tourist chatter reminded me that I did not belong there. Box shrubs clustered around the edge of the pebble path. Behind them were the famous Japanese cherry blossom trees. And, every once in a while, bonsai also twisted and curled. Bonsai symbolize harmony and balance. They are grown with purposeful imperfection and the asymmetrical triangle used for their design symbolizes a continuation of life.

Japan was definitely worth the trip. It was a little frightening at first to walk around in Kyoto, so I suggest you use the subways until you get the hang of the streets. I found the Japanese were varied in their reception of an English tourist. Some grinned hugely at my accent and were willing to try to understand me, but some got annoyed at my lack of vocabulary and avoided me. Nevertheless, I wholeheartedly encourage you to plan a trip to Japan and to make sure you have the Shugakuin Imperial Villa at the top of your 'to do' list!

Matthew set down his quill and stared at his ink-stained fingers. He thought about how Blossom would have loved the Imperial Villa. Shaking his head as if to rid himself of the thought, he placed the leaves of cream paper in a brown envelope and wrote:

Travel column: *Japan*
by *Matthew Stevens*
For: The Daily Telegraph

He plucked his hat off its hook and shrugged on his green corduroy coat. His scuffed, battered briefcase in one hand, and the rattling doorknob in the other, he let himself out of the flat.

The sidewalk was cool in the early evening. Birds were singing and families were strolling home from a day at the park. *Bird song is the best kind of music in the world*, thought Matthew. Tired mothers pushed buggies with exhausted babies who drifted off to the rhythmic bumping. It had been a gorgeous day. The sun had been dazzling, the air heavy with blossoms and bird chatter. But now that evening had come, coolness rushed back in, as if trying to chase people off.

When Matthew reached the *Daily Telegraph* office, he took off his hat and stepped inside.

"Hello, Leslie." Matthew smiled at the secretary who was hunched over some papers at her desk in the foyer.

"Hello, Mr. Stevens." Leslie smiled and straightened up. "We were worried about you when we heard about the earthquake in Japan. I hope you were alright," Leslie asked with concern on her normally bright face.

"Oh yes ... I was alright ..." Matthew hesitated. *How had she heard about the earthquake?* "The epicenter was in the northern part of the island. Is Jane in her office?"

Leslie waited a second as if for more information, then said, "Yes, Jane is in."

Matthew thanked her and strode along the short hallway until he came to an open door with a little plaque on it reading: Jane Cunningham, Secretary and Typist. Matthew knocked lightly. Jane glanced up from her work and beckoned him inside.

"I'll be with you in a second, sir." Jane finished typing a sentence and then greeted Matthew: "Hello, Mr. Stevens."

Matthew said hello and handed her the brown envelope.

"I'll type it up straight away and get it to Mrs. Smith for tomorrow's edition. How was Japan?"

"Wonderful," Matthew replied without further explanation.

"It must have been amazing!" Jane prompted, but when she didn't get any details, she moved on. "Mrs. Smith is out at the moment, but she left a message. You're to go to France next. It has been a long time. Four years, wasn't it? Such a beautiful and romantic place," Jane ended dreamily, her eyes a little out of focus.

"Yes, France is a popular holiday destination. I like going there myself. I'll see you when I get back," Matthew answered quickly.

"Make sure you come back with a lovely story to tell."

Back outside, Matthew adjusted his briefcase and started down the narrow alleyway next to the office. At the end of the alleyway, he turned right onto a quaint street with trees lining the sidewalks and tulips in every garden; their petals faded in the twilight. At number 29, he took the steps up to a burgundy door two at a time. He hoped dinner would be ready. He rapped four times and then went to the kitchen window and tapped. A woman with his green eyes and brown hair glanced up at him and grinned, her eyes crinkling. She left the counter, leaving a man in the kitchen, and after a few seconds the front door opened.

"Matthew! You're a bit late!" She laughed.

"I know, sorry. I had to stop by the office."

They hugged, and Matthew followed her inside and placed his briefcase by the shoe rack. He took a deep breath in of spicy coconut coming from the kitchen.

"How are you, Gabrielle?"

"I'm well. And you?"

"Very well, but starving. Are you cooking curry?"

"Arthur's making his famous spicy masala."

They walked into the kitchen, but before Matthew could say hello to his brother-in-law, a flash of long flowing black hair, blue eyes, and small arms flew into his embrace.

"Matthew!!!"

Matthew hoisted the girl onto his lap as he sat down on a kitchen chair.

"Hello, Nancie. Has Robinson Crusoe satisfied your hunger for adventure?"

"Of course it hasn't! I want to go traveling with you, uncle! Where are you going next?"

"Mrs. Smith wants me to go to France. It's a holiday favorite and people want to know all about it all the time," Matthew explained.

"Can't I go with you?" Nancie didn't look at her mother because she already knew the answer. She always said no, and she knew Matthew would probably say no as well because she could barely remember the last trip they had been on together but she continued to ask him every time he came over anyway.

"Sorry, Nance, I can't take you. Anyway your mother wouldn't let you," Matthew said genially, but his gaze didn't quite reach her eyes. He looked over her head and suggested they set the table.

Matthew chased Nancie round in circles until the last spoon was laid and then they both flopped down on the red rug, exhausted from running and giggling. They lay there, laughing their heads off, until Arthur and Gabrielle came in with the masala and salad, and then they leapt up to their places at the table.

Dinner was an energetic meal. Nancie kept up a constant flow of conversation, gabbing about nothing and making up terrible jokes that she would laugh at hysterically, making everyone else laugh, so that they could share her joy.

After the dishes were washed, Matthew and Nancie went to Nancie's room where he read to her from *Alice's Adventures in Wonderland*, the new book he had brought. At one point, when Alice was walking through the woods and she saw the Cheshire cat, Matthew stopped reading.

"That reminds me of when Blossom and I went to Colorado. Blossom tried to climb a tree to see if the peak of the mountain would seem any closer, but when she came back down she said it didn't make a difference." Matthew chuckled at the memory but his voice died away quickly.

"Do you miss Blossom?" Nancie asked. "I do. I wish she were still here to show me the fun rocks to climb."

Matthew put down the book, and Nancie snuggled next to him.

"I miss Blossom very much, Nance," he said. "I miss her more than I thought was possible to miss anyone in the world."

———————————————

"I miss her more than I thought was possible to miss anyone in the world."

Matthew unlocked the door to his quiet apartment and flicked on the light bulb. He hung up his coat and hat and on his way down the corridor placed his briefcase on a wooden chest full of books.

Matthew put water on the stove to boil and watched its still surface slowly agitate with tiny bubbles coming up from the bottom of the pan. It was funny, Matthew thought, how they came up in such perfectly straight lines and then disappeared when there was no more water to move through. *Like raindrops*, he thought, *going in the opposite direction.*

Matthew found the teapot, put in some black tea leaves, and poured the boiling water on top. While the tea was steeping, he went over to the bookshelf where all the European travel books were and ran his fingers along their spines.

"Ah-ha!" he said aloud when he found the one he wanted. He thumbed through it to make sure it had a chapter on Paris and then continued to search for other books. By the time his tea had steeped, there was a teetering pile of paperbacks about France resting on the armchair.

He settled down with his tea and books and read long into the night. He visited Paris, Strasbourg, Lyon, and many other places besides. Matthew read so long that he fell asleep in his chair.

When he awoke, he found himself as he had been the night before, apart from the fact that his empty teacup had tipped in his lap and several books had fallen to the floor. He quickly picked them up and placed them back on the chair. In the kitchen, he set his teacup on the counter and looked at the clock: 6:30. Matthew decided he might as well start the day, so he reached for a mason jar from the cupboard, took the peanut butter and soy milk from the refrigerator, a banana from the fruit bowl, and the hot chocolate powder from the shelf. He put everything in the jar and the blender whirred it all together.

As he sat at the table to drink his smoothie, he heard a knock at the door.

"Gabrielle! Nancie!" he exclaimed in surprise when he saw who it was.

"Matthew! I'm sorry to disturb you so early in the morning but I just got a call from work, and I have to go in straight away. Arthur has already gone so I was wondering if you could look after Nancie for a few hours?"

"Yes, of course. Have you had breakfast yet, Nancie?"

"No." Nancie yawned and leaned against her mother.

"I was just about to have mine, so you can join me," Matthew took her hand. "Go on, Gabrielle, or you'll be late for work."

"Thank you, Matthew! I'll pick her up at lunchtime or I'll call," she shouted back as she rushed down the hallway.

"Come on, Nance. It looks like you

got out of bed a little too early this morning," Matthew chuckled.

Nancie yawned again in reply.

Matthew led her into the living room. He hastily moved all the books off of the armchair and onto the coffee table so Nancie could curl up in it. Next, he set about cooking a hot breakfast. He baked apple muffins and fried eggs (he didn't like scrambled eggs and neither did Nancie) and then blended up Nancie's favorite frozen berry and yogurt smoothie. The warm smells of Matthew's cooking drifted over to Nancie, and she roused slowly and rubbed her eyes of sleep.

"Matthew, why do you have all these books about France out? You're about to be there; you don't need to read about it!" she proclaimed.

"It never hurts to know more about where you're going. Anyway, most of these are travel guides." Matthew turned back to the counter, away from Nancie.

Nancie held up one of the books. "This one isn't. Look, *The Hunchback of Notre-Dame*, and this one isn't either . . . or this one." Nancie held up several books.

"Oh? I must have put the guides in my room then," Matthew quickly busied himself by cracking eggs into a hot pan.

"Matthew?"

"Yes, Nance?"

"What kind of adventure do you think you'll have in France?"

Matthew smiled and finished salting the eggs. He loved it when Nancie asked him that question.

"Well now. I'll sit by the Seine while drinking a glass of Bordeaux and eating Camembert on freshly baked baguette. I'll watch the sun turn the water to liquid gold and set the trees on fire. Fairy lights will twinkle in the dying light and the romantic hush of French voices will drift along with the current of the Seine. Butterflies will land next to me and tiny forget-me-nots will nod their heads. Aubrieta and black-eyed Susans clustered at the base of the bridge will sway in time to the allegretto played on a piano by delicate fingers."

"Is that what France is really like?" Nancie said, amazed.

"Yes." Matthew placed a hot plate in front of Nancie, then sat down with his own breakfast.

"It sounds splendid. I wish I could come. Are you sure—"

"Quite sure. I will take you to the park, though, if you finish up your breakfast."

"But I . . . alright," Nancie sighed and finished her smoothie.

Before they left, Matthew made sure he had his briefcase, a pad of paper, and a pen. He made Nancie wear a sweater, put on his own coat and hat, and then they walked out the door.

The park was relatively large with a playground at the center. Buttercups and tulips covered the bright lawn. It was still chilly outside, but Matthew could tell it would be another lovely day. The only sounds were their voices and those of the birds. When they got to the playground, Nancie went straight to the climbing structure. Matthew wasn't surprised; he knew how much Nancie liked to climb. He sat on a bench near the bottom of the structure and set his briefcase beside him. He took the pad of paper from under his arm and began writing. Every once in a while, he would look up at Nancie to make sure she was alright. He got nervous when she climbed, and he didn't like to take his eyes off her for more than a few minutes at a time. As Nancie was nearing the top, Matthew had an idea spark and was scribbling quickly when he heard the scream. His eyes flashed up and he jumped to his feet. He saw Nancie lose her grip and tip backwards. His blood went cold. *Nancie!* His long strides got him to the structure just as she fell. Matthew caught her in his arms and put her down gently. His arms were shaking badly.

"Are you okay? Are you hurt?" Matthew inquired with a trembling voice.

"I'm okay. I just got scared."

"Never do that again, Nance, alright? You nearly killed me." Matthew sat down next to her.

"Sorry, Matthew." She hugged him, and he held her tightly. That's when he noticed his papers. In his haste to catch Nancie, Matthew had let all the papers fly out of his lap, and they were now strewn all over the ground. Nancie and Matthew went over and started to pick them up. Matthew moved as quickly as possible and whenever Nancie picked one up he took it from her as soon as she had it in her hands. But Nancie saw snatches of his writing, however

hard Matthew tried to hide it from her. She picked up the last one and then stepped back so Matthew couldn't take it. She read the first few lines.

"Thank you, Nancie." Matthew reached out his arm demonstrating that she needed to hand him the paper. "Go play while I finish tidying this up."

But Nancie didn't move. She stayed as still as a statue.

"Go on, Nancie, just don't play on the climbing structure anymore," Matthew insisted.

Nancie still didn't budge and didn't hand back the paper she clutched in one hand.

She began to read off the sheet: "The sun was falling behind the trees, catching them on fire. As it touched the earth with its magnificence, the Seine turned to liquid gold and a soft allegretto started up somewhere high above, played by delicate fingers. Butterflies twirled in the air, dancing to the music. Clustered at the base of the bridge, tiny forget-me-nots nodded their heads and dandelions shook their manes."

She stared up at Matthew in confusion. "This is the story that you told me this morning. Why are you writing the column when you haven't been to France yet?"

"Nancie, come here." Matthew gestured for her to sit next to him on the bench.

Nancie joined him. Matthew took

As Nancie was nearing the top, Matthew had an idea spark and was scribbling quickly when he heard the scream.

STONE SOUP

a deep breath, lifted his briefcase onto his lap, and undid the clasp. Matthew's hands shook as he took out two passports and a few photographs.

"These are the photos from my last trip. And our passports. Blossom's and mine. This was the last photo I took of her before she died." Matthew held up the crinkled photo of a woman in shorts and an orange t-shirt. "She was laughing because I had just told her a joke. She let go of the boulder she was climbing and fell. I couldn't catch her. She was too far away. She shouldn't have died. I ran to help, but I wasn't quick enough. I haven't gone anywhere since. I'm too afraid that something else might happen." He fumbled with one of the passports. The portrait of a slender woman with round amber eyes and chestnut hair gazed up at them.

"She never liked having her photo taken for her passport because she couldn't smile. She said that if she couldn't smile she wasn't who she was," Matthew said in a hushed voice.

Nancie gently took the photos that Matthew had set aside and stared at the top one. It was of the same woman, but this time her eyes were laughing and Matthew was with her. They were standing on a bridge, the water behind them a dull blue because the sky was overcast. The dismal weather had not dampened the young lovers' spirits. They both beamed at the camera. The next photo was of Blossom again, where she sat in front of the Eiffel Tower, the sun kissing her face. The last one was of Blossom with her arms outstretched and her head tilted back as she looked up at the sky and let the rain drench her from head to toe.

"Matthew? Why did you pretend to keep traveling? Why didn't you just stop and tell everyone?"

"I'm not sure, Nance. I suppose I thought that if I continued to write the column, I could pretend that I was getting over Blossom. I also didn't want to disappoint you and was embarrassed that I was scared. Also, I needed the money. How would I pay my bills?"

"You could have come to live at our house," Nancie said.

Matthew hugged Nancie. He didn't know what he would do without her. He held her tight, thankful that she didn't let go. He was still her idol, even if he made gigantic mistakes.

The sky had greyed, and a brisk wind made Matthew pull his corduroy coat around Nancie. The air rumbled with a passing airplane.

"Take me with you to Paris," Nancie said.

Matthew considered his courageous niece and smiled.

Then he stood up and held out his hand, and together they walked with renewed purpose out of the park. In Matthew's free hand, he held his briefcase, considerably lighter than it had been the day before. He was ready to go on a new adventure.

Chinese Calabash Girls

by Ziqing Peng, 10
Nanjing, China

Chinese Calabash I, *Chinese ink, watercolors, and calabash*

Chinese Calabash II, *Chinese ink, watercolors, and calabash*

On my second calabash, I drew a Chinese poem written by Wang Anshi, a famous prime minister of the Northern Song Dynasty. The poem describes the Spring Festival in ancient China. Here is the poem in Chinese and its translation in English.

Spring Festival Eve
by Wang Anshi (1021-1086)
Written during the Northern Song Dynasty (960-1127)

元日
（北宋）王安石
爆竹声中一岁除，
春风送暖入屠苏。
千门万户曈曈日，
总把新桃换旧符。

Firecrackers are shouting goodbye to the last year,
In warm spring breeze people drink tusu wine.
Thousands of households greet the bright rising sun,
Replacing each couplet on the door with a new one.

Joyous Ensemble

by Sabrina Guo, 12
Oyster Bay, NY

A violinist on tour in China contemplates the power of music

In Shenzhen, China, the night before my first performance on tour with the Joyous String Ensemble, one of the youngest string ensembles in the world, I dreamt of a plum. Up close, it was a combination of pink, red, and orange. In front of me, two paths intersected, forming a shape like a cross, with an aqua pond in the middle and a spectacular fountain hovering in midair that had flowing, agile water, spouting melted diamonds and crystals. I looked down and was surprised to see that I was floating above the glass path, which encased running water with huge koi and calypso fish. They swam smoothly and gracefully, whipping their tails in an airy, wave-like way. There were a bunch of trees surrounding me. I could smell fruity scents and the cherry blossoms; the aroma was pure and sweet, not at all strong and overwhelming like most garden scents. I tried propelling myself by swinging my arms like helicopter blades. I went *up . . . up . . .* and *up . . .* as if I might touch the clouds.

The next night, I felt a bright white light on me. Then green. Then blue. Then purple, which made the violin look orange and made my Pirastro Evah Pirazzi Gold's bottom glow in

the dark. The light testing was over. I smiled at the audience and waved, following the others, and tried my best to look straight ahead, not at anyone in particular. There was just this blurry wavering sea of heads stretched in every direction. I raised my violin to my chin, and we began our set.

Accompanying us on the piano was Mr. Julian Yu, the director of the Joyous String Ensemble and an accomplished composer, conductor, and performing pianist. He has been an inspirational mentor, teaching us how to genuinely enjoy the wonders of music. He said that music is not just a sound but also an emotion, like happiness, sadness, regret, or love. He's encouraged us to use the power of music to spread love and kindness. He believes that music can help save lives and change the world. I doubted this at first, but now, I believe that all of these ideas are within reach.

As I played that night, I was brimming with nervousness, but I focused on how happy everyone had looked on the car ride to the theater. My happiest memories of being in this ensemble have taken place right before each performance—everyone excited and ready to communicate with the audience through music. Our first piece was "Summer" by Vivaldi, which slowly morphed into "Smooth Criminal" by Michael Jackson. Adrenaline flooded my body; the energy around the stage was magnetic, and I felt my bow moving with forces that seemed inside and outside of me at the same time. I smiled in my heart and wondered if my friends felt the same. The first set flew by, and then the second, and before I knew it the performance was over! So quickly, it was hard to track individual moments, but by the end, standing up before an audience cheering and hooting—my crazy dad especially, who kept yelling through his cupped hands—suggested it had been a success. I just kept thinking to myself, *keep smiling* . . .

After the performance, we rode back to our hotel, where we were staying high up on the 24th floor. I gazed out the window to the streets busy with people scrambling about, advertising salesmen shoving papers into people's hands, bicycles zigzagging in every direction. My parents called to me, reminding me to get my rest, since the next day we'd be leaving early for Beijing. I flopped into bed, cactus-style, and couldn't help smiling again, replaying parts of the performance before I fell asleep.

I had yellow watermelon for breakfast the next morning. It was soft, not as crisp as the red kind I was used to, but sweeter. It took me a while to wrap my brain around yellow juice and black seeds meshed together. Yet another reminder that I was in a new place, far from home, where I couldn't expect to follow the same routine, or to experience the same tastes, smells, or sounds. Same as the music of chopsticks clinking together like a drum beat, the sound of knobs turning to send hotpots clicking, the flicker of flames erupting under dishes. Around the corner from our hotel, there was a small alleyway with a bunch of restaurants and a bakery. The next morning, when we left to catch our ride, the whole street was alive with spices filling my nose, sweetly offset by freshly baked bread and sugar.

Our second performance was even more nerve-wracking because we would be performing with Master Lu Si Qing, the best violinist in China and one of my idols. The fact that I was going to accompany him seemed impossible. When we first met him backstage, I marveled over his shiny blue jacket and perfectly creased pants. On stage, he stood before us, chasing the melody of every piece. I felt his raw energy as he rocked and swayed, almost like the violin was an extension of his body, the music living inside him all along. Almost every face in the audience hid behind a videotaping phone, which I imagined made us look like little halos of light around our master. We accompanied him for Vivaldi's Double Concerto, another dizzying blur. I remember this intense feeling of fatigue and excitement afterward, as the audience roared in a standing ovation. Each young player received a rose, and I was thrilled to get the reddish purple one I'd been hoping for, one that reminded me of the plum in my dream. We all exited the stage, and I was surprised when we were served glasses of water on a

I started to think every object was part of a story or larger dream that can come alive through travel and music

black tray. I slowly sipped the water, relishing its smooth, sweet taste.

That night, my memory traveled back to my family's earlier visit to Shenzhen. We had visited an antique store, where there were glass displays with little sky-blue vases with clover-like plants that only had one leaf: two thin stalks in each vase. In the corner, there was a long table from ancient times with a large wooden turtle sitting on it. My parents used to tell me these animals are symbols of wisdom, and I think that's true because they live for a long time and move so slowly, like they've seen it all and don't understand any hurry. I walked over to the table with my father, who told me how to check if it was authentically as old as it appeared. You look for stripped logs placed horizontally on top, with wooden planks below for support. After we examined it, we could tell it was truly an ancient table. In the U.S., we seem to value the physical appearance of things over their history or the traditions and stories implied by them. I started to think every object was part of a story or larger dream that can come alive through travel and music.

At the Shanghai concert, we were surrounded by people everywhere. We were on an enormous platform, and there was the audience—behind us, next to us, in front of us, and above us. Not only was this the biggest show yet, but this time we were raising

money through ticket sales and autograph signings for a 14-year-old boy's mother who needed a lifesaving surgery. The boy was a talented singer, but since China doesn't have many performance events for his age group, he lacked the opportunity to raise the money for his mother alone. The leader of our group is Justin Yu, the 11-year-old son of our director, who is already a world-famous cellist. The boy came out to sing with him for one of the numbers. It was a very emotional moment, feeling the boy's spirit there on the stage, and afterward, I watched some people in the audience wipe their eyes through a thunder of applause. It was the first time that I had ever performed with a higher purpose in mind, beyond wanting to share my love of music with the world, for a family in need. The tour ended, and we received a letter from the boy's father with news that the surgery had worked. While Mr. Yu had told us that music could help to save lives, I hadn't quite believed him until I read that letter. We all felt so moved and honored to be part of that success.

Later that night, I had another dream. Time was frozen, and there were a bunch of string instruments floating around, moving one millimeter per second. I plucked the A-string of a violin in midair, which created a big wave of echoes that blasted my eardrums. The strange thing was,

I could see the sound waves. The A-string made a strawberry-colored wave, D made a yellow wave, while G was sienna, and E was green. Each instrument produced different colored waves, as if they were part of a realm behind the music. Sometimes I wonder if my dreams are synesthesiac, with sounds forming colors through my memory. All the music swirled around my brain at night and pranced around like horses. I wondered if this was all part of living the music, not just practicing and playing it, but feeling its forces upon me, like a liquid that had begun to pump through my heart and lungs, sustaining me through these weeks. Somehow, I played three more concerts with the same energy as the first, and time only seemed to speed up with each—this continual flow of motion that I became more accustomed to, making it harder to separate out individual memories afterward.

I have visited China many times before. Ever since I was three, I've been traveling with my parents to Shenyang to visit my extended family. Usually, we stay at my aunt's house, where they have a fish tank and a little bonsai tree I like to watch my aunt trim. I also like the feel of the tiny leaves, sharp like needles. They always make me think of a miniature world that exists beyond my imagination. Invisible birds and rivers making inaudible sounds. Some mornings, if we wake early enough, we walk to the morning market, where we shop for everything from fried pure milk to jewelry and barbecued squid. Nearby, there is also a sushi restaurant with fresh octopus and salmon rolls. We

always eat in the room where the floor makes noises like tapping ice. Above, there is a chandelier: like glass stars suspended in the air, dangling from a thin hook, encrusted in a zodiac of birthstones. The breeze from the AC causes them to swing from side to side as if they were flowers swaying to a forgotten melody.

These memories transport me back to the moment I am living now, in the wake of last summer's China tour. Sometimes I feel music is a special language of memory between times and places. Music reminds me of an open door to a clear sky. Sometimes, I feel what you want to say can be conveyed better in music than in words. Music carries my feelings, the same way memories do, one thing leading to the next and the next, all through shared emotions between people, placing those people within reach of one another. Sometimes I think memory and music work together like a dream: I start remembering one place and all of its images seep out in a colorful spiral of smells and tastes and sounds, all capturing the soul of a place, a period of time. And then I wake up from that dream and wonder how I got from there to here and back again, as if my memory is one continuous map, this circle of song printed inside me.

Gilmanton at Night

by Anya Geist, 12
Worcester, MA

The crickets chirp, sing to the starry night.

The floorboards creak and moan of old age.

The wallpaper stands rigid, but cracked and peeling.

The motorcycles rev and talk back and forth by the road.

The two old Volvos settle in on the grassy lot.

A musty, old-yet-comforting smell seeps everywhere in the house.

I turn over in bed, to look at moonlight streaming through the gaping crack in the
     shade.

Across the street, the antique store is boarded up,

Its precious relics waiting until tomorrow.

The corner store is closed, sodas and water closed up,

Coffee makers quiet, until the morning brew.

Down at the pond, the bathhouse looms quietly, old green paint on the outside.

Swimsuits and towels hang on racks in rooms, swaying in a soft breeze.

The day's sand tracked in is leaking through the old planks on the floor,

Falling onto the ground beneath.

The raft bobs in the pond, surrounded by dark glistening water.

Up the dirt road to Drew Farm,

Wild animals roam the backyard.

In the attic, the lights are off.

In the room at the back, mattresses, chairs, tables, and papers are left sprawled out

In the middle of planning.

In Airy Cottage, the lights are out,

The radio, always playing orchestras, is off and quiet.

Back in the Little House, all the screen doors are locked

And the porch furniture stands still on the porch.

This is Gilmanton at night.

The House

The cicadas chirp a lullaby to the night.

Their buzzing seems obtrusive at first

But grows to be comforting and content.

Inside, the tiled floor sits cold with all its rivets and dips.

Shutters are locked shut to the windows,

Hatches battened down,

Giving the impression of the quarters of a ship

Sailing through the long, dry grasses of Southern France.

In the beige bedroom, I lie on the twin bed, my shoulder leaning against the wall.

My friend lies across the room, snoring peacefully.

Outside, down the hallway, the fifth bedroom lays vacant.

The other three are occupied, their doors shut tightly.

The steep, tiled stairs lead the way down to the first floor,

Its high ceiling grand but inviting.

The two L-shaped couches in the back living room host card boxes

From games previously played.

These floors are new and wooden.

The windows there still show outside, onto the small cracked patio.

The kitchen is on the front left side of the house,

Cramped but piled with food

And giving way to the laundry room with its low, stooped ceiling.

The dining room table is cleared off,

Its blue tablecloth lit up by the moon that shines bright through the windows.

The alcoves in it are in shadow, mysterious and dark.

The great front door creaks on its old hinges.

Breezes whish through the air,

Spreading the smell of overripe fruit from the trees.

The cars and table sit on a rough gravel.

Through a grove, the pool sits dark.

Its sloshing can be heard, a welcoming sound.

Five chairs sit under an umbrella, relaxing.

A yard of dry grasses stretches until a set of bushes.

From the yard, the whole city seems to be seen.

All of the narrow streets and alleys and squares of Aix-en-Provence.

The mountain of Sainte-Victoire looms in the distance,

Standing where it can just be seen.

Returning through the small grove, the house is sleepy and tired.

The shutters are closed and the windows on the first floor are empty and dark

Even as the moon shines on the front of the house.

The old, worn stone is cool to the touch in the dry night.

Back in bed, I lay under the blanket, chilly

And think of the house perched on its hill

Sleeping under the canopy of night.

Portfolio

by John P. Anson, 7
Kerala, India

The Sky at Night and Day, *oil pastels*

Beautiful Forest, *oil pastels*

Train that Going Through a Forest, *oil pastels*

Eternal Friendship

by Blanche Li, 9
Danville, CA

*A girl struggles to overcome an old fear in order
to accept a new friend*

My mom and I walked through the narrow hallway, noticing all the people around us. I saw a girl in a purple floral dress standing next to her dad. She looked a little younger than I was. I wondered if we were going to be friends. After that, I saw a cast on the girl's right arm, a type of cast I had never seen before. It looked like decorated plastic. Quickly, I glanced away because I knew it was rude to stare. Still, what was that? It didn't look like a cast. I thought it was unusual. Absentmindedly, I strolled the rest of the way to the classroom.

When we were finally inside, I saw that four students were sitting in their chairs and were unpacking their cellos in a great rush, as if they were police searching bags. One of the students even chipped his cello because he was in such a hurry to be the first to unpack and get the best seat. I looked up at the ceiling. It looked kind of like those dance ceilings full of beams. I guessed they were used for supporting the floors above it.

Just then, I noticed that the girl I had previously seen was taking off her arm! I was blank for a minute. Then I knew it. Her right arm was actually artificial. Next, she took something out of a large grocery bag. It seemed like an advanced bionic arm. It was tan and white. Its shape made me feel as if the arm were twisted all around. I could see the technology at work. She handed the bionic arm to her dad, who was a tall and silent man. His attention was focused only on his daughter. He twisted it a few times on her arm and then "Click!"—it was on.

During the group lesson, I learned from our teacher that the girl's name was Kylie. Kylie's bionic arm had two clips. One was fastened to a modified bridge that supported the strings of her cello and one was fastened to her bionic arm. This way, when Kylie played, the bow wouldn't slide off the cello. Her dad also put a Bow-Right on the bridge, a two-piece metal frame that was fastened to both sides of the bridge. It was looped by rubber bands and many small pieces of cushion. I pondered why Kylie needed so many cushions on her cello. Finally, I understood that this way, the cello would not get chipped or scratched.

I started wondering if I should pay attention to Kylie and be friends with her. Sometimes I have nightmares about people with disabilities. Once I met a boy who had lost two of his fingers. I didn't know if I was going to have a nightmare about Kylie. Maybe not. I wasn't sure at all. Sometimes, all these nightmares start to pop into my head. I didn't know if I was going to have terrifying dreams about her. I thought she might scare me off in my dream. But I was still hesitating. The only problem was I still wanted a friend.

Kylie was still sitting next to me. When she was playing, I noticed something else. Her other hand's fingers were half the length of my own. That brightened my heart up. She made me feel like she was amazing and talented. I couldn't believe she could play the cello.

When Kylie left early that day because she was tired, a girl in the class asked, "What happened to her?"

My teacher just replied, "She was born like that." I wasn't sure if my teacher really meant it. Maybe it was just a secret that Kylie, her family, and her teacher shared.

One month later, my teacher set up a free 30-minute play-together for Kylie and me. We got to play duets, holiday songs, and games with each other. It was really fun. I realized that Kylie was a great, energetic girl. She asked questions, said "hi" to everyone she saw, and was never afraid to make mistakes. Gradually, Kylie and I became friends. Slowly, my fear of nightmares about Kylie disappeared. I learned that the nightmares come to me only if I let them. If I think about them too much, the nightmares overtake my brain. It is kind of like they are gum stuck to the corner of my mind. Once they are there, I can't get them off. They only loosen when I'm sleeping, and then the devastating dreams about snakes and ghosts happen. If I don't let them come into my head, they won't come. And in each of my schools I have been to, I remember at least one of my friends who had a disability. I now knew that disabilities were normal. All my friends who had disabilities could be the same as me. They could eat ice cream, they could play games and instruments, and they could always have smiles on their faces.

Then one day, news from my teacher overloaded my brain. Kylie was coming to a six-day cello camp with me in Washington! I wanted to jump up and down and laugh with joy! I could not believe it. How would she play in front of a crowd without being frightened? If I were her, I would be terrified that I would make a mistake, and I would be scared that people would look at me as if I were someone to gawk at. I could imagine this because there was once a boy at my old school named Josh who always called me "lima bean girl" when I had a scar on my face. And guess what? After a few minutes, all my friends came to call me that. No one likes that kind of attention.

I learned that the nightmares come to me only if I let them

I waited and waited for the day to come. The day I would be able to talk to Kylie and have fun again. Finally, it came.

The day I met Kylie at cello camp was a cool day with the sun shining its bright rays over us. I was really excited to talk to her.

The lessons were 12 hours long. We had to stay with each other all the time. At first, I thought fear would return to my brain. But I knew that it was just a silly thing for a girl like me to think of.

Our teachers grouped Kylie and me into a pair. We shared music stands. Kylie helped me find which building to go to. Once we got there, I quickly unpacked and helped set up our benches and stands. Kylie had a great memory. She remembered the right music piece we needed for our lesson. On the last day of camp, we had a recital. Our music was several pages long. While playing, our right hands were occupied by the bow so we had to use our left hands to quickly turn the page. When I turned the page, it was very likely that the rest of the music on the stand would drop. When it was time to flip the pages, Kylie held the other side of the music on the stand. This way, we could move onto the next music seamlessly. After the recital, Kylie and I gave each other a Bow-Five. We had collaborated so well. Even our camp teachers couldn't help noticing it.

Kylie told me that she has two bionic arms. One has a stripe pattern and one has a rainbow print. She also told me that her bionic arm grows with her. One afternoon, during the lesson

break, I held one of her bionic arms and gazed at it in wonder. Kylie looked at me. Without a word, she reached out her hand and touched my face. I turned my eyes to her. I could feel her friendship orbiting my body. It was a gentle, friendly, and warm feeling. It felt like everlasting friendship.

To my parents, I am a wonder. To Kylie's parents, she is a wonder. Making new friends is also a wonder. There are lots of wonders in the world. Open your hand, grab them, and they will be within your reach.

The Juggle Man

by Analise Braddock, 7
Katonah, NY

One day I went to the juggle place and on a shelf sat the juggle man.

He said to me you took a juggle now give it back to me.

The owner of the juggle place said to go home and then she called the police.

The police said outside there is young poor Sally with balls in hand but cannot juggle.

Then the police said on a Monday you took a suitcase on Tuesday you took a toothbrush and on Friday you poured milk.

What a bad girl you have been.

Color City, *paper collage*

by Adhi Sukhdial, 7
Stillwater, OK

Honor Roll

Welcome to the *Stone Soup* Honor Roll. Every month we receive submissions from hundreds of kids from around the world. Unfortunately, we don't have space to publish all the great work we receive. We want to commend some of these talented writers and artists and encourage them to keep creating.

Fiction

Annie Baker-Young, 8
Ava Horton, 13
Aaron Huang, 12
Marilena Korahais, 8
Liliana McCowan, 11
Selina Ni, 11
Pip Reese, 8
Sarah Zimmerman, 12

Poetry

Talia Chin, 7
Amity Doyle, 9
Yaelin Hough, 12
Celia Miller Pitt, 12
Kathleen Werth, 9
Sasha Yelagina, 9

Art

Sarah Berry, 13
Story Kummer, 12

Visit the *Stone Soup* store at Stonesoupstore.com to buy:

- Magazines—individual issues of *Stone Soup*, past and present.

- Books—our collection of themed anthologies (fantasy, sport, poetry, and more), and the *Stone Soup Annual* (all the year's issues, plus a flavor of the year online, in one volume).

- Art prints—high quality prints from our collection of children's art

- Journals and sketchbooks for writing and drawing

...and more!

Don't forget to visit Stonesoup.com to browse our bonus materials. There you will find:

- 20 years of back issues—around 5,000 stories, poems, and reviews

- Blog posts from our young bloggers on subjects from sports to sewing—plus ecology, reading, and book reviews

- Video interviews with *Stone Soup* authors

- Music, spoken word, and performances

StoneSoup

MAY 2019

VOLUME 47 / ISSUE 5

StoneSoup

*The magazine supporting
creative kids around the world*

Editor
Emma Wood

Director
William Rubel

Operations
Jane Levi

Education & Production
Sarah Ainsworth

Design
Joe Ewart

Stone Soup (ISSN 0094 579X) is published
11 times per year—monthly, with a
combined July/August summer issue.
Copyright © 2019 by the Children's
Art Foundation, a 501(c)(3) nonprofit
organization located in Santa Cruz,
California. All rights reserved.

Thirty-five percent of our subscription
price is tax-deductible. Make a donation at
Stonesoup.com/donate, and support us by
choosing Children's Art Foundation as your
Amazon Smile charity.

POSTMASTER: Send address changes to
Stone Soup, 126 Otis Street, Santa Cruz, CA
95060. Periodicals postage paid at Santa
Cruz, California, and additional offices.

Stone Soup is available in different formats
to persons who have trouble seeing or
reading the print or online editions. To
request the Braille edition from the National
Library of Congress, call +1 800-424-8567.
To request access to the audio edition via
the National Federation of the Blind's NFB-
NEWSLINE®, call +1 866-504-7300 or
visit www.nfbnewsline.org.

Check us out on social media:

Editor's Note

Often, the work in our issues is just as
concerned with animals and the natural
world as with humanity and civilization—
not by choice, but by necessity: it reflects
our contributors' interests. But, in this issue,
people and civilization (cities! cars! castles!)
are the main subjects. Patrick Lusa's poem
"Numbers" captures the hustle and bustle
of everyday life; Anna Shepherd's story
"Twenty Questions, Twenty Answers"
explores the complicated-but-close
relationship between two sisters; and Mia
Fang's digital portrait "Lady in the Willows
by the River" (on the cover) places a person
squarely in the center of our usual cover
landscape.

We hope you enjoy reading and looking at
the many other works that appear in this
issue, and that you leave feeling inspired to
send us some people- and car-filled stories,
poetry, and artwork.

Letters: We love to hear from our readers.
Please post a comment on our website or write
to us via Submittable or editor@stonesoup.
com. Your letter might be published on our
occasional Letters to the Editor page.

Submissions: Our guidelines are on the Submit
page at Stonesoup.com, where you will also find
a link to our Submittable online submissions
portal.

Subscriptions: To subscribe to *Stone Soup*,
please press the Subscribe button on our web
page, Stonesoup.com.

On the cover:
"Lady in the Willows
by the River"

**by Mia Fang, 13
West Lafayette, IN**

StoneSoup
Contents

FICTION

POETRY

ART

PORTRAITS: A MULTI-ARTIST PORTFOLIO

Bird in the Clouds, *Nikon Coolpix L830*

by Hannah Parker, 13
South Burlington, VT

Twenty Questions, Twenty Answers

by Anna Shepherd, 11
Brooklyn, NY

An infuriating game of twenty questions pushes Jenny to scour her childhood memories

Only ten minutes had gone by since the last rest stop, but to me it felt like an hour. My knee bounced. My leg jiggled. My fingers drummed out syncopated rhythms on the door handle.

"*Jennifer*," said my older sister, Ula, "stop tapping."

I gritted my teeth and began slapping the side of my thigh instead. "It's Jenny."

"*Jennifer*, you're still making noise."

"My name is Jenny!"

"Ula, Jenny, stop bickering," said Mom in that stiff, controlled voice that meant she was trying very, very hard not to yell. "Especially you, Ula. You're 15. You should know better."

Dad turned around in the passenger seat. "Girls, you're stressing her out. Why don't you play Twenty Questions?"

"Yes," I said instantly. Ula groaned, but I noticed the look of satisfaction in her brown eyes.

"I'll start," she said in a practiced drawl.

"Fine."

The car fell silent while Ula thought of her object. I stared out the window at the wall of leafy green trees parading down the side of the road, bars of Mozart and Seitz and Boccherini running through my head. My own face—straight, thick black hair framing yellow-hazel eyes—looked dispassionately back at me. After a while, I switched to thinking about strange things that could happen as a result of insufficient AI attempts: *A self-driving car is driving down a road. A tree falls across the road, and the car drives into it and explodes. However, right before it explodes, the car sends a record of what has happened to all the other self-driving cars. Instead of concluding that you should stop if a tree falls across the road, the cars all conclude that you should not drive near trees.* I smiled at the image of cars inexplicably avoiding large swathes of forest.

"All right," Ula announced. "I'm ready." *Finally*, I thought, turning from the window. My sister's eyes were narrowed, as if in challenge. Her curly blonde hair had frizzed up around her face, making her look like some sort of evil villain in a comic book.

"Is it a vegetable?"

"No."

Ugh. Already I just felt like lying

down and going to sleep. "Is it an animal?"

She hesitated. "No." The word seemed drawn-out, uncertain. That caught my attention. Ula was never unsure of something in Twenty Questions—or any game, for that matter. At least, she never showed it.

"Is it a mineral?" I almost asked, but caught myself. Since there were only three categories—vegetable, animal, or mineral—it had to be. Furious at my mistake, I took a deep breath and said, "Is it bigger than a bread box?"

"No."

"Is it a sort of big rock?"

"A *small boulder*. No."

"Is it a regular object?"

"No."

"Can it be seen if I look outside?"

"No."

I hated how calm she was, how robotic, how unfazed by my questions. If this were a battle, I thought, she'd be winning.

"Have we seen it before?"

"Yes."

I blurted out the first question that came to my mouth. "When was the last time we saw it?"

Ula's mouth curled into a mocking sneer. "That's not a yes-or-no question."

I gritted my teeth.

"And it counts."

"Was the last time we saw it more than one year ago?"

"Yes."

"More than two?"

"Yes."

"More than three?"

"Yes."

"More than four?"

"No."

So when I was seven.

Okay, this was not fair. But I knew I couldn't back down now.

I cast my memory back to important things that had happened four years ago. That was the year Dad had hurt his foot, leaving him unable to drive and with a limp. And the thing he had dropped on his foot was . . .

Oh. The Christmas tree.

Which would be classified in the vegetable category.

I searched for other things, and my mind was drawn to a sweltering July day in Washington, D.C. Ula and I had had identical dripping raspberry gelato cones, which we licked desperately as we wandered with our parents around Capitol Hill. Despite my efforts, my hands and face had been glazed with bright red liquid.

We had walked through Eastern Market, and even though I saw the same thing every day, I had been mesmerized by all the crazy kinds of produce for sale. The gelato on my face and hands somewhat mopped up, I had gingerly felt the scales of an artichoke, nervously prodded a pineapple's serrated leaves, and generously tasted every plate of fruit samples, stopping only when my parents (and Ula) had dragged me away with angry scolding.

Then, at Ula's and my plaintive requests, we had gone to the library, with its blissfully cool aisles of bookshelves and its little reading tables by the windows. I had plopped down at one of them with a foot-high stack of *Magic Tree House* books I knew I wouldn't be able to finish while Ula prowled the shelves.

Something about that blissful day, so full of possibilities, so free of obligations, felt important. But nothing about it had anything to do with minerals.

We had left the library and continued down the sweltering street. Ula and I had run back and forth along the red-bricked sidewalk, gathering up handfuls of fallen flowers from the crape myrtles and presenting them—I more proudly than Ula—to our parents. Secretly, I had swiped several sprigs of mint from a thick clump growing in someone's front yard and peeking through the black-painted fence, thinking to use it for tea later.

Something about that blissful day, so full of possibilities, so free of obligations, felt important. But nothing about it had anything to do with minerals. Reluctantly, I shifted the focus of my mental metal detector.

Soon, it felt as if I had gone through every memory I had of the year 2014. There was my birthday in August—a water fight at Lincoln Park, with high-velocity squirt guns and hundreds of water balloons. And Ula's in March, spent holed up inside our not-exactly-gigantic apartment with ten preteens who were antsy from eating too much candy. There was the first day of school, the last day of school, the time I won the math competition, the time Ula won the chess camp tournament, and the time I won the vocabulary word fashion show. (I won it the year after that, too.) There was the day Ula had held a funeral for the nest of baby mice we'd found starved to death in the wall of our house—which the rest of us only participated in because Mom and Dad felt obliged to encourage Ula's love for nature and animals, and I felt guilty and rude to be the only person in the family not attending. There was moving day, when we moved from our old apartment into a bigger one two blocks away. That was a terrible day for everyone, because not only was it drizzling the yucky kind of lukewarm summer rain but the moment we left our apartment building some construction workers came by and bulldozed it flat.

"Um, is it the bulldozer?"

"The *what*?"

"Never mind."

"It counts."

I sighed. Suddenly, I thought of something. "Is it that statue in Lincoln Park?"

"No, and by that way, we see that almost every day."

I groaned. This was kind of like thinking you could fly, jumping off the roof of a building, going splat on the sidewalk three stories below, and then waking up in the hospital and wondering why the heck you thought you could fly in the first place.

I leaned back in my seat and closed my eyes. This drive was taking so long.

If only we could get to Aunt Megan's house. Then I wouldn't have to bother finishing this stupid game. I squeezed my eyes tighter, trying to recall what she looked like. Red hair, piled up on top of her head in a sort of beehive . . . or was I thinking of Grandma in those old photos?

Definitely Grandma.

Anyway, this wasn't my fault. I hadn't seen my aunt and cousins, or their house in Upstate New York, for several years. Not since I turned—

I sat bolt upright in my seat. I could almost feel the light bulb going off in my head. I shut my eyes again. Wasn't Aunt Megan's house on a lake?

"Is it the lake Aunt Megan's house is on?"

Ula narrowed her eyes at me. "Aunt Megan's house isn't on a lake. Gramps's is. And . . ."

"*That counts*," I finished under my breath.

With a jolt, I realized I was at 15. Only five questions left. I made a growling noise deep in my throat. *Why does Ula have to win at everything?* But I also knew, somewhere inside me, that I was too interested at this point to give up. I desperately wanted to know what this object was.

I took a deep breath.

I will do this. I would show her.

Think, my brain commanded. And so I went back to my only lead—that summer day, spent wandering our home.

"Please, can we see the cherry blossoms?" Ula had begged. And my parents had given their consent, even though it was much too late for cherry blossoms, because we had all known that Ula would find beauty in even the saddest, brownest, most wilted handful of flowers.

We had boarded a train on the subway, heading to the Mall. We had gotten off at our stop and climbed the steps to the surface again, emerging into the hot, too-bright sunlight. The Washington Monument had risen, blindingly white, in front of us.

I loved that part of the city. Everything was in various shades of white, cream, and beige—even the sidewalks. My seven-year-old self had looked down at the ground, which was made up of light-brown gravel that was getting in my worn red sandals. I had been reminded for some reason of the pebbles sunken into the ground in front of CHAW (Capitol Hill Arts Workshop).

I blinked. Turned to Ula. "Is it your favorite CHAW pebble?"

"My what?"

"The blue pebble. Next to the *C* in CHAW. You know, where it spells out CHAW in the concrete. In front of CHAW." *Stop rambling*, I told myself.

"Oh. That. No."

Four questions left.

By the time we had reached the cherry blossoms, we were sweating profusely, despite having stayed in the shade the entire way there. While Ula danced among the drooping, slightly shriveled trees, picking up every fallen flower she could find, I had looked sleepily across the Tidal Basin. Only a few boats had bobbed in the water, and I had been glad that I wasn't in one of them. Briefly, I wondered if Ula's object was a boat, then just as quickly dismissed the idea. Last year, I remembered, we had ridden on one ourselves.

Another thought crossed my mind. Recklessly, I asked, "Is it a cloudless sky?"

Ula snorted. "The last time I saw a cloudless sky was before I was born."

"That's not—"

"In other words, cloudless skies are nonexistent."

"What an optimistic thing to say."

"If I were an optimist, my life would suck. I would be disappointed by everything."

I ignored her and plunged back into the vivid waters of my memories. I had been startled out of my drowsy haze by Ula's voice crying out. "What is it, Ula?" Mom had asked, a trace of worry in her voice.

"Mom. Dad. Jenny." Ula had sounded as if she were crying.

"What is it?" I had called, overcome with worry and sympathy for my big sister.

"Look." When we had raced over, we had seen a baby sparrow lying on the ground underneath one of the cherry trees, its left wing broken. It was dead.

"Help me bury it," Ula had pleaded. When my parents were reluctant, she had snapped, "Well, then I'm taking it home and doing it myself!"

"If you bury it here, you have to do it by yourself," Mom had said.

"Fine!"

After what had seemed like forever, Ula was done. She had even found a small, gravestone-like rock to place on top. We had listened to her short speech in honor of the bird, and then Dad had suggested heading back home. Everyone had readily agreed.

No sooner had we turned onto our street than clouds suddenly swept over the sun and rain came pouring down. By the time we reached the door, we had been drenched.

And then suddenly it hit me. It was so simple, so obvious, and so devilishly Ula . . .

"Is it water?"

"If we hadn't seen water in four years, we'd be dead."

"Oh." Suddenly I felt so idiotic, like I did whenever I played chess.

And I had two questions left.

This is hopeless . . .

For the first time, I just felt like giving up. I could give two half-hearted guesses, let Ula reveal the answer, and the whole thing would be over. I wouldn't have to bother with any of this. I wouldn't have to try anymore.

After all, it's just a game.

"Is it a brick?"

"No."

"Is it . . . "

I trailed off as we pulled into a driveway. Looking out the window, I saw a two-story house with an attic, painted a bright, cheerful yellow. There wasn't a lake in sight.

"We're here," Mom announced.

I let out a sigh of relief. *Safe.* Gratefully, I reached for the door handle. But

But just as my fingers grasped the warm metal, something clicked in my head.

Love Stone, *iPhone*

by Tatiana Hadzic, 11
New York, NY

just as my fingers grasped the warm metal, something clicked in my head.

A mineral. Smaller than a bread box. Irregular shape. The more I thought about it, the more sure I was that I was right. For once, everything fit.

I turned around. Ula was still in the car. I said to her, "It's the rock that you put on the sparrow's grave." Then, wanting to share my brilliant revelation with someone, I added, "You hesitated when I asked if it was an animal because you weren't sure if you wanted to make it the sparrow itself. That's why."

Ula was now opening her door. With her back to me, she said, "No."

I gaped. "What?"

"I said no. I don't choose stupid things like that. You're wrong. I win." She opened the door and got out of the car.

Desperately, I called after her, "Then what is it?"

Ula's voice floated faintly back to me. "I don't have to tell you if I don't want to."

"But—"

"It's just a game. It doesn't matter anyway."

"Yes, it does!"

She ignored me.

Stunned, I watched through my window as my parents and Ula headed for the door, dragging our luggage. I could see my cousins Cecily and Emma pushing the door open now, with Aunt Megan behind them. Her hair was the color of her house.

"You're lying," I said to no one.

I had been right. I was sure of it.

A Magnificent City

by Ziqing (Izzie) Peng, 10
Nanjing, China

Something beautiful for us might be poisonous for others

I'm living in a magnificent city. In the morning, when the first sunlight illuminates the earth, the buildings seem to wear a beautiful yarn shirt. The world revives, people get to work. Cars make a beautiful picture, like a glittering lake.

In the afternoon, flowers blossom, trees and grass make a marvelous photo. Children play happily. There's laughter everywhere.

In the evening, colorful lights open. The city looks like the dark sky with shining stars. The wind blows. Slowly, the city becomes quiet. All the lives are sleeping. The lively city becomes mysterious and poetic. Everything is sleeping except the lights. They change every second to make magnificent pictures. They light the sky and make night into morning.

But the magnificent lights also cause problems. Some small turtles are born on the beach, and they need to go back to the sea. They only know that the sea is light and take the city as the sea because the city is much lighter than the sea. When they miss their way, they may die.

So not every magnificent city is good for wildlife. Something beautiful for us might be poisonous for others.

Cranes and Christmas Tree, *Canon Rebel T4i*

by Nicholas Taplitz, 13
Los Angeles, CA

Numbers

by Patrick Lusa, 11
Stafford Springs, CT

1 winter day at
2 in the morning there are
3 people sleeping as
4 owls are hooting before they go to sleep at
5 a.m.
6 in the morning and the owls have stopped hooting,
7 birds are chirping as they search for food.
8 dogs are barking,
9 cats are hissing as they fight at
10 in the morning, there are
11 people driving to lunch at
12.
13 days later, there is heat again.
14 people are swimming in the
15-mile lake.
16 cars are driving to exit
17, taking people to work.
18 days have passed now
19 people are in school getting bored to death.
20 people are running the
21-mile race.
22 days later, the heat is getting stronger,
On the 23rd, days are getting longer.
The world seems to turn faster.
The racers run faster.
The light is still putting up a fight.
24 hours after midnight.

The Sky

The sky seems endless.
All of the birds fly in it.
The huge blue abyss.

Shadow in the Sun, *gouache and acrylic*

by Isha Narang, 13
Austin, TX

Two Princes

by Lia Taylor, 12
Elkins Park, PA

When his father, the king, asks him to choose a wife, Prince Richard realizes he can't marry a woman

Once there was a beautiful kingdom called Galavor. Giant trees and impossibly green grass flooded the land like a smile on a baby's face. The sun would always shine without a doubt, warming the vast kingdom. The king, King Charle, seemed reasonable and fair. His dark, stiff beard and squinty eyes created a wise and trustworthy appeal. Everyone was happy and everyone adored their ruler.

One warm June day, King Charle and his only child, Prince Richard, were eating a breakfast of omelettes and fresh fruit. They ate alone, as the Queen had passed away a few years prior, and all of Richard's brothers had passed away at a young age. As per usual, the only noise was clinking cutlery. Prince Richard's soft, platinum-blond hair occasionally fell into his emerald green eyes. His hands almost blended in with the porcelain chinaware. He was in premium health, but his complexion matched his mother's, at least in his last memory of her. His bony body made the prince appear puny, but he was stronger and nobler than any man within the kingdom.

Suddenly, King Charle broke the silence. "Son, while I hope to live much longer, we do have to acknowledge that I am getting older. In two months' time, you will turn 21, and by then you shall be engaged to the woman of your choosing. Then you and your fiancée will get married and have a coronation, for it is an event I wish to be present for. Today, you shall travel to the next kingdom, Spañia, to search for a wife."

"While I do not disagree with you, Father, I would like to ask: why you are planning to step down from the throne so early in your life? You are only 60 years of age. You must remember, I am your youngest child, as my brothers have long passed. But, very well. If that is what you wish, I must obey. I will pack after breakfast," responded Richard.

"Very well," said King Charle. The men continued to eat in silence.

At about noon, when the sun was high in the sky, Richard mounted his black stallion, gave a small wave to his father, and set off on his two-day journey to Spañia. About two hours into his ride, he began to think about what he searched for in a wife. Romantic, independent, strong . . . As he tried to picture his perfect bride, he realized that each time he imagined her, she wasn't the slim, graceful woman that is thought to be the most beautiful. Instead, she was more handsome than pretty and had a sturdy build. He realized that marrying and starting a family with a woman filled his heart with dread. He only wished to befriend women. He thought he was starting to hallucinate. So, after only three hours, he stopped for a nap beneath a willow tree.

He arrived at the palace of Spañia around two o'clock in the afternoon, when the kingdom was at its hottest. The palace was built at the top of a tall, brown, and rocky cliff. While Spañia was just as beautiful as Galavor, it was pretty in a different way. It was warm and mystical. The royal family greeted him at the gate: King Ferdinand, Queen Isabel, Princess Isabel (the eldest sister), Princess Mia (the youngest sister), and Prince Francisco. They were all kind and very welcoming. While Isabel was the prettiest of the princesses, Mia took the most interest in Richard right away. Richard knew picking a bride would be difficult, especially considering he was attracted to neither of them. Instead, he took a strong interest in the prince, Francisco.

Lucky for Richard, it was Francisco who showed him around the palace and helped to get him settled in his room, which was between Princess Isabel's room and Francisco's room. As Richard put his things away, he noticed the massive and beautiful garden outside his window.

At six o'clock, dinner was served. Richard was placed between Isabel and Mia, and across from Francisco. The King and Queen sat at either end of the long, rectangular table. Throughout the evening, Richard had boring, two-sentence conversations with both princesses. ("How was the trip?" "Fine." Or, "The salmon is quite delicious." "Yes, it really is.") Finally, Richard remembered the garden.

"I couldn't help but notice the beautiful garden you have here," said Prince Richard.

"Ah, yes," said Francisco. "I love it. It's where I spend most of my time. If I'm not gardening, I'm wandering, or reading under a willow tree. But, really, it's nothing much. If you like, Richard, I can show you after dinner?"

While Richard's hair fell in his face, he wondered what it would be like to have Francisco's dark complexion and stiff, yet wavy, black hair. He was the most attractive man he had ever seen. He liked his kindness too. He admired how humble he was.

"Of course! That would be fantastic!" Richard exclaimed.

"Great. I'll meet you in your room at 7:30," decided Francisco.

At 7:32, Richard was still waiting in his bedroom, which was quite luxurious. He was starting to worry. "What if he has forgotten?" he thought. "Maybe I should go check on Francisco, to remind him of our—" Richard was not sure how to define it—"date?" Richard thought it was a date, but did Francisco? Did Richard want it to be a date? Richard was now more nervous than ever. As he stood to check on the prince, there was a short and rhythmic knock at the door.

"Richard? Sorry I'm late. Are you ready?" called the voice of Francisco, through the door.

"I'll be right out, and don't be sorry, it's alright," replied Richard. A second later, the two men stood together in the corridor. Richard found Francisco especially dashing. Was this a date? It seemed the answer was yes. To his own surprise, Richard smiled at the revelation.

"Shall we?" Francisco put out his arm. Richard reluctantly rested his hand atop Francisco's arm. He didn't *want* to want to, but he did. What was this new feeling? Was it . . . attraction? This was something he had never felt before. He never thought he would fall for anyone, especially a *prince*.

Back home, Richard had never met anybody who was gay. It was not allowed, because his father, King Charle, had made a law against same-sex couples. If they were found out, they would be banished. Richard never understood this, but everyone knows better than to question a king's judgement. Richard wasn't in Galavor now, though.

Francisco led Richard through the gardens. As they walked, Francisco started a bouquet of his favorites, the flowers he nurtured the most. A white rose, an orchid, a tiger lily, a peony. After two hours of laughs and banter, the bouquet had grown full. Francisco gently placed the flowers into Richard's hands. There was a silence, but not awkward. They each gazed into each other's eyes.

"I don't want to marry either of your sisters," said Richard. His pale cheeks turned bright red with embarrassment. The contrast made him look even paler.

"I know that. If you were to marry them then why would you be here, on a date with me? You . . . you do know this is a date, right?" Francisco seemed confused. "You came here to find a fiancé; I thought you had chosen me."

"Umm, no . . . I don't know. My father wouldn't approve. We could never inherit the kingdom . . . " mumbled Richard.

"We'll figure it out. A happy kingdom needs happy rulers. I know you don't like my sisters, so—be with me?"

"I- I don't know. My father is a scary man." Richard took a deep breath, inhaling the thick scent of his bouquet. The bouquet that Francisco had given him. Francisco, the only person he could clearly and fondly see in his future. "Okay, but we need a plan, for our future."

"Isabel and Mia, they are just magnificent with secrets. They never intended on marrying you anyway. They'll be in the study"

The four stayed up all night suggesting ideas. Overthrowing Galavor would not be popular among citizens. Isabel was next in line to rule if Francisco was unable, and she intended to take that chance. Many ideas were proposed, all shot down.

"What if you founded your own kingdom?" proposed Isabel.

"You could run away, take Pegasus," added Mia.

"Anyone from Spañia or Galavor could come with us, to be citizens of a new land," suggested Francisco.

"Yes! This could work! We'll lead on Pegasus with our citizens in boats below," Richard exclaimed.

"And King Charle will never have to know. We'll work by night," Mia explained.

"No, no. He needs to know. I will confront him tomorrow. May I take Pegasus? My horse is ill, and it will make traveling faster," said Richard.

"Of course!" said Isabel.

Pegasus was a large white mare with a wingspan longer than a man is tall. Gentle in nature, yet strong at heart. Richard climbed aboard cautiously, but soon realized he was perfectly safe, and the draining two-day trip became an exhilarating two hours. It filled the timid and confused prince with confidence.

As Pegasus started her descent to the castle grounds, Richard noticed the king waiting patiently outside the castle.

"Hello, Richard, have you found a fiancée?" asked King Charle.

"Yes, I have." Richard said this confidently, yet inside he was dreading the moment.

"And her name?" prompted the king.

" . . . Francisco. His name is Francisco," said Prince Richard, sheepishly. And with that, he took off, back to Spañia, feeling a mix of emotions. Brave, proud, worried. He had fled before his father even had time to react.

A few days later, everything was ready for the escape. Richard was overjoyed that he could spend his life with the one he loved so dearly, but there was the familiar emptiness of loss, an emptiness he hadn't felt since the death of his mother.

Flying, the two princes could see everything for miles and miles, including the large ship of hopeful citizens. Then, somebody below shouted "Land ho!" A loud cheering erupted, then quickly faded as they saw the state of the land. Death flooded the landscape. Ashes and dead grass spread as far as the eye could see. The joy melted from people's faces. Nevertheless, Richard and Francisco guided Pegasus to the ground. As they landed, the ship was pushed up onto the shore.

Everyone was uneasy, except for their leaders. The princes felt the earth calling to them, begging to be nourished and lived on.

In unison, the princes announced, "Behold, our new kingdom! We shall call it Terracinis! We will create life upon this ashy land. We will live with the land, not on it. We will find beauty in this demolished plain." They said this with such confidence and hope that the people were able to understand.

The land appreciated this and became beautiful right before their eyes. The grass was greener than grass should be, but was undeniably healthy. The air was fresh and the flowers could bring tears to eyes with their exquisite beauty. The land saw the hope and love in the hearts of the princes and gave them sweet fruit, in ample amounts. A crystal palace rose from the ground and a sweet, quaint village swirled up from the ashes. Birds placed crowns fit for a king onto the heads of the princes.

"Long live the kings!" cheered the crowd of citizens, awestruck and joyful. The people of Terracinis lived happily ever after.

Portraits: A Multi-Artist Portfolio

Editor's Note

In visual art, a portrait is traditionally a painting, drawing, or photograph that depicts a person's face. Before photography was invented in the 1800s, people would usually commission portraits of their friends and family so as to have an image of the person they loved. Important and wealthy individuals—like the monarchs in Europe—might have many portraits painted of them throughout their lifetime. But a middle-class person might only have one or two. And someone in the lower class—perhaps none. So, for a long time, a portrait was associated with status. Today, a photographic portrait is cheap: you can get your best friend to take a professional-looking photo of you with your phone on 'portrait' mode. But, because of the time and skill required, the painted portrait still remains rare.

An excellent portrait is not necessarily the one that most accurately or realistically portrays its subject; it is the one that somehow captures the subject's inner being—that gives the viewer some sense of who that person is, not just what they look like.

In this portfolio of portraits, four different artists are exploring the form in their own unique ways. By using a variety of materials to make up the face in her portrait, Sritanvee Alluri emphasizes how each of us is composed of different pieces of the world: of what we read, hear, watch, and think. In her two portraits, Amalia Ichilov uses soft, visible brushstrokes to create a more realistic—yet somewhat dreamy—representation of her subjects, who appear refreshingly 'normal', like someone you could run into on the street. Using Autodesk Sketchbook, a drawing and painting software, Leo Melinsky has turned his attention not to people but to dogs—and succeeds in capturing their personalities: Ernie—standing, mouth closed, looking off the page—appears high-strung and hyper-alert, waiting perhaps for someone to throw his ball, whereas Hazel—drooling, sitting, relaxed—seems easygoing. Finally, Isabella Webb, in painting Queen Elizabeth II, reminds us of the history of portraiture, with an image that captures the Queen's friendly-but-always-formal attitude.

In Through One Ear and Out the Other, *mixed media*

by Sritanvee Alluri, 12
Austin, TX

Portrait of a Woman Standing Against a Blue Wall, *oil pastel on paper*

STONE SOUP

Portrait of a Freckled Young Woman, *oil pastel on paper*

by Amalia Ichilov, 9
New York, NY

Ernie, *Autodesk Sketchbook*

by Leo Melinsky, 12
Clayton, NC

Hazel, *Autodesk Sketchbook*

The Queen, *oil paint*

**by Isabella Webb, 11
Berkshire, UK**

Gone Fishing

by Mia Fang, 13
West Lafayette, IN

When Lily's father loses his job, he enlists in the army to support his family

Chapter 1

I lay on my bed, wracked with worry. Horrible thoughts floated on my conscience. I buried my face in my pillow, my long hair spread over the silk. I tried pushing the thoughts away, with no luck. It was hard concentrating on anything these days. I had pushed my friends away, and spent less and less time with my mother. I knew she was worried too, but I had to admit I was angry. I play the scene over and over again in my head: why did it have to be my family to suffer?

A month ago, my life couldn't have been more perfect. I had sat at the table waiting for Father to come home. Wonderful smells rose from the pot of stew. Cloves of dried garlic and mushrooms hung from the ceiling. The light of the setting sun seeped through the window, casting a warm glow on the kitchen. I watched as the soft figure of Mother stirred in herbs and spices, her long, strawberry-blonde hair flowing down her back. Like Father, I had a head full of flame-red hair and a face swarming with freckles.

Mother was 18 weeks pregnant and her stomach was really starting to swell; I couldn't imagine what it would be like to have a sibling, if Father would love him or her more than me.

Soon, the front door swung open with a creak and the tall figure of Father stood in the doorway. He set his bag down with a heavy thud and hung up his hat and scarf. He walked in, shaking the snow from his hair without speaking. It wasn't like him. He sat down wearily as if the weight of the world was resting on his shoulders. I ran up and hugged him, clinging to the plush arm of the chair. I looked into his eyes, which seemed more tired than usual. He gave me a small smile and playfully rubbed my hair, though his smile faltered and a grim expression took its place.

"Holly," he said, turning to Mother. "I have some bad news to share with you and Lily."

Mother turned around calm as ever, and slowly sat down next to Father. Her presence was reassuring.

I sat quietly and listened, a bad feeling creeping up my gut. But I wasn't afraid then. Mother had that effect on people.

"It's my job," Father said, looking

down. "I got laid off today. I'm to collect my last paycheck tomorrow." He looked up at us. "I'm really sorry. I s-should have tried harder."

Mother and I, we wrapped our arms around Father, unsure of what to think or of what lay ahead.

I laid in bed staring at my wallpaper: bright colors beamed from my walls, fields of livid flowers, a small cottage bordered in a white picket fence. My eyelids felt heavy. Worried whispers floated through the floorboards.

That Sunday I woke up to warm smells coming from the kitchen. I walked down the stairs, floorboards squeaking under my feet. Father stood grinning with an apron tied around his waist.

"Morning, sunshine!" he called and placed a bowl of oats in front of me.

"Where's Mother?" I asked.

"She wasn't feeling up to it this morning. She's in her room right now. I think it would be wise to leave her alone for right now."

That's not like her, I thought. Mother was a put together, down-to-earth woman, and was always the calm one. I wondered what was upsetting her so much.

"Don't worry too much, Lily. I was thinking we could go fishing today, just the two of us. We will have to stop by town to get some bait before we

head off, though."

We walked into town. I was dressed in a plain, light blue Sunday dress with a Peter Pan collar. It's a nice dress, but not my best by far. It was perfect for a day of fishing.

We walked down the cobblestone streets. I walked slightly behind Father. His tall figure perfectly hid me from the crowds. I slouched, keeping my head down, hoping to make myself seem smaller and less noticeable. I'm a shy girl, and talking to strangers was never my thing. Mother always told me how much I was like my father, but in my opinion we couldn't have been more different. I watched as Father tipped his hat to a gentleman walking by with a polite "How do you do?" I cringed just thinking of a social interactions, and felt more grateful than ever for Father's protective shadow.

We loaded our little rowboat on a lake with our bait, fishing poles and lunches. Here on the lake, there was a peaceful silence, away from the crowds and people. Away from the vendors and markets. I felt safe here. It was Father's and my special place here, where we had come so often. I climbed into the gently rocking boat and straightened my posture.

Father rowed the boat off the shore, the paddles breaking the water's surface, sending ripples out on the emerald lake. Fog spread across the lake, weaving its tendrils over the still waters. The outlines of faraway moun-

Only two months, I thought, then Father will be back.

STONE SOUP

tains were barely visible, green with all the lush vegetation. I breathed in the fresh air, smelling hints of pine and the familiar earthy smell. Ancient evergreens and willows stood tall along the shore watching over us like guardians.

Father cast his line, and I followed shortly after. We sat like that in a silence for a while and, after an hour with no catches, he turned to me.

"Lily, you know we have a beautiful big house with a stove and three stories, but anything beautiful costs money."

I loved our house, decked with its colorful wallpapers, its big windows, and spiral staircases.

"Well," Father said. "Since I lost my job, it will be hard to keep our house and pay taxes. The bank might evict us if we don't get payments in soon."

"Will we have to move?" I asked. "I don't want to!" *That was our home, and for the bank to take it would be so unfair!*

"Yeah, I figured you wouldn't want to," he said with a chuckle. "I found a new job that will support our family."

"That's so great! What kind of job is it?"

"I'm going into the military."

Chapter 2
Anger and Guilt

I sat looking out my window without seeing. *Only two months*, I thought, *then Father will be back.* They had stationed him in Russia to fight in the Second World War.

When he left, I began noticing how big of a hole he left in our fami-

ly. Walking into the master bedroom with only one side of the bed occupied. Hoping for him to magically walk through our door. Suddenly, I began noticing his scent everywhere—on the laundry hung out to dry, on the couches and chairs. My heart ached for his presence, and I knew Mother wasn't doing much better, but that didn't stop me from thinking horrible thoughts I know I shouldn't.

Why couldn't Mother get a job? Then Father would still be here. Why couldn't she help out the family more?

But as soon as those thoughts entered my mind, I felt a wave of guilt. It wasn't her fault. But thoughts are addictive, dangerous, contagious.

Mother knocked at my door. "Supper's ready, sweetie."

I didn't answer. I heard her footsteps descending the stairs. I felt a wave of homesickness even though I was at home. I flopped down on my bed and slowly drifted off to sleep.

When I awoke, the sun had set and moonlight sent shafts of light in my bedroom. I felt a dull pain in my stomach, hunger. I walked downstairs and wondered if Mother was still up, but found the kitchen empty. My bowl of soup was still on the table with a spoon laid neatly beside it. Again I felt the guilt and quickly ate my soup, which had gone cold. I went upstairs hoping to apologize to Mother, only to find her asleep. Not wanting to disturb her, I walked back to my room, footsteps heavy, and fell into a deep slumber.

Chapter 3

Chapter 3
The Day the Sky Came Crashing Down

The days went by as slow as dripping molasses, one day after the other. We barely ventured out of the house, with the exception of a few trips to the town market. Mother fell into a kind of work phase. She dusted, washed, and polished everything. Not a single insect dared step in our house. Clothes were organized, every nook and cranny was scrubbed, and all kitchen utensils were organized from largest to smallest. When I asked about the cleaning, she had said, "I couldn't help noticing how dirty everything was recently. Besides, that way your father can come home to a clean house." But I knew she was worried.

On a Wednesday, we decided to visit the local library. Mother, toting her heavy belly, put on her nice sun hat and a bright yellow maternity dress. Dressed up, Mother looked more like her put-together self. And I, who was so glad to have a reason to get out of the house, wore one of my favorite white dresses with small roses embroidered into the fabric.

As we walked down the streets full of people, I started to slouch and looked at my feet.

"Look up, Lily," said Mother. "And straighten your posture."

I did what was asked grudgingly, feeling noticeably more vulnerable. When it was too overwhelming, I slid behind Mother where she couldn't see me and resumed my crunched up pose.

We walked through the grand entrance of the library, and immediately the noise and commotion of the streets began to die down. The library held tall cedar shelves, full of books in leather covers all with the same gold script. Mother and I each chose a book and headed home.

As we walked, the sky was clear and the birds hummed. Flower vendors had booths overflowing with blooms. I couldn't help but shake free of my worry and enjoy the scenes, but my moment of bliss soon diminished when I saw a boy on a bike turning into our street. The boy rode around the town every day delivering the bad news to the families of soldiers.

"You don't think we will get any news, do you?" I asked Mother.

"No, no, I'm sure he is just going through our street to get to the next. Don't worry," Mother replied, but her face was pinched with worry, and she quickened her pace.

Cold sweat ran down my back. I could tell the bike boy was nearing our house now.

Mother, sensing my impatience, said, "You can run. I'll be fine."

As soon as the words left her mouth, I broke into a sprint. It wasn't a very ladylike thing to do, but, at that moment, I didn't care.

I heard the pounding in my ears every time my feet hit the pavement.

My mouth felt dry, and I was having a hard time breathing.

I could see the boy more clearly now, and I was hoping, praying for him to pass our house.

But my prayers were not answered, and the boy halted just outside our door. I crumpled to the sidewalk, not processing that it was actually happening. I had so much hope, everything was supposed to go as planned. I was supposed to win the game, have a happily-ever-after.

Everything was a blur, nausea swept over me, and I had trouble hearing. Mother came, she talked to the boy. She was crying, she never cried.

I couldn't move, the boy came and crouched by me, I could feel his hand on my shoulder.

"I'm sorry, Miss."

I fainted right there and then.

Honor Roll

Welcome to the *Stone Soup* Honor Roll. Every month we receive submissions from hundreds of kids from around the world. Unfortunately, we don't have space to publish all the great work we receive. We want to commend some of these talented writers and artists and encourage them to keep creating.

Fiction
Reiyah Jacobs, 13
Ella Jeon, 11
Lissa Krueger, 11
Haeon Lee, 11
Grace Malary McAndrew, 12

Poetry
Gia Bharadwaj, 12
Rhône Galchen, 11
Harry Kavanaugh, 10
Uma Nambiar, 11
Billy Ren, 11
Christina Smyth, 11

Art
Catherine Gruen, 12
Natalie Johnson, 13
Sarah Pledger, 12
Sophia Torres, 11
Calci Wolfe, 13

Visit the *Stone Soup* store at Stonesoupstore.com to buy:

- Magazines—individual issues of *Stone Soup*, past and present

- Books—our collection of themed anthologies (fantasy, sport, poetry, and more), and the *Stone Soup Annual* (all the year's issues, plus a taste of the year online, in one volume)

- Art prints—high quality prints from our collection of children's art

- Journals and sketchbooks for writing and drawing

        ... and more!

Don't forget to visit Stonesoup.com to browse our bonus materials. There you will find:

- 20 years of back issues—around 5,000 stories, poems, and reviews

- Blog posts from our young bloggers on subjects from sports to sewing—plus ecology, reading, and book reviews

- Video interviews with *Stone Soup* authors

- Music, spoken word, and performances

StoneSoup

JUNE 2019 VOLUME 47 / ISSUE 6

StoneSoup

The magazine supporting creative kids around the world

Editor
Emma Wood

Director
William Rubel

Operations
Jane Levi

Education & Production
Sarah Ainsworth

Design
Joe Ewart

Stone Soup (ISSN 0094 579X) is published 11 times per year—monthly, with a combined July/August summer issue. Copyright © 2019 by the Children's Art Foundation, a 501(c)(3) nonprofit organization located in Santa Cruz, California. All rights reserved.

Thirty-five percent of our subscription price is tax-deductible. Make a donation at Stonesoup.com/donate, and support us by choosing Children's Art Foundation as your Amazon Smile charity.

POSTMASTER: Send address changes to Stone Soup, 126 Otis Street, Santa Cruz, CA 95060. Periodicals postage paid at Santa Cruz, California, and additional offices.

Stone Soup is available in different formats to persons who have trouble seeing or reading the print or online editions. To request the Braille edition from the National Library of Congress, call +1 800-424-8567. To request access to the audio edition via the National Federation of the Blind's NFB-NEWSLINE®, call +1 866-504-7300 or visit www.nfbnewsline.org.

Check us out on social media:

Editor's Note

This is an issue about potential, possibility, and change. In Isabel Swain's story "Innocent but Dire Words," a young poet dreams of a better future for herself, while in Vandana Ravi's short story, a girl dreams of simply another place. In Grace Jiang's poems, nature comes to life again, after its seasonal death and hibernation, and in Andrew Wu's story sequence "Nature in my Eyes," nature changes in our eyes, as we attempt to see it from the angles and experiences of different creatures. Change is inevitable: we change, the world changes, time moves along. And, in the spaces between, in the time when it feels as if nothing is changing, we dream of the change that might happen. And yet when that change finally does occur—when yet again the rose blooms—it still feels miraculous. After reading this issue, I hope you will feel inspired to think and write about change—in the world or in you, past or future, real or imagined.

Happy summer!

Letters: We love to hear from our readers. Please post a comment on our website or write to us via Submittable or editor@stonesoup.com. Your letter might be published on our occasional Letters to the Editor page.

Submissions: Our guidelines are on the Submit page at Stonesoup.com, where you will also find a link to our Submittable online submissions portal.

Subscriptions: To subscribe to *Stone Soup*, please press the Subscribe button on our web page, Stonesoup.com.

On the cover:
"Flight Through the Cosmos"

**by Hannah Parker, 13
South Burlington, VT**

StoneSoup
Contents

Fist, *acrylic*

by Claire Jiang, 12
Princeton, NJ

Innocent Yet Dire Words

by Isabel Swain, 12
Portsmouth, RI

A book lover dreaming of a better life uses poetry to cope

Like the mythical creature,
It calls out a sound.
Just not a pleasant one;
A torture in its own way.
Siren.

I hold my ears and tell myself to breathe. *One, two, three, four . . . 12, 13 . . . 20. This will pass; don't worry. It's just a siren, you don't have to have another Freak Out, Lila. It's okay, it's okay. See, it's leaving? Okay, okay.* I open my eyes, slowly uncurl myself from my Freak Out Stance, and take one last deep breath.

I shake myself off; it's over now. I peer out the dirt-encrusted window and see a hazed-out dawn. I look at the clock which shows me that it is 6:17. Two hours and 13 minutes left. In the far distance, a careless person pushes a little too hard on the gas and their car makes that God awful noise that makes me wince despite myself. After doing a pointless once over of the three-room shack that is supposedly for two, I scan this "house" (not home) for a woman who doesn't deserve the title of mother. I prefer to call her by her first name, Ilene. She's barely ever here. Figures. Last night was the Fourth of July; she probably ran off to San Francisco with only the clothes on her back trying to fill her never-ending want for "adventure." She's nicknamed her spontaneous outings "longings" in order to make them sound more magical. Let me assure you, it doesn't work.

After I do my usual morning routine—make the bed, dust the window (singular), eat breakfast (dry cereal)—I get dressed and ready to go. By now it's 6:50, which means one hour and 40 minutes . . . Well, better just treat it like it's a normal day, even when my stomach is churning as a way of calling out, *Don't do it!* I just hope that Ilene's back on time.

Once I've located and thrown on my only decent pair of shoes, I thrust the door open and breathe in the hot air.

A moving ghost,
Too large to maintain.
Clear as day, yet blinding.
I stumble through like a wounded
    soldier;
Life
    Before I give myself over to the

overwhelming humiliation that will happen in about an hour and fifteen minutes, I decide to go to my comfort place, the library. My neighborhood is not spectacular in any way, except for maybe the dusty, old makeshift library. To me, this ancient building is the closest thing I've ever had to a home. I love the way it's always been there for me as though it was the parent I never had. The people and books there have become my family to run to whenever I need a home base. It's the only place I know that didn't move when I did.

When Ilene first had me, she was still living with her parents because she was so young. A month after I was born, she ran away on a train to this small town in Nevada. For the first two years we lived with Wanda, an old widow who took us in. However, she died the day before she and Ilene were going out to look for potential apartments for us to stay in. Since nothing in her will was dedicated to us, we were left to our own devices. It took my mother three months to find a steady job that she could use as a money source. And even then, it only lasted for six months. When she finally had enough money to buy us a somewhat bearable apartment, it was a small, overheated two-room that was extremely uncomfortable for a four-year-old and her single mom. Since then, we've been evicted from 32 various apartments, shacks, and Airbnbs. Usually, we overstayed our welcome or my mother hadn't paid the rent. Either way, we still moved our 10 or so possessions to yet another dingy, uncomfortable place in the same dingy, uncomfortable neighborhood.

Needless to say, I've gotten pretty used to reliving the same nightmare over and over again. As I unthinkingly play one-person soccer with a rock along the sidewalk, I rehearse exactly what I'm going to say in one hour and five minutes. I've had everything planned down to the syllable for three weeks now. I'm just praying they don't ask anything about my living situation. Ilene better be there and sober, or else I'll be immediately excused. No parental guardian, no acceptance. This is the only opportunity I've ever had, and I will not let my self-centered, sorry excuse for a mother dictate whether or not it goes my way for once. I feel myself start to panic.

The definition of fear,
Powerful yet the weakest.
I find myself consumed.
It rules my thoughts,
Anger

When the library's welcoming facade comes into view, I release a tired breath in an audible sigh. It's a beautiful place built of brick and wood. Morning glories reach all the way to the top as though they are trying to protect the knowledge that lives here. The faded windows have frames of magenta that come straight out of a fairy tale. But this is just the outside— so little compared to the interior that I long ago memorized. A dozen spacious rooms with stained-glass windows taken right out of a church. Soft leather seats surrounding dim fireplaces. And then, the shelves themselves. Their oak wood carvings tinted with well-worn paint. They are the perfect pieces to hold the most wonderful things on Earth.

I'm practically skipping towards the door when I'm hit with a shock of ice-cold water. My gasp is involuntary. It takes me a few freezing moments before I look up to where the attack came from. My gaze focuses in on a broken gutter. The bolt holding it to the side of the roof falls to the ground as if to shove it in my face. *Well, this is perfect, isn't it. Now I have to go back to my house and change into awful-looking clothes.* In my head, a battle is unfolding over whether I should still go into the library or not. This is something that comes with the Freak Outs: anxiety and confusion over very small and unimportant things. I decide that I still have time to pick out one or two books for my later reading pleasure.

When I enter the library, the librarian looks up at me and scowls. She must be debating whether or not let me browse in sopping wet clothes. After only 30 or so seconds she looks back at the computer she's sitting in front of. Her quick fingers with long, talon-like nails scrape at the keyboard. It's the exact kind of background babble that you'd expect from a library in Nevada; it is dry and annoying, just like the weather.

I make my way over to my favorite genre's shelf. Historical fiction. I love losing myself in events that happened in the past. Something feels so great about being a part of something that can never change. It feels solid and hopeful. I've read books on everything from World War I to the Trojan War. Usually in the perspective of a young teenage girl with dark black hair. These books are very predictable once you've read them all your life. My hands skim the worn-out copies, and they cover my hands in a thin layer of dust. I decide on a novel about a war in ancient times. These are my favorite because they're so mysterious. I mean, the story is basically just an illusion of time. While I file through the pages, my mind wanders. Specifically, drawn to the events ahead.

Two weeks ago, I had walked into the library first thing in the morning. In my peripheral vision, I had seen a pin drop. No, that's not a joke on how quiet it should be in libraries; I literally saw a pin drop. My head turned toward the source, and I found a poster floating to the floor.

My hand reached for it out of curiosity. The crisp, new edges were orange, as was the rest of the paper. But the appearance doesn't matter, it's the content that I'm here to tell.

Brand New Opening!!!
The New School on Evergreen Avenue, Smith Hill, will be opening very soon and prospective students are welcome to interview on Friday, July 27 at 8:30 a.m.

This is something that comes with the Freak Outs: anxiety and confusion over very small and unimportant things.

All above the age of 10 are welcome! Cost will vary based on information gathered at the meeting.
Please note that no child will be accepted into the Smith Hill School if they do not have a legal parental guardian with them for the meeting.

In my head, possibilities had taken over. *What if you could convince Ilene to do this? What if you got in? What if you went to school?* This is the kind of thing I'd been waiting for my whole life. Finally, something could go my way. Then, I folded up the paper and stuffed it in my pocket. I rushed out of the library, and I didn't remember the pin I left on the ground until I was halfway home. I figured I would have to wait awhile until Ilene got home and then even longer to get her in a good enough mood to actually ask her about the interview. But I was pleasantly surprised when I found her lying in bed at home.

"Hey, Mom." Though it pained me to call her that, I knew it gave me a better chance at yes. "Are you asleep? I have something I need to ask you."

Ilene smiled—I assumed because of my unusual affection towards her. Funny how she finds so much pride in being lied to.

"I'm awake, honey. What do you need?"

"Well, there's this school that is opening up, and they are having interviews to apply soon. But, I can't go without a legal guardian and I was wondering if maybe . . . " This was hard for me to finish because I knew she could crush my newfound dreams with one innocent yet dire word. " . . .

I was wondering if you would come with me?"

I heard Ilene sigh in thought. She seemed out of it, and I hoped that would bend to my favor. Her nail touched her forehead—something I do, too. I hated myself every time I did it because the movement, so small, connected me to her.

"Well, I suppose it wouldn't hurt, would it?" She said after a moment's consideration. I couldn't believe it was that easy.

Looking back on it now, that should have been a sign that it wouldn't work. I mean, if Ilene never makes it back to the house on time, then it really would have been a sign. For now, though, I just have to focus on the best possible outcomes.

Once I check out the book, I turn around to face the door. It is huge, with smooth varnish that makes it glisten even in the artificial lighting. Step after step, I walk towards it. I don't know why but I've always been intimidated by this door. I guess it is the force that decides whether or not I can enter my favorite place—figuratively, anyway.

Most are greedy for it, but
Few can possess the trait.
Like money, it takes over.
Wonderful yet harmful;
Power.

When I open the door, my movement is greeted with the humid air of the summer. I find myself wishing for that shock of cold again. Now, the damp spot on my clothes is just making it more muggy and hard to move. I start the short trek back to my place

This is the kind of thing I'd been waiting for my whole life. Finally, something could go my way.

and walk along the run-down side-walk. Multiple plants are invading the cracks that fill the concrete. They look like they have escaped from a prison too deep to notice and are soaring up to the sun while they can. I can relate to that. Once I reach the hill that overlooks my abode, I can see a figure standing by our door. My shoulders relax as I'm reassured that she is here.

I stumble down the hill towards the two shadows: one of a shack, one of a woman. I try not to trample the flowers that have popped up along with the rest of spring, although I'm pretty sure a few were sacrificed in the process. When I make it to the bottom, I realize that this woman is not, in fact, my mother.

Her posture is too perfect and her hair is up in a too-tight bun. I bet her face is red from tension underneath all that make-up. In her skinny arms is a clipboard that has unnaturally crisp white papers on it. I almost laugh at the scene: a proper businesswoman in the middle-of-nowhere Nevada stand-ing beside a run-down shack that's decorated with rust and rot. I almost laugh until I remember she's not Ilene. *Why is she here? Where is my mother? I won't be accepted, I won't be accepted, I won't be accepted . . . keep it together, Lila.* But already my thoughts have been thrown onto the back of a bucking horse; they won't stop moving and are just trying to hold on.

The thought of them brings
    revenge.
They are twisted sisters,
Moving together always.
Their cousin: regret;
Betrayal and trust.

"Who are you and why are you here? You may not know it, but right now, I'm supposed to be in an office. With my mother, starting the one op-portunity that I have ever had. And yet here we are, and please, do tell, why that is."

I speak in a deadly peaceful voice, like the calm before a storm. My words are clear as day, and I sound about ten years older than I actually am. I'm trying to unnerve her; I bet she's never heard a 13-year-old talk to her like an adult. It works; the woman's face falls and she looks momentarily concerned. For me or for herself, I don't know. The woman who may just about ruin my entire life smiles a plastic smile that could easily make the healthiest person in the world be sick. She pulls together her face like a pro; I'll give her that.

"Hello there, darling! I'm Carla Hemingway from the Nevada Child Protection System. I'm here because your mother, Ilene Quortiez, was found unconscious on a park bench in San Francisco and was brought to the hospital. I know this news must be shocking and that's why . . ."

*My mother is in the hospital? She left
me for real this time? What happened,
exactly? Why is she unconscious? Has
she woken up? Will she wake up? What
if she doesn't?* I try poetry but it doesn't
work. My last thought before I fall into
the never-ending spiral is, "I told you it
was San Francisco."

Peaceful yet confusing,
Drifting as though you weigh
  nothing.
Welcoming darkness,
Holds you in a lull.
Oblivion.

When I wake up, the first thing
that registers is the pain coming
from my head. My head that's full of
thoughts and poetry, the one that is
my friend and foe. It's been there for
me as the source of my five senses
and an extra: taste, smell, hearing,
sight, touch, and thought. My most
powerful weapon has been diminished
into a helpless object on a hospital bed.
It is now the source of my pain, both
physical and mental. This is when the
memories come back. The horrific
events come running in all at once as
though they are fighting for the most
grief.

In the near distance, I hear a loud
beeping noise that can only come from
a medical machine. My first instinct is
to go into Freak Out Stance, but it hurts
to even think about moving. Instead,
I try poetry, but it seems as though
my words are not coming. They are
abandoning me. I gasp. Beside the bed,
a figure rouses. I don't know who it is,
but the person looks genuinely happy
to see me awake. This is weird because

nowhere in my memory does her face
ring a bell. Granted, I am in a hospital
bed with a traitor for a head, so I probably shouldn't trust what I remember. I
would like some answers, though.

As if on cue, the plastic woman
named Carla struts in. She leans in
beside me and says, in a voice that
sounds like a shout, the most unnerv-
ing words I've ever heard:

"Hello, darling. I'm glad you joined
us. Your mother is in the ICU and has
been diagnosed with severe head
trauma. The Nevada Child Protection
System and I have decided that you
will be placed in foster care upon your
recovery. I know this may seem like
a shock to you and we don't want to
cause any stress . . ."

Just, please,
  Leave
    Me
      Alone in my
Grief

The Rose

by Grace Jiang, 11
Ontario, Canada

A little seed falls on the ground,
it becomes a little sprout.
When the wind blows,
it starts dancing all about.

It sways from side to side,
it bobs up and down.
The little sprout is growing,
it has become a rose.

The rose is growing,
it is taller than a little mouse,
it is taller than a rabbit,
it has become the size of a dog!

The rose stops growing,
it stands in the same spot,
for many, many days
until winter comes.

The frost and snow come,
now it must hide underground.
So, petal by petal it withers away.

The next year it happens again,
and again,
and again . . .

Fawn in a Clearing, *chalk-colored pencils*

by Meredith Rohrer, 10
El Cajon, CA

The Four Seasons

by Grace Jiang

A golden leaf falls on Little Deer's nose,
he jumps around playfully,
"Fall has come! Fall has come!" he calls.
His father bellows, "We must go find more food
or the cold white sheet will bury it all!"

Little Fox jumps around in the white powder,
that once had millions of flowers in it.
Now it is cold and wet.
He whines to his mother, "I must go play with Brown Bear!"
His mother whispers, "You must wait till spring."

Spring has come!
Little Horse is only a month old,
yet he jumps as high as his mother.
"Look! Look! I see a bush of daffodils!"
He prances over to the bush and sighs, "Spring is here."

Two happy birds sing,
"Summer has come!
Food is plentiful,
but we must eat lots
because fall is soon to come."

It is fall again,
Little Deer has grown up.
Now he has his own mate and child.
A fawn calls, "Fall is here! Fall is here!"
He smiles at the fawn and calls,
"We must go find more food
or the cold white sheet will bury it all!"
He sounds just like his father.

Possibility

by Vandana Ravi, 12
Palo Alto, 12

At the first whisper of the unicorn's warm breath in my ear, my worries begin to fade. I lean back against a burnt tree stump and close my eyes. I can feel the dewy grass of the clearing tickling my ankles above my sneakers. The heavy summer wind falls like a mantle on my shoulders. A bitter-tasting lump has formed in my throat, but I let myself sink into the warmth.

Words flit through my mind. Descriptions. *Serene. Sun-drenched. Dappled wood. Magical. Paradise.* They comfort me, as they always do. I steady my mind, focusing on them, on their shapes and colors and structures, the myriad ways they fit together. *Solace. Consolation. Assuagement. Relief.* The unicorn nickers softly. I reach up and rub its muzzle. I let my heart brim with the feeling of luckiness, that I have such a friend to love, such a place to stay. The only place that stays the same. No matter what.

I hear a girl's voice behind me. I turn around. She has two short pigtails and a pink, sooty face. She is grinning. I grin back. The unicorn grunts. I mouth her name, the silent word bursting with joy. For a moment, I pause awkwardly. But she doesn't care about my height, or the fact that I have never, will never, be able to speak to anyone but her. She squeezes my hand and leads me away, the unicorn clopping behind us.

When I am with her, the lump in my throat begins to disappear. So that 20 minutes later, I am able to whisper two words. *Thank you.* And she smiles and nods and squeezes my hand. *Friendship.* It's a beautiful word, the color of winter sunsets and summer tangerines. My mind lingers on the image, and the time passes by. Words float out of my mouth now, light and sweet like spun sugar. At the same time, they form in my mind, as always, unspoken. *Gratitude. Serendipity. Liberation.*

And then all of it is shattered. The sound of a bell ringing echoes against my eardrums, loud and insistent. I can feel the worn, tattered cover of a book in my hand. The golden-lit clearing is gone. The ground underneath me is cold.

Students fill the hallways and cluster around lockers. I should be one of them. The lunch break is over. It is time to enter the world again, to be subject to a classroom of pitying stares ... to try and find the courage I left behind in the unicorn's world.

I rise and wrap the book in my coat. It is close to falling apart. I cannot count the times I have slipped it into my backpack, always comforted by the image on the cover: a sooty-faced, pigtailed girl leading a unicorn into the forest.

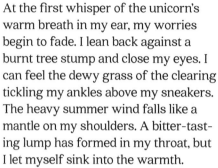

Photography Portfolio: Hannah Parker

by Hannah Parker, 13
South Burlington, VT
Camera: Nikon CoolPix L830

Editor's Introduction

Since November 2017, we have published 15—and, with this issue, now 20—of Hannah Parker's photographs. This issue also marks her fourth *Stone Soup* cover. Hannah lives on a farm in Vermont with goats, a dog, chickens, cats, and a bunny. Given her surroundings, it's no surprise that her subject has always been nature—from flowers and landscapes to her own pets and wildlife.

Though her subject has remained the same, in the two years we've been publishing her work, Hannah's approach has changed and matured. Her early photos often depicted nature in straightforward ways: a flower framed in the center of the photograph, for instance. Even early on, however, she had photographs that had a hint of strangeness, that forced us to see something very normal—a dog, the full moon—in a new way, because of how she framed the subject.

Over time, Hannah's photographs have all become stranger—and so more beautiful and more interesting—as she has experimented with editing techniques alongside new angles and frames. In this portfolio, you will see an oversaturated, almost alien-looking landscape; flowers that look as tall as trees; a landscape reflected in a raindrop; and ghostly daisies.

Even though Hannah has now turned 14, we look forward to continuing to publish the works she submitted in the months prior. We hope her work will inspire many of you not only to take photographs but to rethink your approach to common photographic subjects!

[signature]

Fog over Stowe

Queen Anne Silhouettes

Reflections in a Raindrop

Ghost Daises

Nature in My Eyes

by Andrew Wu, 11
Canton, MI

CHAPTER 1
The Seed

I am a seed who was planted by Native Americans into the rich, fertile soil of the forest paradise of the wilds of Michigan. Each day, forest would grow, and water would flow, Nature would do its thing. This never-ending cycle of creation was the lifeblood of Mother Earth's greatest creation, Life. I am Life, and you are Life. Everything that moves, grows, and flourishes is Life.

Each day Nature would repeat itself. Soon, I began to grow. I emerged from the fertile soil and saw what appeared to be a blinding ball of fire hanging in the sky. The warmth this object gave me was enough to make me happy. I could feel my sprout grow-ing in this heavenly warmth. Was this the meaning of life and Nature itself? Every day I basked in the object's warm rays. I then classified this object as God. At night God would lower down out of view, taking his warm rays with him. Then another object would rise up at night, which was not warm and much smaller. It never ap-peared to take one shape, with a slight change in the structure of the object every night. It had a certain glow, making it seem unnatural and myste-rious. I then came to classify this cold object as Gloom. Gloom would calm me down, and allow me to rest.

One day at sunrise or what was supposed to be sunrise, I couldn't see God. He just wasn't visible. I wondered why and quickly discovered strange floating balls of cotton were blocking out God. I classified these cotton balls as the Shields of Vision. They kept getting darker and darker until, I felt a drop of what I'd never felt before, which was touchable but not solid and broken when touching anything. It made me feel better than when God was out. It felt like nourishment, a soothing drop of liquid. Thundering booms followed the rain. I called these Boomers. The next day when God was visible again, I was especially happy because I have not gone through a day without God until yesterday. God was especially bright for some reason to-day, and he seemed to outshine Nature itself.

A few weeks later I had become a big sprout growing out of the ground. I saw more of the wondrous world upon me, huge lumps of rocks with white peaks, plants of my own kind, trees of a tremendous height. I saw Nature! Na-ture was beautiful, elegant and grand!

A few months later I grew into what Native Americans called "naadą́ą́" or in American language, "corn." Days went by and I grew taller and taller. Inside the bulb on top of my stalk grew a fine, tender kernel of corn. As the days went by I began to feel older, crinklier. A few months ago, God had bathed me in soothing warmth, but up to this point I felt like

Everything that moves, grows, and flourishes is Life.

he was burning me with inhospitable heat. I felt dry with God visible. I felt burnt and wanted no more. Eventually crows started eating my corn, and a few days later, my corn was an empty cob and fell out.

By then I was reduced to nothing but a dry empty stalk lying on the ground. Now I had learned the true meaning of Life: be created, wither away, create, and destroy. I had been created as a seed, created a corn cob, absorbed water, and eventually withered away myself. This was my fate and I was ready to accept it.

CHAPTER 2
The Insect

I am a minuscule insect inside an egg, a small egg. These eggs were laid by another of my own kind. I was just a puny creation of Nature and the Universe itself. I would hatch into a marvelous spectacle of Nature. I would discover the meaning of Nature and accomplish what no insect has accomplished before. I was soon to be hatched and discover amazing things, but for now I had to wait a couple of days.

A few days later, I hatched, along with the other eggs that were laid by my mother. Each of our tiny limbs and joints emerged from out of the shells from which we were made. This was the first time I had seen the outer world, which was a spectacle of true beauty. I started to walk away from my birthplace, my sisters, and brothers. It was something completely new, something that was almost telling me to solve the mystery. But the mystery of what? The mystery was Nature perhaps, or could I somehow solve myself? The idea of solving mysteries was a pleasant thought to my head.

As the days passed, I began to shed my old skin and grow a new one. It may not seem very interesting, and actually it seemed weird, but this is how Nature works. It creates new things and replaces them with newer things. This is Nature. I had settled to a spot 10 miles from my birthplace. I

live in a Pine Tree next to a majestic 130-foot high waterfall. At this point I was a decent sized Stag Beetle, and my jaws were two centimeters long each. I had my own territory, and my brothers and sisters had theirs. Occasionally, I found a trespasser and, as usual, I threw them in a place they would never get out of. I was basically the King of Bugs in my domain. But I felt empty, incomplete, and it was like a part of my life was gone before I was born. For some reason, from the start of my life, I wanted to solve a mystery. But this mystery was a mysterious mystery. I myself didn't even know what this mystery was.

When I was roaming around in my domain looking for food, I came across the miracle of life— a deer was being born. I was watching, and felt like I had to find the meaning for this, some mystery that relates to everything. Did the mystery relate to life? If so, this could be the biggest clue to solving the mystery.

As days passed, I began to think about this mystery. I began to discover more clues. However, I was not aware that I was aging and withering away. I was running out of time to solve the mystery. I could feel myself getting closer and closer to catching it, but it seemed to keep scampering away. I felt like I was missing an important key to the mystery. All the clues lined together to form Nature. I had to solve Nature, why it took place. I had to do it before I withered away, but none of the clues, alone or combined, gave an answer.

I was running out of time, I could feel my aging but still no answer. "Wait," I thought to myself. "Nature doesn't exist as one, but many; there is no one answer to that many things. Nature happens because of itself. It is a cycle that happens in the wild." Had I found the answer? Did I solve one of the greatest mysteries on Earth? If so, I would wither away with pride, with a hope of someone new taking my place. This was my fate. Nature was doing its thing: to Create, to Destroy, and to Replace. Goodbye, green world. See you soon.

I was basically the King of Bugs in my domain. But I felt empty, incomplete.

Eyes of the Savanna, *acrylic*

by Alicia Xin, 13
Scarsdale, NY

CHAPTER 3
The Fish

An egg was once laid in a pond. Inside that egg was a fish; that was me. As my egg began to soften and thin, I slowly began to break free. I emerged with an unknown purpose which I would soon begin to realize. As I hatched along with all my brothers and sisters, I began to realize that I looked different. I looked more like a Koi Fish than a Salmon. Well, even if I looked different, I bet I was smarter than the other fish. I felt wise, knowledgeable, like I'd had another life before this. I slowly followed a stream leading from the pond to a small lake. My instincts told me to go there. I was not aware that this was the place where I would discover the mystery that I would solve.

I followed the stream and encountered a fork in the road. I knew which way to take by instinct. I took the right path and eventually followed it to a small lake. I saw not many of my siblings had made it—only 40 percent of them had made it. I did what any Salmon would do: I started looking for food. There were big insects swarming but none of them were in reach. The hunger I felt was immense even compared to huge lakes. As a response to my hunger, I jumped up four feet and snatched an unexpecting Beetle. The bug filled my hunger, and I was no longer starving.

As I began to swim around in my new, temporary home, I began to wonder. I wondered about what made this place seem so special. It just seemed like a regular lake, but there was more to it. I felt this lake was an answer, an answer to some great, important, unanswered question. I wondered about this "Question." It could be something related to Life, Nature, or anything along those lines, though those topics seemed "solved" or "figured out." I noticed birds cheerfully chirping as if nothing wrong could happen. Everything seemed so peaceful.

Maybe the answer to peace was the thing I had been looking for. It all seemed so clear now. If the answers to Life and Nature were already solved, Peace would be the next. This seemed like an easy topic, but it wasn't as easy as it sounded. There must be a deeper meaning for all of these. I felt I needed to solve this. This was my life mission, and I had to do it. If I failed to solve Peace before I died, I would even regret living. This became my life goal.

A few days later, I swam around my lake in search for clues about Peace, but found nothing. If there were no clues to the answer to Peace, did that mean Peace was only a result of Chaos? Have I just solved a great mystery of the world? Even though that was unlikely, it seemed like I had. I thought some more and it made sense, I had just solved the idea of Peace. I

I felt this lake was an answer, an answer to some great, important, unanswered question.

could live the rest of my life in Peace,
enjoy the wonders of the world and,
more importantly, live my life the way
it should be.

CHAPTER 4
The Bear

As a bear cub, I always wondered about Mother Earth, our home planet. My mother told me that we lived on a planet named Earth who is everyone's proud mother. I admired Earth mainly because of her size and power. She was not to be reckoned with. My mother told me about the Gods who created Mother Earth. These Gods were even more powerful than Mother Earth. I wondered why the Gods created Mother Earth, maybe for Peace? Maybe just to create something, or even to bring happiness to the Universe. Whatever the reason, I'm sure it's a good one.

As I grew older, I started going off on my own to explore the wilderness. I saw butterflies, flowers, and lakes. The Sun that cast his light upon Mother Earth was out. Mother Earth's surface seemed perfect and almost completely natural. Why was Mother Earth so perfect and what was her reason for existence? As I explored, I found nothing that gave hints to my question. It seemed like Earth was here because of a major coincidence. Everything seemed natural, and everything was in the place it was supposed to be. How can something so Natural have everything in the exact place? Living creatures are the most amazing creations of Mother Earth. They have diverse forms, though each originated from the same ancestor. No other

known planets have such diverse life. It was probably just a big coincidence. But that coincidence has made Mother Earth one of the most special places in the Universe.

When I was one year old, my Mother sent me to live alone. I lived next to a river, where I would eat fish every day. This supply of fish was the perfect kind of food. Mother Earth was the only thing keeping me alive, and she was one of the only places where there was life. None of this seemed to be planned out. This was only a coincidence. That seemed to be the reason for Mother Earth's existence and various forms of life. The only possible answer to Earth's greatness was the greatest coincidence of all time.

Now, when living on my own, I felt in charge of an entirely new aspect. Every day, now and then, I would find something peculiar. Some days were just more special than others. It was strange to think a normal day was more special than another normal day. I lived my life normally and occasionally ran into another bear, and I would snarl and they would go away. When I was younger I felt more excited, but now I feel monotonous about my day. Every day is just the same as another. I wish something amazing would happen.

One day, when looking for food, I found a peculiar rock at the bottom of a crystal-clear river. I went forward and picked it up. What I noticed about this rock was that it was as clear as the lake itself. I could only see the rock because of its outline. It looked special as if it was a gift from the Gods. I decided to keep this rock, and as soon as I had it with me, a huge school of salmon crossed the river to my side. I was shocked at the sight of so many salmon. That day was the best day. I had found the sweetest and ripest berries, the best weather, and no competitors. I knew this was the rock's cause. This rock was a miracle, a grace, something I wished to keep forever. I could live happily with it, accomplish my dreams, and live my life the way I wanted.

Why was Mother Earth so perfect and what was her reason for existence?

Sun Flower, *acrylic*

by Sloka Ganne, 9
Overland Park, KS

The Place Where It Isn't

by Eliana Schaffer, 11
Los Angeles, CA

One girl's quest for perfection

There was a space. The space was empty, but, if you think about it, it wasn't an absence; it was a presence. It didn't belong. Inside her heart, there was the absence, or presence. In her heart was an empty space, or filled space, and it just didn't belong. The rest of her heart, though, could take years to describe thoroughly. There was art, there was math, there was writing, there were jokes, and there was family. What was missing? In the very back, there was sorrow, but sorrow had its place. Of course, it was hidden. Everyone has sorrow hidden in them. It is human.

But everything about this girl was normal. Except for the absence, she felt as if she was complete. Not special, not out of the ordinary, but she was fine. You could almost say she was perfect, but even in perfection, there are flaws. You see, even in perfection, it is hard to learn, to improve, and to do better. You cannot set goals, not achieve, for what is there to achieve in perfection? The perfection, as the girl saw it, was something she loved. But not until she learned of what that perfection did to her did she realize what it took from her.

Every day, she would watch the other children get scolded, and taught, and corrected. She laughed and thanked the gods for what she had achieved.

Two days later, the girl was crying. She was crying, and crying. For she was told by her teacher that she had to stay home from school.

"Why?" the girl cried out. She was upset at the teacher. So, so, so upset. For that teacher, unintentionally, had spoiled her lifelong journey toward perfection. She had never cried. Even as a baby. Now she let it out, and, surprisingly, it felt good. She approached her teacher. Screams and screams were aimed at the teacher. The teacher looked hurt. What was hurt? It didn't make the girl happy. There was something else, like the opposite of happiness. Then, she hugged her. It was a solution. Why would she need a solution?

The solution helped. It filled up the hole of hurt. The hurt was still there, but it was covered, and the covering made her happy. It was an accomplishment, and that felt good.

The Monster

by Ivy Cordle, 9
Princeton, NJ

Some people think that monsters
are bad, that monsters are scary
hairy and mad, but maybe
just maybe if you hear a roar
outside your bedroom door
and you invite the sound in,
maybe you won't see a scary,
bad, mad, monsterest creature;
you'll see a scared, sad, lonely
creature instead.
And when you say "come to my bed,"
you see the monster shrink
just a thread, and when
the monster is snuggled up
close, you feel the monster
shrink a foot. By the time
you've laughed and played
a game, the monster is
the same size as the helmet you
wear when you're
polluxing the polluxes out of your hair.
After you read the monster
a book about a band, the monster
could fit in your hand. As your
eyes were trying to stay awake,
the monster disappeared just like
that but all you can do is
hope the monster hopefully,
just hopefully, will come back.

Letters to the Editor

Dear *Stone Soup*,

I recently got a subscription to *Stone Soup*, and I love it! It is the perfect opportunity for me because my biggest passions are reading, writing, and drawing. I have not submitted anything yet, but I most definitely will in the future.

On a different note, after reading this particular newsletter, I wanted to say that there was one thing that really stood out, mostly because I could relate to it. The other day, while I was at school, my grandma, who was babysitting me at the time, read through my latest *Stone Soup* and was very impressed. She was even more surprised when I got home and told her the entire magazine was written by children my age! Afterwards, my grandma showed the issue to my parents, who also thought the work was exceptionally good.

So, when I read the segment in the Saturday newsletter about *Stone Soup* being for everyone, not just children, I completely agreed. I just wanted to make sure you knew that your statement about *Stone Soup* being for adults too has most definitely been proven true. Just ask my grandma!

Sincerely,
Charlotte McAninch, 11
Chicago, IL

This letter was written in response to our March 9, 2019 Stone Soup Saturday Newsletter.

Dear Ms. Wood,

Having a piece accepted by a magazine is an amazing experience—more than anything, it's a validation, a sort of proof that hours of reading, writing, and revising have paid off. My favorite thing about *Stone Soup* is the wide range of publishing opportunities it offers: a nature lover can blog about their finds, a composer can send in a piece of music, a reader can write about what they read, and there is still space for stories and poems.

Stone Soup's website is what started me on book reviewing; when I found out that "writing about books" could actually be published, I started to dig short commentaries out of my notebook and turn them into multi-paragraph pieces. Getting a review published was immensely encouraging for me, and I began to write more and more, eventually venturing into the world of short stories and poetry. Reviewing has changed the way I read and think about what I read. In a way, being accepted by *Stone Soup* changed my life.

The stories which are featured in the newsletter every Saturday are, I think, a great way of giving newsletter readers a taste of what's out there—without even visiting the website or opening the magazine. I wonder if, perhaps, you could also feature poems or content from the blog more often; shaking things up might bring more attention to the different genres published in *Stone Soup*. I really enjoy reading the writing of kids who are my age. For me, it's a form of inspiration—if they can do it, so can I!

Some really beautiful, evocative writing appears in *Stone Soup* every month. I'm continually being impressed by what my peers can do, and it gives me the determination to keep going. Thank you, *Stone Soup*!

Sincerely,
Vandana Ravi, 12
Palo Alto, CA

Do you have something to say about something you've read or seen in Stone Soup? If you do, we'd love to hear from you, and we might print your letter on our Letters to the Editor page! You can write us a letter via our Submittable page (choose "submit" on our website menu and follow the link), or leave a comment on our website.

Honor Roll

Welcome to the *Stone Soup* Honor Roll. Every month we receive submissions from hundreds of kids from around the world. Unfortunately, we don't have space to publish all the great work we receive. We want to commend some of these talented writers and artists and encourage them to keep creating.

Fiction
Alexander Antelman, 12
Anya Geist, 12
Savanna Hopson, 13
Keira Krisburg, 11
Macy Li, 13
Grace Malary McAndrew, 12
Ilya Rosenbaum, 11
Alexa Troob, 12

Poetry
Sascha Farmer, 11
Ruth Gebhardt, 11
Leah Koutal, 11
Zaid Nazif, 10
Zoe Smith, 11
Alexa Zielkowski, 12

Art
Sage Millen, 11
Cameron Purdy, 9
Kathleen Werth, 9

Plays
Liana Zhu, 10

Visit the *Stone Soup* store at Stonesoupstore.com to buy:

- Magazines—individual issues of *Stone Soup*, past and present

- Books—our collection of themed anthologies (fantasy, sport, poetry, and more), and the *Stone Soup Annual* (all the year's issues, plus a taste of the year online, in one volume)

- Art prints—high quality prints from our collection of children's art

- Journals and sketchbooks for writing and drawing

... and more!

Don't forget to visit Stonesoup.com to browse our bonus materials. There you will find:

- 20 years of back issues—around 5,000 stories, poems, and reviews

- Blog posts from our young bloggers on subjects from sports to sewing—plus ecology, reading, and book reviews

- Video interviews with *Stone Soup* authors

- Music, spoken word, and performances

StoneSoup

 VOLUME 47 / ISSUE 7

Stone**Soup**

*The magazine supporting
creative kids around the world*

Editor
Emma Wood

Director
William Rubel

Operations
Jane Levi

Education & Production
Sarah Ainsworth

Design
Joe Ewart

Stone Soup (ISSN 0094 579X) is published
11 times per year—monthly, with a
combined July/August summer issue.
Copyright © 2019 by the Children's
Art Foundation, a 501(c)(3) nonprofit
organization located in Santa Cruz,
California. All rights reserved.

Thirty-five percent of our subscription
price is tax-deductible. Make a donation at
Stonesoup.com/donate, and support us by
choosing Children's Art Foundation as your
Amazon Smile charity.

POSTMASTER: Send address changes to
Stone Soup, 126 Otis Street, Santa Cruz, CA
95060. Periodicals postage paid at Santa
Cruz, California, and additional offices.

Stone Soup is available in different formats
to persons who have trouble seeing or
reading the print or online editions. To
request the Braille edition from the National
Library of Congress, call +1 800-424-8567.
To request access to the audio edition via
the National Federation of the Blind's NFB-
NEWSLINE®, call +1 866-504-7300 or
visit www.nfbnewsline.org.

Check us out on social media:

Editor's Note

You'll quickly notice this issue is more than
a bit different than our other issues. There
are no stories, artworks, or poems—only
reviews! (I talk about the value of critical
reading and reviewing in a longer note on
page 4.)

The other thing that makes this issue
different is the way we put it together: most
of the reviews were commissioned. This
means that instead of passively waiting for
writers to submit on their own, we actively
reached out to both former contributors
and current reviewers for our website. We
asked them specifically to review a classic
book, poem, or film from a list we at *Stone
Soup* compiled. I hope the results inspire your
summer reading!

Letters: We love to hear from our readers. Please
post a comment on our website or write to us via
Submittable or editor@stonesoup.com. Your letter
might be published on our occasional Letters to
the Editor page.

Submissions: Our guidelines are on the Submit
page at Stonesoup.com, where you will also find a
link to our Submittable online submissions portal.

Subscriptions: To subscribe to *Stone Soup*,
please press the Subscribe button on our web
page, Stonesoup.com.

On the cover:
"Tree Library"
watercolor

**by Li Lingfei, 10
Shanghai, China**

StoneSoup
Contents

The Value of Critical Reading
by Emma Wood, Editor

In addition to being Editor of *Stone Soup*, I am also a university instructor. When I teach creative writing, I like to tell my students that the most important part of the class is not writing but reading because reading will you teach you how to be a writer.

As you sit there, eagerly turning the page to find out what will happen next, you are also taking in sentence structures, vocabulary, pacing, and the many other features that make up a poem, a story, or a book. On top of this, you are learning about what kinds of books have already been written. If you want to be a writer, it is crucial to learn about the history of the genre in which you want to write. All writers build on the work of other writers. Writing that is not built on this foundation of knowledge is often, like a house without a foundation, unable to stand for long. Finally, when you read, you are also learning about your own tastes: What do you like to read, and why? This can often help you uncover interesting insights about yourself.

But all reading is not equal. Have you ever been told "You are what you eat"? Well, the same is true for what you read. If you want to be a mystery writer, read mysteries; if you want to be a poet, read poetry. But you don't want to read just any mysteries or poems: you want to read the best mysteries and the best poems (with some breaks in between for some literary "junk food"!). The best writing and art is that which rewards close study and rereading. It is the novel or poem that you can't stop thinking about, the one in which you find something new each time you read it. It is classic literature.

The review is a place to celebrate reading—but not just any reading: close and critical reading. Writing a review pushes you to engage more deeply with a text than you might have otherwise. It opens up a dialogue between you and the book and the author, allowing you to discover more about yourself and the text in the process. In my experience, writing critically about a work I already love makes me love it even more: it makes visible all the previously invisible threads that make it so incredible. I realize now what I should say to my creative writing students is that reading *critically* will teach them how to be writers.

You will notice that one of the reviews in this issue is a review of a film. Although I am talking specifically about books in this introduction, movies, paintings, sculptures, and other visual modes can be "read" as well, and it is just as important to engage critically with work in these mediums as well.

With this in mind, I ask you to try to write at least one review this summer. Read, listen, watch; then re-read, re-listen, re-watch. And, finally, think critically about what you've just encountered. See what it feels like to spend time, outside of class, thinking through a work you really love (or hate).

We look forward to reading the results!

Novel Reviews

Frankenstein
by Mary Shelley

Before I begin this review, I want you to think of everything you think you know about *Frankenstein*. What comes to mind even when I think of *Frankenstein* is the classic depiction from the old horror movies. The insane doctor with a German accent screaming, "It's alive!" as lightning lights up the sky and magically brings his new friend to life. A hideous monster who speaks in broken English. In the book, none of that happened. The lightning thing never happened; Victor never said, "It's alive!"; and the monster was, according to Victor, quite attractive (with the exception of his somewhat unsettling eyes, but I'll get to that later). Rather than the science fiction horror story of the silver screen, the original book was actually a profound and grim commentary on the dangers of unethical science.

The novel, written by Mary Shelley in 1818, opens with Captain Robert Walton aboard a ship drifting through the North Pole. He spots none other than Victor Frankenstein, stranded on the ice and looking very displeased indeed. He takes Victor on board and, naturally, wants some context as to why this scientist is stranded in the middle of the North Pole. Victor launches into an exhaustive life story told in excruciating detail from the very beginning.

Victor, born in Italy to a German family and raised in Geneva, Switzerland, is a brilliant scientist who grew up reading the works of outdated alchemists and scientists. This motivates him to get a real education and pursue science as a career. This whole bit bored me to tears, and I'm sure it will do the same for you, so I'm going to skip on to the juicy part: Fast forward to years later. Victor has dropped out of college (no, he was not a doctor, not even close) and decided that he's going to go dig up some graves, stitch some body parts together, and bring his new creation to life. Grave robbing and playing god. Classic midlife crisis.

To someone like Victor, this is a completely normal thought process. Victor does indeed bring this creation to life, though it's never said how (screenwriters had to make up the lightning thing all on their own). He also never says, "It's alive!" His reaction is more of an "Oh, cool."

Contrary to the classic Hollywood nightmare, said monster is actually very beautiful. The monster's only fault is that he has terrifying eyes. Victor is, in fact, so afraid of the monster's eyes that he declares the experiment a failure, ditches the monster, and leaves the monster to his own devices. Deadbeat dad of the century right there.

The monster wanders out into the world, curious and kind and eager

Reviewed by
Valentine Wulf, 13
Seattle, WA

to learn. The monster soon finds out, however, that people are afraid of him. He is naturally confused and scared and runs into the forests of the Swiss Alps. There he is lost, wandering around and discovering the world for the first time, given that he's basically a giant baby.

The monster learns to speak by listening in on a rural family in the Alps. He begins to understand that all his misfortunes are caused by Victor, the one person who was supposed to take care of him. From there, the monster decides to seek revenge on his creator. I won't spoil the rest!

Victor, out of arrogance and disregard for anyone but himself, brought the monster to life without regard for the consequences of his actions. When this backfired, instead of accepting responsibility for his mistake and either killing the monster or raising him properly, he hightails it out of Switzerland and leaves the monster to fend for itself rather than face what he has done.

Victor isn't a mad scientist, nor is he a hero. He is someone whose life fell into ruin because he only thought about himself; he let his ego dictate his work. To all the people who say "Frankenstein was the doctor, not the monster"—in this story, there are two monsters. And one of them is indeed named Frankenstein.

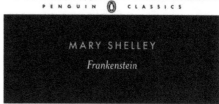

Penguin Classics: New York, 2003; originally published in 1818.

A Little Princess
by Frances Hodgson Burnett

I consider myself privileged. I have a wonderful family, live in a big house in the suburbs, and I go to a highly ranked school. My family really cares about me. I have a great life with wonderful opportunities and perform well in school and in the extracurricular activities I participate in. I am most likely a child who is awfully spoiled. Although I can see it so clearly now, there was once a time that I thought I did not have a very good life. There was always someone who had something better than me. So what if I had a cookie in my lunch? Someone else had two cookies, and obviously, two cookies were undoubtedly superior to one cookie. I was a disagreeable young girl and coveted more than I had. I didn't see how lucky I truly was.

Now I know that it was an amazing miracle that my little first-grade self plucked *A Little Princess* from the shelf one bitterly cold winter morning.

As I studied the book cover for the very first time, I was captivated by the girl my age in a rosy pink frock on the cover. *A book about someone my age?* I excitedly pondered in my head. I saw the title, *A Little Princess*, printed on the cover in a cursive font I admired. *A girl my age who was a princess? This is going to be a good book!* I had no idea how true that statement would turn out to be.

When I started reading the book that very weekend, I was treated to descriptions of smoggy, turn-of-the-century London. This was where rich, clever Sara Crewe went to a dignified yet stingy old boarding school. Sara was no ordinary girl, though. She was undoubtedly kind. Instead of being friends with the popular mean girls, she sparked friendships with the misfit students and younger girls. She was also a star student, yet she didn't brag about her cleverness to her peers. She was truly a lovely little girl.

I immediately found distinct similarities between Sara and me. We both had an intriguing look, that was different yet pretty. We were both very clever and deemed "smart" by our teachers and peers.

But as I read on, I found so much more in this book. As I traveled through heartbreak, hardships, and cruelty with Sara as my companion, I uncovered a true secret of life. As she was abused, starved, and cruelly mistreated, Sara was still gracious. She was tenderly chivalrous to all those she crossed paths with, even when they greeted her by barking orders at her, even as she labored over difficult work. Seeing this, I had a sudden epiphany. I stopped reading all at once and thought long and hard. If Sara could be magnanimous in a time of great trial, shouldn't I be even more so when I had so much more to be gra-

Reviewed by
Ava Horton, 13
Gresham, OR

cious about? Couldn't I give so much more to those in greater need than I was? I had the power to be gracious and kind. That was when I decided to use it.

A Little Princess taught me to be a friend. It also taught me to be kind and grateful. I never neglect to say "please" or "thank you" because I know, though small, those simple words can be extremely powerful.

You know you've found a great book when it transforms your thought process. Now I know how lucky I was to find a little princess on the shelf that fateful Monday morning.

Harper Classics: New York, 1998; originally published in 1905.

A Little Princess
by Frances Hodgson Burnett

What does a person really need in order to be happy? If you were to lose every tangible thing which gives you joy now, what intangible things would make life still worth living? The novel *A Little Princess* by Frances Hodgson Burnett answers these two questions from the point of view of an eleven-year-old with a response which is ultimately simple, sweet, and surprisingly wise.

The wealthy, pampered Sara Crewe finds herself alone in a new country when her doting father leaves her at a London boarding school. As she adjusts to her new life, her character turns out to be surprisingly different from that of the stereotypical rich, spoiled girl; she uses her advantage and intelligence to help those of her classmates cast off by the other girls. But when Sara's father suddenly passes away, leaving behind nothing but debt, her life is turned upside down. Transformed from a veritable princess into an unpaid scullery maid, she loses all the expensive comforts she is used to. However, Sara's kindness, tenacity and imagination afford her new joys, eventually bringing her all the way to a happy ending.

There are two intertwining themes in *A Little Princess*: the power of imagination and the power of kindness. When I first read the novel as a quiet "dreamer" third-grader,

I was surprised and impressed by the way Sara conquers her troubles: by imagining that she is a princess. Telling herself that she is above those who ridicule her, she ends up making her dream a reality by striving to act better than her tormentors—even if it means hiding sadness or biting back anger. She notices and appreciates the small joys in her new life, pretending to be elsewhere when her sadness overcomes her. Sara's ability to find joy in apparent bleakness is so great that friends who visit from their comfortable rooms go away envying her bare, drafty attic; her tenacious cheerfulness beautifies her poverty more than money and expensive furniture do for her peers.

The second recurring idea in *A Little Princess* is the impact of kind actions. Sara's painstaking kindness to many characters, including the scullery maid Becky, spoiled toddler Lottie, learning-challenged Ermengarde, and even a lost monkey, repeatedly comes back to help her when she needs it most. Her resolution to be a princess in actions, if not in wealth, is one which continually acts in her favor—giving her hope, self-respect, and sustenance just as she strives to give it to others.

Years after first reading the book, I still try to apply its themes to my own life. A touch of imagination and kindness has helped me through countless hard days and added joy to easy ones;

Reviewed by
Vandana Ravi, 12
Palo Alto, CA

rereading Sara's story now lifts my spirits. *A Little Princess* is the essence of what we can live for, of how we can deal with hard times, whisked into a story just close enough to a fairy tale that its moral feels more like a familiar friend than a stranger.

I've loved reading the classics ever since I was old enough to understand them. I carried them with me on school trips, piled them next to my pillow, and quoted and cherished their words wherever I went. But they aren't just special to me because of their universally relatable plots or old-fashioned language—although I enjoy those elements too. Classics—older books which have survived generations—tend to carry with them a host of life lessons, buried in the pages like treasure waiting to be found. These lessons can remind us of what we care about, offer advice when things get difficult, and shine a few rays of hope into our lives when we most need them. That is my favorite thing about reading: its power to guide the reader through real life.

If you were to lose everything, what intangible things would make life still worth living? There are a few answers to that question. Imagination. Hope. Kindness. Friendship. And maybe, as a comforting map to help you find the purpose you're looking for, the imprint of a good book on your heart.

A Tree Grows in Brooklyn
by Betty Smith

A Tree Grows in Brooklyn by Betty Smith is the story of a Brooklyn girl with Irish ancestors who grows up at the beginning of the 20th century with all the hardships that come from not having enough money in the house, a drunkard for a father, and a mother who prefers her son to her daughter. Although Frances Nolan's life is riddled with complications, she never ceases to find beautiful places and things in life—like the flower in the bowl at the library that changes with every season or the little school 12 blocks away that she dearly wants to attend.

We follow Francie from her birth to womanhood. We meet her singing father and her hardworking mother, her three aunts and her saint-like grandmother, as well as Cornelius (or "Neeley" for short), her little brother who is so favored by their mother. As Francie grows older, she realizes how poverty limits her family, and she knows she doesn't want to grow old poor. So at the age of 14, Francie gets a job, pretending she is 16, to help bring in more money for her family.

A lot of the story's main ideas are about life lessons, about poverty, and what it was like to be a girl, then a woman, at the beginning of the 20th century.

One of the sharper life lessons of the story is when Francie learns that not everyone appreciates the truth. She has started to write stories based on her surroundings, but her teacher does not approve. Francie used to write beautiful, made-up stories which Miss Gardner loved, but when Francie starts to write stories about drunkenness, poverty, and hunger Miss Gardner gets angry:

> "You were one of my best pupils. You wrote so prettily. I enjoyed your compositions. But these last ones . . ." she flicked at them contemptuously. ". . . poverty, starvation and drunkenness are ugly subjects to choose. We all admit these things exist. But one doesn't write about them."
>
> "What does one write about?"
> . . .
> "One delves into the imagination and finds beauty there . . ."

Francie and the reader understand that Miss Gardner is wrong because truth is also poverty and hunger and drunkenness. This is by no means all of what truth is, but it is still truth. To say that beauty is the only truth is to only see half of reality. After this conversation with her teacher, Francie realizes for the first time that educated people might see her life as revolting.

I read *A Tree Grows in Brooklyn* just after finishing *The Chosen* by Chaim

Reviewed by
Claire Rinterknecht, 14
Strasbourg, France

Potok. *The Chosen* is a novel set in Brooklyn about Reuven and Danny, two Jewish boys who become best friends and have to live through the silence that Danny's father inflicts upon Danny. It was interesting to read two books set in the same location but at different time periods. *A Tree Grows in Brooklyn* is set around World War I, and *The Chosen* is set around World War II. In *A Tree Grows in Brooklyn*, Francie walks home down Graham Avenue, and she notices everything:

> She was excited by the filled pushcarts—each a little store in itself—the bargaining, emotional Jews and the peculiar smells of the neighborhood; baked stuffed fish, sour rye bread fresh from the oven, and something that smelled of honey boiling. She stared at the bearded men in their alpaca skullcaps and silkolene coats . . .

Similarly, in *The Chosen*, Reuven walks with Danny down the street where Danny lives. He notices how:

> [T]he street throbbed with the noise of playing children who seemed in constant motion, dodging around cars, racing up and down steps, chasing after cats, climbing trees, balanc-

ing themselves as they tried walking on top of the banisters, pursuing one another in furious games of tag—all with their fringes and earlocks dancing wildly in the air and trailing out behind them.

These two passages are very similar in their description of the streets in Brooklyn, even though more than 20 years and two world wars separate the two stories. Readers get a real sense in both books of how varied and alive Brooklyn was.

A Tree Grows in Brooklyn is beautifully written and entrances the reader from the first page. I recommend it for mid to older teens. It is not a simple read because of the style of writing, which often includes the Brooklyn slang from the time. One example of the slang in the book is when a mean little girl spits in Francie's face but Francie doesn't cry. The little girl says, "Why don't you bust out crying, you dockle? Want I should spit in your face again?" To "bust out crying" is just like to burst out crying, but "dockle" does not have a modern definition in the dictionary because it was part of the local slang in that period. I had to search a little to find any kind of meaning and finally found that a dockle is a sort of doll or bundle of thread, but, in this quote, "dockle" is clearly an insult.

It is difficult to capture the feeling of *A Tree Grows in Brooklyn* because the way Betty Smith writes is almost otherworldly. But at the same time, the things she writes about are so realistically concrete. The following quote conveys some of the otherworldly but realistic aura of the book.

> The tree whose leaf umbrellas had curled around, under and over the fire escape, had been cut down because the house-wives complained that wash on the lines got entangled in its branches ... But the tree hadn't died ... it hadn't died. A new tree had grown from the stump, and its trunk had grown along the ground until it reached a place where there were no wash lines above it. Then it started to grow towards the sky again.

This quote is both beautifully written and is an elegant metaphor for Francie's life, as she was cut down often but also found a way around her troubles in order to grow and thrive.

A Tree Grows in Brooklyn is very much about a woman's life in a man's world, and Francie's life represents all of the struggles and obstacles women faced. But her life also represents the beauty and achievements that brave women have lived through. I hope future readers will find it as special as I did.

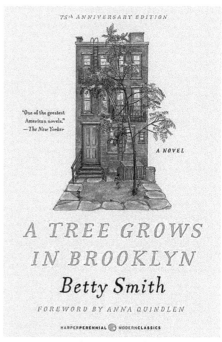

Harper Perennial: New York, 2018; originally published in 1943.

See also: Potok, Chaim. The Chosen. Penguin Random House: New York, 1996.

From the Mixed-Up Files of Mrs. Basil E. Frankweiler
by E.L. Konigsburg

Raise your hand if you like art. Yes? Good. Raise your hand if you like adventure. Excellent. Now raise your hand if you like books. Spectacular! As it happens, there is a book that can satisfy all of those things—*From the Mixed-Up Files of Mrs. Basil E. Frank-weiler* by E. L. Konigsburg. A blend of mystery, adventure, and a little history, *From the Mixed-Up Files* is instantly recognizable as a classic book for the ages.

The main character, Claudia, feels that her life is riddled with unfair treatment, such as having to constantly do chores for very little allowance. So she resolves to run away from home with her younger brother, Jamie, (mostly because of his transistor radio and all the money he's saved up) on the Metro-North train and live in the Metropolitan Museum of Art in New York City for a little while. She plans to learn as much as possible about the museum in the time that they will spend there. While hiding in the museum, Claudia and Jamie notice that people are swarming to see an angel sculpture. Claudia wonders why everybody is so excited about it, so she finds a *New York Times* and reads an article on the angel, which says that it is suspected to be by Michelangelo. She decides to solve the mystery of the statue's origins, and in doing so will satisfy her real motive for running away: to have made a significant change in her life by the time she goes home.

The story is told as a series of letters written by a character who only appears at the end, Mrs. Basil E. Frankweiler, who is recording Claudia and Jamie's tale in a letter to her lawyer, Saxonberg. Mrs. Frankweiler's asides to Saxonberg are hilarious. Another aspect of the story I enjoyed is how relatable it is. Anyone with at least one sibling knows how incredibly exasperating they are at times (I myself have a little brother); however, on occasion, you are glad to have them around. *From the Mixed-Up Files* captures this relationship perfectly, and subtly encourages siblings to get along more

Reviewed by
Nina Vigil, 11
Katonah, NY

by focusing on the positives. Another way the author creates a sense of relatability is by describing the many frustrations children have in life (Claudia's "injustices") and also our desire for adventure and excitement. I have always wanted something really exciting like a grand adventure or mystery to happen to me, although this wish has unfortunately not yet been granted!

Stone Soup put this book on their list of classics, and I wholeheartedly agree with the decision. *From the Mixed-Up Files of Mrs. Basil E. Frankweiler* demonstrates all the defining qualities of a classic, and it deserves this honor. For those of you who haven't read it, go read it. For those of you who have read it, good; now go read it again.

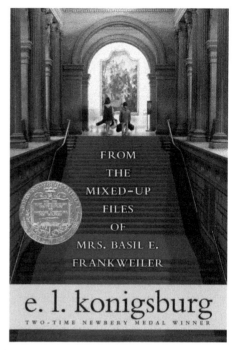

Atheneum Books for Young Readers: New York, 2007; originally published in 1967.

Boy: Tales of Childhood
by Roald Dahl

My mother always told me tales from her childhood. Most were happy stories that made me laugh. Others were sad and made me worry about her. Sometimes she told me stories about her own mother, my Yiayia, who had an even harder childhood, raised in a small village in Greece. My mother told me that without experiences, even hard ones, sad ones, and ones that make me cry, a writer will not have anything to write about. Roald Dahl puts his experiences of life, both happy and sad, in his autobiography, *Boy: Tales of Childhood*.

Roald Dahl, the proud author of many funny children's books, isn't the same on the inside as what he seems like on the outside. After reading *Boy*, I learned that he had a hard, troubling life as a kid, and those experiences are the ones that inspired him to write this

Reviewed by
Marilena Korahais, 8
Whitestone, NY

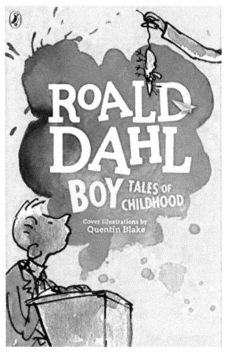

book.

This book is not like others I've read. It begins with a memory of his dad working on the roof of their house; his dad tragically falls off and breaks his arm. The nearest doctor was drunk, and he dislocated the poor man's arm. Because of this, Dahl's father had to get it amputated and later invented a tool that helped him cut and eat his food with one hand.

Dahl also shares his experiences at boarding school where he was often mistreated. But, he also shares happy times, like the time he and his friends put a dead mouse in the mean candy-lady's store. Dahl's life was full of different emotions, and I realized I am very lucky that my life is filled with happiness. Still, everybody has had some sad experiences, even if they haven't had a lot of them.

Though I wish Dahl's life wasn't full of melancholy events, I believe that is part of the reason he is such a good writer. Most kids know about *The BFG*, *James and the Giant Peach*, and *Matilda*, but they may not know who Dahl was and what his life was like or how this affected his writing. Without these experiences that made him who he was, he may have had nothing to write about at all. I treasure his stories the way I treasure the stories from my mother and grandmother.

Puffin: New York, 2016; originally published in 1984.

Number the Stars
by Lois Lowry

Number the Stars is about Annemarie Johansen, a Christian girl living in Denmark during World War II. She is best friends with Ellen Rosen, a Jewish girl. When the Nazis decide to "relocate" Denmark's Jews, Annemarie and her family hide Ellen to keep her safe. Later, Annemarie helps get Ellen's family and other Jews across the sea to Sweden, a country that was Nazi-free. At the end of the book, Annemarie has to summon all her bravery to make a trip on her own that will decide the fate of the Jews her family was trying to save.

Bravery is an important theme in the book. Annemarie is put in countless situations where she has to be brave or the consequences would be terrible. I admire her very much for this. I also try to be brave. It is a quality I would like to have. However, I don't feel brave or think that I am. There are silly things that scare me; for example, I get scared if there is an insect nearby. I know this is silly, but still, I am not brave when I see a bug. In the book, Annemarie also says that she does not feel brave. However, when it is necessary to be brave, she is. Fortunately, I have never been in anything close to the terrifying situations Annemarie faced. Still, the book inspired me to think that if someone could be brave in such terrible and scary situations, then maybe I could be brave, too, in the silly situations that I find myself in. All

I have to do is try.

Another part of the book that spoke to me was a scene involving the Star of David necklace Ellen always wore. In the scene, Ellen has to quickly remove the necklace before the Nazis march into the room. Since there is not enough time to undo the clasp, Annemarie rips the necklace off.

I identify with Ellen because I also have a Star of David necklace. My necklace was given to me by my great-grandmother who survived the Holocaust. At the time of the Holocaust, being identified as Jewish through wearing such a necklace could endanger your life. Still, even though my great-grandmother went through the Holocaust, she wanted to give the necklace to me. I think that this is because she thought wearing such a necklace was important. The necklace is a symbol of my culture, and of Ellen's. And that culture is part of our identity no matter what happens. At the end of the book, Annemarie fixes Ellen's necklace to give back to her one day. She knows that, like my great-grandmother, Ellen would still want to wear her Star of David necklace.

My great-grandmother was from Lithuania. When the Nazis invaded, she was put in a ghetto. Before the ghetto was liquidated, she and my great-grandfather escaped. Her family friends hid her afterward. She later

Reviewed by
Maya Viswanathan, 13
Champaign, IL

moved to Israel and then America, where I was born. Because of her experience and the experience of my other great-grandparents in the Holocaust, this book was especially meaningful to me. It is also important to me to remember the Holocaust so that something like it never happens again.

The Holocaust was a horrible tragedy and therefore reading about it is often very difficult. But, as far as Holocaust books go, this one was less dismal. And so it is a good book to read if you haven't learned much about the topic. Even if you do know a lot about it, I recommend reading this book, because it focuses on good people who helped the Jews. In Denmark, people were very much against the Nazis. The book demonstrates how people helped the Jews escape and then took care of their possessions after they left. This book illustrates the kindness of the non-Jews in Denmark. We can learn from them that, even in the face of such danger, it is still worth it to help and be kind to others—a lesson that can't be discussed too much.

I read this book a few years ago, and I recently read it again. Both times I enjoyed it a lot and learned a lot. This book is a meaningful story about an inspiring, brave girl who did what was right, and it was even funny at times. If you have never read *Number the Stars*, I strongly recommend reading it.

HMH Books for Young Readers: New York, 2011, originally published in 1989.

The Book Thief
by Markus Zusak

A snow-clad cemetery in Germany, a few months before World War II. A girl cannot believe her brother has just died, as she and her mother witness the burial. A black book drops to the snow without the owner's knowledge. The girl picks it up and clings to it. Her debut in the career of book thievery. Some hours later, the girl and her mother go their separate ways. The girl goes to her new parents. She does not know where her mother is going.

Liesel Meminger (the aforementioned girl) is adopted by Hans and Rosa Hubermann of 33 Himmel Street. The Hubermanns are not rich. They decide to raise Liesel because they are getting an allowance for it. Despite this, Liesel could not have a better father than Hans Hubermann. Hans comes to Liesel's room after her frequent nightmares and comforts her, or sometimes plays the accordion for her. The same cannot be said of Rosa. Though she loves Liesel, she is constantly addressing her as "pig," often accompanied by a beating. Liesel soon adapts to life in Himmel Street, befriending Rudy Steiner, one of her neighbors. Liesel and Rudy play football with the other kids, go to school together, and also go on thieving adventures. (Their loot mostly consists of food and an occasional book.)

It is Hans who discovers Liesel's first stolen book. (She was lucky it wasn't Rosa!) Liesel never learned how to read and Hans has little education. Yet, they manage to finish the book, with Liesel learning how to read in the process. Perhaps these reading sessions develop a love for reading in Liesel. And perhaps this is the reason Liesel feels a compulsion to steal books.

The narrator of *The Book Thief* is Death. What does death have to do with a girl stealing books, you say? But the book is not just about that; it is also a story based in World War II Germany where death had the leading role. Death is not just an observer; he is as much a character as Liesel herself. Death is a wonderful narrator. Often, he includes his flashbacks and images of the future. His narration is also not dry and boring. Death can be funny; he can be friendly. In fact, he is more human than most people think.

During the Holocaust, propaganda was common. Hitler fooled the majority of Germans with his words: Germans only read books which were approved by the Nazis; the media was used to create the impression that Hitler was Germany's savior; Nazis used media to convince people that Jews did not deserve to live. For this reason, the author puts a lot of emphasis on the power of words. Those who can tame words can gain

Reviewed by
Ananda Bhaduri, 13
Guwahati, India

a lot of power. Liesel, for instance, is one of these "word shakers." By the end of the book, not only can Liesel read novels on her own, she has also started writing the story of her life. (A girl living under Nazi occupation, writing the story of her own life . . . That seems familiar.)

The Book Thief is a bundle of themes. It is about "pure" Germans risking their lives to help Jews, the power of words, death, and war. However, unlike most Holocaust books, it does not focus primarily on Jewish characters. *The Book Thief* is unique because it presents us a rare perspective on living as a non-Jewish German in Nazi Germany. If you haven't read *The Book Thief*, you are missing out on one of the best Holocaust books.

Knopf Books for Young Readers: New York, 2016; originally published in 2005.

Film Reviews

When Marnie Was There
A Studio Ghibli Film

When Marnie Was There is the last movie released by the famous Japanese animation studio called Studio Ghibli, and the first I saw that got me hooked on anime, a style of Japanese animation. The story follows Anna, a young teenage girl suffering from asthma, who is sent to the country by her foster parents to live with her relatives for a while. One day, she comes across an empty house known as the Marsh House. She returns to the house time and time again to find no one living inside until, one day, she finds a young girl named Marnie who insists that Anna never tell anyone about her. As the movie progresses, we learn more about Anna and Marnie's personal backgrounds and life stories, and finally, about how their two lives might intersect . . .

There are three reasons I absolutely love this movie. First, I felt great empathy toward Anna. Anna is a shy and lonely girl who is trying to fit in, and I am also shy. Marnie is a good friend to Anna: she is kind and lighthearted and always tries to cheer Anna up.

Secondly, I appreciate that the two girls don't have a normal friendship. Other movies about friendship typically show friends having fun until a problem occurs that tests their friendship—and then the friends either reunite or break up and drift apart. For example, *Bumblebee* (part of the *Transformers* film series) is about a young girl and a robot who become close friends. They have various fun adventures during the movie until the girl finds out Bumblebee is being hunted by other robots. *When Marnie Was There* is different because Anna and Marnie never get to really know each other. There seems to be a mystery or secret that's keeping them at a distance from each other. And so, this creates suspense and leaves the viewer waiting for more. Who is Marnie? Is she a real person? Is she a ghost? Is she a figment of Anna's imagination? What is their relationship? The plot is never pieced together, and it's up to you to figure it out. This is a concept I have never seen before in a movie.

Finally, I love the animation. Most other anime films have gross characters and ugly worlds. For example, *Spirited Away*, another Studio Ghibli film, has a really twisty world with really ugly characters; they all look old and wrinkly. But in *When Marnie Was There*, the animation is realistic, and you can see everything perfectly just like in the real world. Unlike Disney animation, the anime in this movie is more beautiful because you can see all the details on the birds, flowers, and trees, and you feel like you're in Marnie's world. Disney animation has mostly empty worlds, and the setting doesn't feel alive. This is because the Disney world focuses primarily on the story happening in the movie and not on world-building.

This movie, while insanely good, does have some flaws. You see, the entire movie is literally Anna going to Marnie, and nothing else; there are barely any scenes in the movie that are not related to the friendship between the two girls. Another annoying thing is that the movie is really slow. Anna learns about Marnie very slowly. So you always have to wait for Anna to find Marnie over and over again and also wait patiently through many unnecessary scenes of Anna drawing, doing chores, etc. What's up with this slow waiting? Other than those two flaws, I feel this movie was extremely clever for a friendship story.

If you like a fast-paced thriller or action like the *Harry Potter* movies, then this movie is not for you. This movie requires deep thinking. Overall, *When Marnie Was There* is a wonderful Studio Ghibli movie and will stay in my mind as one of the greatest emotional movies of all time. There is pain, sadness, hope, and loss, and that is why I cried at the end!

Directed by Hiromasa Yonebayashi, 2015.

Reviewed by
Abhi Sukhdial, 11
Stillwater, OK

Poetry Reviews

"Hope" is the thing with feathers
by Emily Dickinson

"Hope" is the thing with feathers -
That perches in the soul -
And sings the tune without the words -
And never stops - at all -

And sweetest - in the Gale - is heard -
And sore must be the storm -
That could abash the little Bird
That kept so many warm -

I've heard it in the chillest land -
And on the strangest Sea -
Yet - never - in Extremity,
It asked a crumb - of me.

THE POEMS OF EMILY DICKINSON, edited by Thomas H. Johnson, Cambridge, Mass.: The Belknap Press of Harvard University Press, Copyright © 1951, 1955, 1979, 1983 by the President and Fellows of Harvard College.

Reviewed by
Kate Choi, 14
Seoul, Korea

What is hope? Why do we feel hope? And why is hope so important to us? In a story from Greek mythology, hope was famously the only item to remain in Pandora's box after it released the evils of the world, demonstrating just how valuable hope is to us: had hope escaped from our possession, humanity would have been unable to survive the evils of the world.

Emily Dickinson believed in the power and value of hope just as strongly. Famously reclusive, this 19th-century American poet remained largely unpublished during her lifetime, by her own choice. After her death in 1886, however, her poems were discovered and published by her close friends and family. Since then, Dickinson has grown to become one of the most mysterious, emblematic, and loved poets of all time with her short but powerful poems. Much of her poetry is devoted to exploring the nature of life, death, and what she called the "Circumference," the boundary where the reality that we know meets that of the sublime—God, for example, or for the less religiously inclined, Truth with a capital T. Dickinson was the first poet to really capture my attention when I was younger, and she is now one of my all-time favorite writers.

In her beautiful poem "'Hope' is the thing with feathers," Dickinson explores the power of hope and what it means to us as humans. In the first stanza, she introduces hope as a bird that "perches in the soul" and forever keeps us company to bear us through difficult days. In the second stanza, Dickinson emphasizes how only the most terrible situations could cause hope to falter, though hope becomes an even greater comfort to us when life is at its most difficult (a "gale" is a strong wind, while "abash" is to make someone disconcerted). Finally, in the last stanza, Dickinson brings home her message of how hope is always with us without ever costing us anything, no matter how difficult or dangerous something may be.

I love this poem first and foremost for its message, and then for its structure and wording, which is also beautiful. The poem isn't very long, but its message is still clear and potent. The rhythm of the words flows smoothly, and the words themselves are simple. I love how Dickinson feels no need to overstretch herself with elaborate and showy writing, and instead chooses to relay her message as simply as possible, which brings me closer to the poem and only heightens the impact of her message.

Dickinson is well known for the seemingly hidden meanings and complex symbolism in her work. Though this particular poem of hers is relatively simple, I, like Dickinson and her "hidden" meanings, have a hidden reason for sharing this particular poem with you today. "'Hope' is the thing with feathers" is, without doubt, an extraordinary, thought-provoking work that showcases poetry at its best. But that's not the only reason I chose to review it. In a time when the world increasingly has to deal with problems both large and small, from climate change to warfare to poverty to politics, it's more important than ever to remember the message of this poem: hope can carry us through the darkest of storms, and even when all else has abandoned us, hope never will. And I hope (yes, I hope) that you will remember it, for hope never stops—at all.

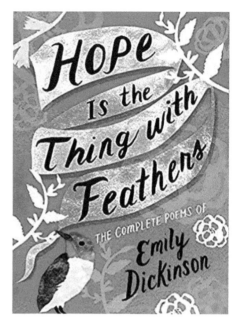

Gibbs Smith: Layton, Utah, 2019; originally published in 1891, believed to have been written in 1861.

The Road Not Taken
by Robert Frost

Two roads diverged in a yellow wood,
And sorry I could not travel both
And be one traveler, long I stood
And looked down one as far as I could
To where it bent in the undergrowth;

Then took the other, as just as fair,
And having perhaps the better claim,
Because it was grassy and wanted wear;
Though as for that the passing there
Had worn them really about the same,

And both that morning equally lay
In leaves no step had trodden black.
Oh, I kept the first for another day!
Yet knowing how way leads on to way,
I doubted if I should ever come back.

I shall be telling this with a sigh
Somewhere ages and ages hence:
Two roads diverged in a wood, and I—
I took the one less traveled by,
And that has made all the difference.

THE POETRY OF ROBERT FROST: THE COLLECTED POEMS, COMPLETE AND UNABRIDGED, edited by Edward Connery Lathem, New York: Henry Holt and Co., 2002.

From choosing what clothes we wear to the career path we devote our lives to, life will always be full of choices. "The Road Not Taken," by Robert Frost, is a poem that describes a traveler who encounters a fork in a road in a forest. Presenting him with a choice between two paths, the poem digs deep into the nature of making choices.

"The Road Not Taken" has a melancholy yet peaceful tone to it. Through the description of yellow leaves, I assume that the season is autumn, when vibrantly colored leaves would be falling around the speaker, blanketing the path. The poem has a peaceful sadness emanating throughout, as the speaker laments being unable to experience both roads. In his indecision, he tells himself that he will follow the other path another day, but then adds, "Yet knowing how way leads on to way, / I doubted if I should ever come back." In the end, he predicts telling the story of his choice with a sigh, wondering what would have happened if he had chosen differently.

Robert Frost wrote this poem for his friend and fellow poet Edward Thomas as a joke, because, on their frequent walks together, Thomas was extremely indecisive about which route they should take. No matter what road they took in the end, Thomas would always regret that they had not taken another path, convinced that it would have led to better sights and better places.

In my mind, this poem is not just about the traveler and his walk through the woods. In fact, picking a path through a forest is not such an important decision. But that decision is a metaphor for many of the life-changing choices people have to make in their "walk" through life. Whether you're traveling through the woods or simply navigating through life, you have to set your eyes on a destination.

I think the poem is telling us that we should think through all of our options, as it will impact the very direction of our journeys. There's no point in concocting a million "what ifs." Every choice you make should bring you closer to that destination. If you've made a wrong turn and there's no going back, just learn from that mistake and stay focused on the destination. Regrets don't change reality. What will change reality is your determination and how hard you work toward that ideal destination.

Reviewed by
Alicia Xin, 13
Scarsdale, NY

STONE SOUP

Stopping by Woods on a Snowy Evening
by Robert Frost

Whose woods these are I think I know.
His house is in the village though;
He will not see me stopping here
To watch his woods fill up with snow.

My little horse must think it queer
To stop without a farmhouse near
Between the woods and frozen lake
The darkest evening of the year.

He gives his harness bells a shake
To ask if there is some mistake.
The only other sound's the sweep
Of easy wind and downy flake.

The woods are lovely, dark and deep,
But I have promises to keep,
And miles to go before I sleep,
And miles to go before I sleep.

THE POETRY OF ROBERT FROST: THE COLLECTED POEMS, COMPLETE AND
UNABRIDGED, edited by Edward Connery Lathem, New York: Henry Holt and Co., 2002.

In the spring of 2017, I traveled with my father as he was doing research on the former death camps in eastern Poland. Driving back to Lublin, we made a stop in the Renaissance city of Zamość. In the central square, we came upon an old man in a feather hat and high boots standing next to a gray horse and carriage. The coachman offered to take us around.

"I'm the last coachman of Zamość," he declared.

Curious, I asked: "What do you mean?"

The old coachman replied in Polish, which I could understand, more or less, because I speak Russian: "I'm an old stupid man still to be driving this horse and buggy."

His words carried me back across the ocean to my native New England. The ride in the old-fashioned carriage at dusk brought to mind the second stanza of one of my favorite poems by the great American poet Robert Frost:

My little horse must think it queer
To stop without a farmhouse near
Between the woods and frozen lake
The darkest evening of the year.

The 48-year-old Frost wrote this melodic poem in Shaftsbury, Vermont, in 1922 and included it in his collection *New Hampshire*. The poem captures a person's travels through the night—and through the unknown. The speaker stops to rest in the alluring quietness of the night. This scene in the poem shows the speaker's peculiar behavior in front of the "little horse." The speaker seeks a break from his commitments and obligations ("promises") in life.

The poem continues:

Whose woods these are I think I know.
His house is in the village though;
He will not see me stopping here
To watch his woods fill up with snow.

The question that has been soaring in my head is: Whose woods are these? Who is the greater "he" in the poem? Is it a person—a farmer or a simple peasant boy? "The woods are lovely, dark and deep, / But I have promises to keep," states the speaker in the final stanza. I wonder again, to whom are these promises given? They could be promised to a specific person or a soul, to God or a higher power, or even to art itself.

To accomplish his meaningful tasks, Frost organized the poem in deceptively simple stanzas with rhymes that travel through the poem like a trotting horse through the woods. The rhyming conjures up the poem's central theme. In the first three stanzas, the rhyme of the

Reviewed by
Tatiana Rebecca Shrayer, 11
Brookline, MA

third line becomes the main rhyme of the first, second, and fourth lines in the following stanza: *here* in the first becomes *queer, near*, and *year* in the second. In the final, fourth stanza the whole poem comes together by employing the same rhyme throughout: deep/keep/sleep/sleep.

Why is this poem called one of the best in the 20th century? I think the poem is like an earring that was lost and later found. It shows human nature simplified into little pieces waiting to be discovered. Frost's poem invites but does not force the reader to keep his or her own promises to people, and to the world.

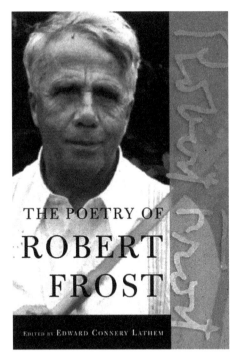

THE POETRY OF
ROBERT
FROST

Edited by Edward Connery Lathem

Henry Holt: New York, 2002; originally published in 1923.

Nothing Gold Can Stay
by Robert Frost

Nature's first green is gold,
Her hardest hue to hold.
Her early leaf's a flower;
But only so an hour.
Then leaf subsides to leaf.
So Eden sank to grief,
So dawn goes down to day.
Nothing gold can stay.

THE POETRY OF ROBERT FROST: THE COLLECTED POEMS, COMPLETE AND UNABRIDGED, edited by Edward Connery Lathem, New York: Henry Holt and Co., 2002.

Reviewed by
Maya Wolfford, 13
Cincinnati, OH

I first came across Robert Frost's "Nothing Gold Can Stay" two-and-a half years ago, nestled in a copy of S.E. Hinton's novel *The Outsiders*. To this day, I have every word of the poem memorized. It is a quick poem that says so much in so little. It combines powerful figurative language and a deeper meaning, crafts beautiful imagery, and creates a fluid sound pattern.

First, anyone who likes the outdoors and outdoor writing will enjoy "Nothing Gold Can Stay." Every line of the poem relates to some sort of item in nature: Frost touches on the Garden of Eden, the sky, and the earth.

With the second line ("Her hardest hue to hold"), Frost also personifies nature as someone struggling to hold onto her prettiest hues in her early hours. Though there are a number of possible readings for this line, it is easily comparable to children in their innocent years: an individual is guiltless and pure early on, which is the "gold" of life, yet innocence is something that stays "only so an hour."

After all, as Frost points out, everything ends. Eventually, a golden flower must join the other flowers on the ground, when "dawn goes down to day." While it is sad that every good thing can't last forever, Frost uses dawn and day instead of day and night to show that there are hopes for the future. He still manages to make the poem optimistic.

Through minimal words, Frost still forms a beautiful scene. His imagery, though confined to just eight lines and forty words, allows any reader to see spring. I imagined a sunshine-yellow daffodil ("Nature's first green is gold") bloom, then wilt. I imagined a violet twilight turn into blackness, ending the dawn. Each word in the poem has a purpose and together forms a visual that any reader can see.

What I love the most about this poem is its number of powerful words. Additionally, the couplet rhyming scheme and similar syllable count in each line give the poem a watery flow. The words and sounds form a cohesive work, instead of a choppy, peppery, scattered slew of letters.

When I first read the poem, I never imagined it would have such an effect on me. "Nothing Gold Can Stay" is a golden piece that any reader would enjoy as it appeals to a wide audience through a gorgeous combination of descriptive words, a layer that is deeper than just a picture, and its concise but nice phonetic pattern. And for all these reasons, I think this poem can stay.

This is Just to Say
by William Carlos Williams

I have eaten
the plums
that were in
the icebox

and which
you were probably
saving
for breakfast

Forgive me
they were delicious
so sweet
and so cold

STONE SOUP

Reviewed by
Twyla Coburn, 13
Portland, OR

"This is Just to Say" is a wonderful and detailed imagist poem by William Carlos Williams. After it was published in 1934, it became one of Williams's most popular poems.

With only 28 words and no continuous rhyme scheme, no meter, and no punctuation, "This Is Just to Say" captures an innocent apology for eating "the plums that were in the icebox," and yet it could mean much more. While many believe that the poem was a note written by Williams to his wife after indeed eating the plums that were in the icebox, others believe that the poem could represent a premature death of a loved one. The plums, while once here and being saved for breakfast, have now been eaten and no longer, well, exist. They are gone. This poem has been interpreted by many, and not one interpretation has been agreed upon. That is part of the beauty of this poem: it is an experience for each reader alone. One reader may see the poem as nothing more than an apology, and another could find another meaning within. The two might never agree, but for each, the meaning of the poem is theirs. That is the way in which we can all connect with this, or any, poem; it can be ours.

The speaker of the poem (either Williams or simply a fictional narrator), who is also responsible for eating the plums, explains the simple reasons for their temptation and ultimate consumption of the plums despite the fact they were (probably) being saved for breakfast. This tells us how much the writer wanted the plums, and how could we blame him? Many people would probably have done the same had they been faced with choosing between eating cold plums now versus allowing them to be saved for later. Nevertheless, the narrator asks for forgiveness. We can wonder what kind of guilt the plums have finally brought the narrator and hope that it was not too much. This poem allows us to connect with the narrator in hopes that he has not come to regret happily eating the sweet plums.

This poem, while lacking length, holds much more. It holds a strong connection with the imagination. With only the words "they were delicious / so sweet / and so cold," we are able to picture and feel the plums Williams so simply and yet vividly describes. We can picture the plums, the icebox, the note. This short poem has a never-ending ability to inspire the pictures that we can create in our minds. Williams's considerate apology is everyone's place for imagination.

Not only does this poem inspire imagination, but it inspires our senses. "Delicious," "sweet," and "cold" are all we need to feel the plums. The word "delicious" fills the mouth, much like plums and the word "plum" itself. Speaking the word "delicious" takes everything of the speaking mouth which is overwhelmed by the dynamic spectrum of movement the word requires. Eating plums requires much maneuvering of the mouth as well. Slowing the quick push intended to work through the skin is the first task, and carefully working around the pit is next. Speaking the word "delicious" takes a similar effort. We move through the "d" to immediately slow to prepare for the climactic "-licious" that we move through with great care. Now, I am not saying that Williams deliberately picked the word "delicious" because speaking it is similar to eating a plum (instead of picking the word because it is one of the more impactful ways of saying that something tastes good), but I can suggest that it certainly inspires the senses and helps the feeling of eating plums reach the reader.

"This is Just to Say" is a great poem—especially as far as poems with fewer than 30 words go!

The Collected Poems of William Carlos Williams

Volume I · 1909-1939

Edited by A. Walton Litz & Christopher MacGowan

New Directions: New York, 1991; originally published in 1934.

Thirteen Ways of Looking at a Blackbird

by Wallace Stevens

I
Among twenty snowy mountains,
The only moving thing
Was the eye of the blackbird.

II
I was of three minds,
Like a tree
In which there are three blackbirds.

III
The blackbird whirled in the autumn winds.
It was a small part of the pantomime.

IV
A man and a woman
Are one.
A man and a woman and a blackbird
Are one.

V
I do not know which to prefer,
The beauty of inflections
Or the beauty of innuendoes,
The blackbird whistling
Or just after.

VI
Icicles filled the long window
With barbaric glass.
The shadow of the blackbird
Crossed it, to and fro.
The mood
Traced in the shadow
An indecipherable cause.

VII
O thin men of Haddam,
Why do you imagine golden birds?
Do you not see how the blackbird
Walks around the feet
Of the women about you?

VIII
I know noble accents
And lucid, inescapable rhythms;
But I know, too,
That the blackbird is involved
In what I know.

IX
When the blackbird flew out of sight,
It marked the edge
Of one of many circles.

X
At the sight of blackbirds
Flying in a green light,
Even the bawds of euphony
Would cry out sharply.

XI
He rode over Connecticut
In a glass coach.
Once, a fear pierced him,
In that he mistook
The shadow of his equipage
For blackbirds.

XII
The river is moving.
The blackbird must be flying.

XIII
It was evening all afternoon.
It was snowing
And it was going to snow.
The blackbird sat
In the cedar-limbs.

THE COLLECTED POEMS OF WALLACE STEVENS: THE CORRECTED EDITION, edited by John N Serio and Chris Beyers, New York: Vintage, 2015.

Reviewed by
Sabrina Guo, 13
Oyster Bay, NY

Wallace Stevens was an American modernist poet who was born in Pennsylvania in 1879. He worked as an executive for an insurance company in Connecticut, but when he had free time, his imagination took over, and he wrote beautiful poems. In 1954, he wrote "Thirteen Ways of Looking at a Blackbird," a gorgeous poem that describes a blackbird on windy days and in cold seasons. Each of the 13 short stanzas shows one perspective of the blackbird without giving the reader any background story. Instead, the poet intertwines imagery, musical terms, and euphoric sounds to engage and encourage the reader to dive deeper when interpreting the poem.

What I like the most about the poem is the imagery, which replaces a strict storyline. Imagery, in any form of literature, is very powerful because it allows the reader to place herself within the scene that's being described. With imagery, descriptions are much more intriguing and vivid to the reader. For example, the lines "At the sight of blackbirds / Flying in a green light" gave me the warm and magical feeling of traveling through sunlight filtered between green leaves.

There are also less straightforward images in the poem that left me entranced and contemplating the meaning of each line. For instance, when I read, "When the blackbird flew out of sight, / It marked the edge / Of one of many circles," I didn't know how to interpret it at first. But then I thought of the last two lines of the previous stanza, ". . . the blackbird is involved / In what I know." This made me think of the bird flying into the narrator's mind and leaving a mark on him, one of the many things he will carry with him in his life.

Along with the imagery, the fifth stanza really stuck out to me because I am a violinist. It reads, "I do not know which to prefer, / The beauty of inflections / Or the beauty of innuendoes, / The blackbird whistling / Or just after." In music, an inflection is a change in pitch, which can be achieved by doing vibrato—that is, creating an echoing sound that makes the note a hundred times livelier. On the other hand, an innuendo is the aftermath of an increase or decrease in volume. It's like the whisper that comes through half-open windows, the sound of wind through curtains. As a musician, I loved how the blackbird is portrayed as a very delicate instrument, and it helped me appreciate the bird's song in a way I hadn't before.

But it's not just musical terms that give this poem its melodic feeling. The poet also uses phrases that sound like what they describe, which gives the poem a fun edge. For example, the first stanza reads, "Among twenty snowy mountains, / The only moving thing / Was the eye of the blackbird." When you read this out loud, the phrase, "twenty snowy mountains," actually sounds like the mountain peaks because the words' stresses move up and down at a quick pace. Say it out loud, you'll see! Also, in the line, "The blackbird whirled in the autumn winds," the words "whirled" and "winds" capture the sound of circular gusts of wind.

As a whole, this poem is packed with graceful imagery and interesting sounds, which left me in a trance after reading it. The writing conveys many feelings and effects: stillness, playfulness, mystery, and nostalgia. Because the poem's meaning isn't straightforward, it pushes readers to ask themselves questions about what the blackbird symbolizes and encourages readers to discover its many meanings. So I want to ask you: what do you think? How do you interpret this poem? What do you think the blackbird means in each stanza?

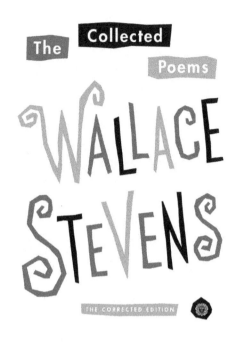

Vintage: New York, 2015; originally published in 1954.

One Art
by Elizabeth Bishop

The art of losing isn't hard to master;
so many things seem filled with the intent
to be lost that their loss is no disaster.

Lose something every day. Accept the fluster
of lost door keys, the hour badly spent.
The art of losing isn't hard to master.

Then practice losing farther, losing faster:
places, and names, and where it was you meant
to travel. None of these will bring disaster.

I lost my mother's watch. And look! my last, or
next-to-last, of three loved houses went.
The art of losing isn't hard to master.

I lost two cities, lovely ones. And, vaster,
some realms I owned, two rivers, a continent.
I miss them, but it wasn't a disaster.

—Even losing you (the joking voice, a gesture
I love) I shan't have lied. It's evident
the art of losing's not too hard to master
though it may look like (*Write* it!) like disaster.

Reviewed by
Kate Choi, 14
Seoul, Korea

We've all lost something at some point in our lives, from keys to wallets to homework assignments. Sometimes we lose bigger things: memories, people. Some of us have lost loved ones: grandparents and siblings, parents and friends. Some of us lose ourselves.

Loss—all of these kinds of loss—are central to Elizabeth Bishop's poem "One Art." In it, Bishop describes how she loses one thing after another, beginning with trivial objects like keys and building up to larger losses: houses, rivers, a continent. A loved one. Those losses, she tells us, were "no disaster," but as the poem goes on, we come to wonder if she really means it as she repeats that "the art of losing isn't hard to master."

Elizabeth Bishop was a leading American poet in the 20th century. Though she wrote many extraordinary poems during her life, "One Art" is easily Bishop's most well-known work, and in my opinion, it is her greatest. What starts off as an observation of loss and a plaintive refusal to recognize that loss is disaster ends with an anguished, heartbreaking denial that even the loss of "you" could have been a disaster.

Throughout her life, Bishop herself endured countless losses, beginning in infancy when she lost her father (she wasn't even a year old). In her grief, her mother fell into depression and had to be hospitalized when Bishop was five. Bishop then grew up afflicted with asthma and spent her childhood alternating between the care of various relatives. As an adult, Bishop lost one lover to death, and at the time of writing "One Art," she had just separated from another longtime lover, a younger woman named Alice. In response, Bishop rapidly wrote out 17 drafts of a single poem in less than a month, a first for her, since she usually spent months perfecting and revising her work. The result was "One Art," a tremendously beautiful and heartbreaking read.

"One Art" begins with its most famous line: "The art of losing isn't hard to master." Bishop starts off slowly, reassuring us that misplaced keys and wasted time are only small losses and encouraging us to practice losing: "Lose something every day," she writes. She tells us what else she has lost, things that gradually start to seem less and less trivial: the loss of her mother's watch, her house, her memories. Still, these losses are not disasters. Here the reader begins to realize that Bishop might not take these losses so lightly after all, though she so bravely pretends otherwise, as she describes the losses of "lovely" cities, continents, and realms, which (she claims) are still not disasters.

But then she reaches the final stanza, arguably the most important one in the poem. Here is where the twist is. The dash before this stanza makes it seem to be almost a postscript, an addition that couldn't be held back. "—Even losing you," Bishop writes here, revealing that the poem is being written for a certain person: "It's evident that the art of losing's not too hard to master / though it may look like (*Write* it!) like disaster." This very last line exposes to us the true nature of Bishop's immense struggle to cope with her loss, despite her repeated assurances otherwise. "(*Write* it!)," she commands herself; those two words are the only ones in the entire poem where her true pain is revealed to the reader, leaving us feeling just as torn as she is.

The best thing about "One Art"— the thing that, in my eyes, makes it so powerful—is how human it is. As Bishop herself once put it, "One Art" is "pure emotion." It approaches loss in a way completely novel, yet so familiar to any of us who have lost something we treasured. Though the speaker continues to deny that loss is any disaster, it is evident that the opposite is true, and that is what makes this poem so compelling. It is deep and powerful, simple but complex. To me, "One Art" is exactly what poetry is at its best, laying bare not only the human mind, but the human heart, however agonizing it may be.

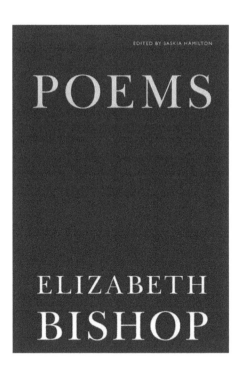

Farrar, Straus and Giroux: New York, 2011; originally published in 1976.

Honor Roll

Welcome to the *Stone Soup* Honor Roll. Every month we receive submissions from hundreds of kids from around the world. Unfortunately, we don't have space to publish all the great work we receive. We want to commend some of these talented writers and artists and encourage them to keep creating.

Fiction
Dora Fields, 11
Jasmine Kang, 11
Irina Kolarova, 12
Sean Lee, 13
Julia Marcus, 12
Izzy Martin, 13
Andres Lopez Perez-Lete, 10
Reese Caroline Stirlen, 10

Poetry
E.K. Baer, 11
Kira Brown, 8
Ariana Daya, 10
Rithika Kangath, 6
Otys Train, 9

Art
Max Fang, 7
Natalie Johnson, 13

Visit the *Stone Soup* store at Stonesoupstore.com to buy:

- Magazines—individual issues of *Stone Soup*, past and present

- Books—our collection of themed anthologies (fantasy, sport, poetry, and more), and the *Stone Soup Annual* (all the year's issues, plus a taste of the year online, in one volume)

- Art prints—high quality prints from our collection of children's art

- Journals and sketchbooks for writing and drawing

  ...and more!

Don't forget to visit Stonesoup.com to browse our bonus materials. There you will find:

- 20 years of back issues—around 5,000 stories, poems, and reviews

- Blog posts from our young bloggers on subjects from sports to sewing—plus ecology, reading, and book reviews

- Video interviews with *Stone Soup* authors

- Music, spoken word, and performances

StoneSoup

SEPTEMBER 2019　　　VOLUME 47 / ISSUE 8

StoneSoup

*The magazine supporting
creative kids around the world*

Editor
Emma Wood

Director
William Rubel

Operations
Jane Levi

Education & Production
Sarah Ainsworth

Design
Joe Ewart

Stone Soup (ISSN 0094 579X) is published
11 times per year—monthly, with a
combined July/August summer issue.
Copyright © 2019 by the Children's
Art Foundation, a 501(c)(3) nonprofit
organization located in Santa Cruz,
California. All rights reserved.

Thirty-five percent of our subscription
price is tax-deductible. Make a donation at
Stonesoup.com/donate, and support us by
choosing Children's Art Foundation as your
Amazon Smile charity.

POSTMASTER: Send address changes to
Stone Soup, 126 Otis Street, Santa Cruz, CA
95060. Periodicals postage paid at Santa
Cruz, California, and additional offices.

Stone Soup is available in different formats
to persons who have trouble seeing or
reading the print or online editions. To
request the Braille edition from the National
Library of Congress, call +1 800-424-8567.
To request access to the audio edition via
the National Federation of the Blind's NFB-
NEWSLINE®, call +1 866-504-7300 or
visit www.nfbnewsline.org.

Check us out on social media:

Editor's Note

This is an issue that looks at relationships from many different angles. The poems and stories (and many of the images too) explore what it means to be a friend, a sibling, a child, and a student. You will notice many of these pieces are set at school. The start of school every fall can be an exciting but also frightening time. I remember always being worried about whether I'd have classes with my friends, and how I would cope if not. I always found a way to cope and usually made new friends in the process!

I hope these pieces will push you to think about the relationships in your lives—how they have changed and shaped you—and inspire you to create art about them, in any form. I also hope they will inspire you to reach out to new friends this school year.

Happy September,

Letters: We love to hear from our readers. Please post a comment on our website or write to us via Submittable or editor@stonesoup.com. Your letter might be published on our occasional Letters to the Editor page.

Submissions: Our guidelines are on the Submit page at Stonesoup.com, where you will also find a link to our Submittable online submissions portal.

Subscriptions: To subscribe to *Stone Soup*, please press the Subscribe button on our web page, Stonesoup.com.

On the cover:
"Flowerwork in the
Sky"
Canon PowerShot

**by Owen Scott, 7
Fayetteville, NY**

StoneSoup
Contents

Give Me Your Hand, *iPhone 7*

by Ziqing Peng, 11
Nanjing, China

The Hello Kitty Shirt

by Una Dorr, 12
Brooklyn, NY

*After years of trying, Kiera is finally popular ...
so why isn't she happy?*

From afar, Kiera fit in perfectly at MS 452. Watching her pick at her peanut butter and jelly sandwich while fanning herself with her homework folder on this late September day, an unsuspecting onlooker might give her a glance and deem her an average seventh grader, not particularly interesting and far too obsessed with clothes, hair, and makeup. This onlooker, seeing her talking naturally with the group of girls surrounding her, would suspect that this was simply an ordinary day for Kiera, that she had known these girls for years. In assuming this, the onlooker would be entirely wrong.

While it didn't show, this may have been the most important moment Kiera had experienced in the 11 years that she had been alive. Ever since her family's SUV had finally pulled up in front of her new house in Brooklyn after the drive from New Jersey early that summer, Kiera had waited for this moment. Finally, after nearly a month of relentless effort, she had been accepted by the popular kids at their lunch table, and therefore into their group of friends. If she were to embarrass herself in front of these people, this new friendship she had formed would crumble in front of her eyes—something that she wouldn't let happen, no matter what.

Every day of being thought of as the quiet one, the friendless one, the lonely one who sat with a book in the corner of the playground during recess, vanished from Kiera's mind. Now she was speeding down the road to what she had only dreamed of in years before: popularity.

"Oh my gosh. Eric is *so* weird. Like, he literally wears the same pair of sweatpants *every day*. How gross is that?" Mia's voice rang through the bustling lunch room, somehow managing to be louder and more significant than any of the other voices in the crowded cafeteria. Sitting across from Mia in the center of the table, Kiera tried to time her giggle with the rest of the group. Together, they sounded like a bottle of soda fizzing, or perhaps a pack of joyful hyenas ready to pounce on their prey. Other people from different tables cast the group of girls annoyed glances, but this was not apparent to Kiera. Even Eric's upset face didn't matter. She was absorbed in her own circle of friends, who were so perfect and so beautiful and so amazing, and, more importantly, so existent. In this way particularly, they were different from her friends from when she lived in New Jersey.

Life went on for Kiera. She became closer with the girls, and by mid-October, she had mustered up the courage to invite them to her house for dinner one night. That Thursday, a few hours before the group was due to arrive, Kiera did some last minute, very necessary work. She pulled her parents out of their room, sat them down across from her on the couch, and stared at them intensely.

"You are not the world's most embarrassing parents," Kiera started.

"Well, yes, when we gave up our model Santa collection, I think that we stepped down to the world's second most embarrassing parents," Kiera's mom said with a grin.

Rolling her eyes, Kiera continued. "*But*, as I was *trying* to say, you certainly aren't cool or anything. So please, *please*, stay out of my business when the girls come over. It means the world to me."

Kiera's parents nodded, but as she stood up to tidy her room, she heard one of them mumble quietly, "What happened to our little Hello Kitty?"

The girls came, gossiped, ate, and then left without Kiera's parents saying anything more than "Yes, this is vegetarian." Ella had just gotten her ears pierced, and all she could talk about was how beautiful they were, and how it hadn't hurt a bit when she got them. Kiera found herself thinking about how boring the conversation

had become, and how she really didn't care about the brand new holes in Ella's ears. Alarmed, she pushed the thought out of her mind and leaned in closer to hear about all the different options for earrings that Ella had had to choose from.

The next day in school, Ms. Perez, everyone's least favorite teacher, decided to switch the current Science tables. Harper and Kiera exchanged annoyed glances, as they had only recently been seated next to each other. Many students groaned bitterly for the same reason. Ms. Perez, they thought, must be made of nothing but pure evil.

Harper, Mia, and Ash were seated at the same table, and Kiera heard Harper squeal "Yes!" in her high-pitched voice. Kiera looked down sullenly. Hadn't Harper just been moaning about being moved away from her?

As she grumbled, Kiera felt a sudden movement to her left. She jerked her head up as a tiny girl hopped onto the chair next to her, and promptly rested her feet on the shiny plastic table as if she were sitting in her living room at home. Looking around to see if anyone else had noticed, Kiera found a giggle bubbling in the back of her throat. The girl, who Kiera remembered being called Claudia, looked at her warily, one eyebrow arched to the extent that it seemed as if it might come off of her face entirely.

"What are *you* looking at?" she smirked, the accusation clearly fake.

Kiera clamped her lips shut to hold

in her laughter, but she was unable to control herself. As her mouth was shut, a rambunctious snort burst out of Kiera's nose. Claudia grinned at the peculiar noise, and Kiera grinned back. They were silent for a moment, pursing their lips to keep from laughing as they stared at each other. Then, all of a sudden, they erupted in laughter. It wasn't as if anything was particularly hilarious, yet Kiera found herself gasping for breath between laughs. Only when they realized that Ms. Perez was staring daggers at them through her cat-eye glasses did they finally stop laughing.

That period of Science, despite the evil teacher, held the record for the best Science class Kiera had ever experienced. Kiera was far from a troublemaker, so angering Ms. Perez should have upset her, but she was too busy talking to Claudia. It was as if this girl brought out a whole different side of her: Kiera, for the first time in her life, felt funny, unique, and charismatic, even. When the bell rang for sixth period, the two girls walked towards the cafeteria next to each other, mimicking Ms. Perez's condescending British accent and bossy, overly posh air.

When they arrived at the lunch room, Kiera invited Claudia to sit with her at her regular table. Claudia's face brightened, but following Kiera's finger to the table where Mia, Harper, Ella, and July were already unpacking their lunch boxes, a frown developed across it.

"Oh, gosh no. Sorry, but if I sit there, those girls will literally kill me," she said, a look of disgust unhidden on her face.

Surprised, Kiera replied, "Them? They aren't so bad. They're really nice actually! I know they might seem shallow or something, but I bet they'd really like you if you'd just be nice to them, you know?"

Claudia only shook her head and laughed quietly to herself. "Look, you seem nice and all, but those girls? They're just plain mean. I'm serious. Sit with me if you want, but only bad will come if I sit with them."

As Claudia waited for a reply, Harper noticed Kiera standing by the lunch room doors. Smiling brightly, she waved her over. Kiera looked at Claudia, and then at Harper. Finally, she turned back to Claudia, and mumbled, "Bye. I-I gotta go."

Claudia shook her head again and walked over to an empty table as Kiera turned to go to hers, which by now was almost filled with her friends.

When she arrived at the table, the girls were talking about the new Science seats. When she told them who she was sitting next to, they all groaned simultaneously.

"Poor you," Mia said with a swish of her neat blonde ponytail. "She is such a dork." Kiera wanted to respond, but she knew that it would only make things worse. And, she reminded herself, she had promised that she would try her hardest to keep her friendship with these girls. Telling them that she wanted to be friends with Claudia might murder her reputation, so why would she do that?

The weekend passed far too quickly, as always. Kiera spent it sitting in her room watching Netflix and thinking about Mia, Harper, July,

Ella, and Ash. She reassured herself that just like the people in the show she was watching, she and these girls were destined to be friends. Who had invited her to sit with them when Kiera was new? The girls. Who was nice to her when she got lost around the building? The girls! Claudia hadn't even tried to be kind to her in the beginning of the year. She may be funny, but really, Kiera thought, she was nothing compared to her other friends. On the way to school that Monday, Kiera promised herself that she would stop trying to be friends with her, that she would completely give up on her. However, Kiera had never expected it to be so difficult.

When Kiera stepped into homeroom, a wave of nausea rolled over her. Claudia stood in front of her rusty purple locker, struggling to wiggle out of her oversized navy sweatshirt. Underneath the sweatshirt, Kiera saw her interesting outfit.

She wore a pair of average blue jeans, cuffed to display a pair of beat-up Converse, and on the top, she wore a white T-shirt. This wasn't the strange part. No, the strange part was the cartoon image that had been ironed onto the T-shirt. It was a picture of a white cat with beady little eyes and a massive bow in front of one of its ears. Under it, in hot pink bubble letters, the words "Hello Kitty" were inscribed. Kiera remembered that cat. In fact, Kiera remembered that very image, ironed onto a very similar white T-shirt.

She had received it as a birthday gift in fifth grade, during the height of her Hello Kitty obsession, and had worn it at least once a week until the beginning of the summer after sixth grade. Then, after speaking with her cousin about the current trends in New York, she had put it, along with the rest of her Hello Kitty clothing, into a plastic garbage bag. Stuffing it in the back of her closet in case she wanted some extra fabric for a sewing project, she declared that if New York found Hello Kitty silly, then she did too. She remembered telling this to her parents as a way to ask if she could take a trip to the mall, and watching as her mother looked at her strangely. After all, Hello Kitty had always been Kiera's favorite character, and it was so unlike Kiera to give her up. Her mother understood that she wanted to fit in in New York, but she thought that Kiera was taking it too far.

During school that day, Kiera felt as if she were floating through the halls. As her friends gossiped and whispered during lunch, Kiera hovered next to them like a ghost, watching Claudia at her table. Old Kiera wouldn't have hesitated to befriend her: she was funny, kind, smart, and had the same interests as her. But, she reminded herself, old Kiera was gone. She was dead. Burned up. Down the drain. Turned to dust. That was final, she thought, and turned towards July to catch up on the gossip. Everything was going to be alright, she thought—until she heard what they were gossiping about.

"That girl is literally killing me. I mean, Hello Kitty? How could *anyone* be so babyish? I mean, the *sixth* graders wouldn't even wear that." July laughed as she readjusted the knot

Old Kiera wouldn't have hesitated to befriend her: she was funny, kind, smart, and had the same interests as her. But, she reminded herself, old Kiera was gone.

in her shirt. "You know, we might as well be good people, don't you think? Maybe we should tell her how stupid she looks. Come on, let's go."

Once again, Kiera felt sick to her stomach. Not being friends with someone was a piece of cake, but bullying them? That was a different story.

"No! Guys, umm, maybe it's just a costume? Like, she's mocking little kids or something? I mean, we really shouldn't talk to her. Because she's a dork," Kiera tried, immediately regretting saying something so implausible. They just waved off her comment as if she had never spoken and wandered over to where Claudia was eating rice and beans out of a thermos. She looked up, and seeing Kiera, smiled weakly. Kiera didn't mean to, but on instinct, she smiled back.

"Hi Claudia. We were just noticing your mature, flattering outfit. It really highlights your eye color! Nice job," Harper said sarcastically. She slid onto the bench next to Claudia, and smiled with her perfect teeth. The others joined in, teasing her, telling her that they hadn't seen anything as hip as Claudia's outfit—hip for kindergarteners, that is.

After saying a particularly rude comment about how pigtails and a pacifier would complete the look, Ella looked at Kiera, and grinning broadly, said, "Right, Kiera? Don't you think?"

Kiera looked at Ella, and then at Claudia. Once the insults had started, Claudia had found a particular interest in her thermos, and only now did she look up at Kiera, her eyes big, innocent, and injured looking. But the rest of the people were looking at her so encouragingly, hoping for a top-notch insult. And they were her friends. *And they would stay her friends forever.* Sweat slipped down Kiera's forehead despite the cool fall weather, and her heart felt as if it was about to beat out of her chest. Her voice was practically a whisper, but somehow, she was able to manage a feeble, "Ha! What are you, six?"

Immediately, she felt the damage that she had done. Claudia let out a long breath: she had clearly been holding it while Kiera had hesitated to speak. Then she looked at Kiera pityingly, shaking her head. She was smiling sadly, like it was Kiera who had been hurt, not her. At this, Kiera realized that it was true. Claudia didn't care what the other girls had said. Claudia was only upset for Kiera, who had done such damage—to herself.

That afternoon, Kiera speed-walked home by herself. Her father said hello to her from behind a crumpled copy of the *New York Times* as she unlocked the front door. She hardly even noticed him—she was heading for her room. Heading for her closet, specifically. After a forceful twist of the unpolished doorknob, her room displayed itself in all its glory: its constantly chipping white walls that had yet to be repainted, the twin-sized bed wedged into the corner, and of course the closet, partially blocked by a cardboard moving box that Kiera still hadn't found the time to deal with. Kicking the box aside with her sneakered foot (she hadn't bothered to take her shoes off when she had rushed through the door), she pulled the door open and immediately began fishing through her things. It was surprisingly cluttered, given that she had only had a few months to start her new collection of garbage, and it took a while to swim through the randomly placed items towards the back of the closet. Finally, she found what she was looking for. A small glimpse of black garbage bag had never made her feel happier.

Kiera pulled it out of the closet and laid it on the uncarpeted floor of her room. It took her a moment to untie it, but once the knot came loose, she began hurriedly dumping out the contents onto her floor. Hello Kitty-themed sweatshirts, t-shirts, pajamas, swimsuits, pants, and a few pairs of Hello Kitty underwear spilled out in a heap of vibrant color. Kiera sorted through them, tossing them over her shoulder one by one. About halfway through the pile, she spotted it: the white tee with the ironed-on picture. She blew out a relieved breath, pushed her clothes out of the way, and proceeded to finish the Social Studies project that was due the next day.

It was just a Tuesday. An average, October Tuesday, yet it felt like a momentous occasion for Kiera. Less than a week ago, Kiera had met Claudia, and now here she was, sacrificing her reputation and her friends for this girl. She felt a little bit crazy, and scared too. Her plan might backfire and make her lose all her friends, because Claudia might think that she was mocking her. But it was worth a shot, she decided, pushing through the double doors of MS 452 into the messed-up world of middle school.

First period was Science. Kiera fidgeted anxiously in her seat, tapping her fingers rapidly against the plastic table and waiting for Claudia to arrive. No one else had noticed her T-shirt yet, as she had only just zipped down her jacket to reveal the design. The minutes passed slowly, as if the ringing of the late bell had been postponed by a few years. As the bell finally started to ring its shrill scream, Claudia came hurtling through the door, determined not to be marked late. Just in time, she slid into the seat next to Kiera, and pulled her planner out of her bag to copy the homework for the day. Feeling Kiera's eyes on her back, she turned around in her seat, homework planner in hand. Her expression morphed from annoyed to surprise in a matter of seconds, a clear clue that she had noticed the beady-eyed little cat and the words underneath. Kiera's breath caught in her throat as she tried to read Claudia's expression. Was she happy? Sad? Angry? Did she even understand the gesture? Seeing her face soften and turn into a wide smile, it was clear that she understood.

Folding her arms across her chest, her eyes gazing directly into Kiera's, she opened her mouth and spoke in a steady voice. Her voice louder and more significant than any other voice could ever be, she said with a wink, "What are you, six?"

Sunset Silhouettes, *Canon G9X*

by Anya Geist, 12
Worcester, MA

Coconut Pudding

by Tristan Hui, 12
Menlo Park, CA

To save her life, Thu must take his younger sister on a long journey from rural Vietnam to the city

I used to be Grandma's favorite. She told me it was because when I was born, she was the first to hold me. "No one can replace you, Thu," she would say, taking me onto her lap and stroking my dark hair. "No one."

Bao, my older brother, was Grandpa's favorite. Grandpa's life had been centered around him, and sometimes it seemed like I was Grandma's only *cháu trai*, her only grandson. I loved it.

One humid June day, the gentle waves rocked our house as I docked the sampan boat and skipped inside.

"I'm home from school!"

"Good!" Grandma was sitting in the rocking chair, repairing a fishing net. "Thu, come here."

I was 12 and almost as tall as she was, but Grandma let me onto her lap. I leaned into her, expecting her to stroke my hair and tell me how no one could replace me. But instead, she took my hands and looked me in the eye. "I'm getting older, Thu. My daughter has two sons and my son has a daughter who lives in America. My husband has long passed, and I've done everything I need to do." She smiled sadly, her Khmer accent slightly lilting the Vietnamese words.

I knew almost immediately what she meant. She was ready to die. "Oh."

She laughed then patted my hair, a shouting peddler outside breaking the silence between us. A gull cawed, and Má called us to dinner. The moment was lost, and we never spoke about it again.

But in July, Má found out that she was pregnant. I would have a little sister.

Everything changed.

When Grandma heard that, she vowed to live until that baby was born.

As Má's belly grew, so did our responsibilities. I ran errands at the floating market instead of playing *katrak* behind school with Xuân. Grandma mended old baby clothes instead of my favorite shirts, the ones she'd promised to patch. Bao went fishing alone or helped Cha with his paperwork. Cha worked extra hours at the sales company, and I took Má to Dr. Accola's office nearly every week, missing school most Fridays.

Minh was born on a bright February morning, nothing like anyone had expected. And not necessarily in a good way.

She was a sickly child from the

start. Her limbs were thin, and she didn't drink enough milk. I didn't think she would live, and even Dr. Accola was skeptical. But Grandma loved Minh with all her heart, and I guess that was enough.

Now Minh can talk and walk, though she's not steady on her feet. Grandma still loves her, but I think she lost most of her steam after Minh learned to talk. Even she has realized how old she is by now.

On Monday, I stay home from school. Minh has a fever, and Má is peddling vegetables in the south, so I take her to Dr. Accola's office across the village.

"She just has a cold. Check back with me in two weeks." Dr. Accola flies around the dim, one-room office like an agitated bird, trying to get everything done at once. She's had a busy week. I can tell by the way she's acting.

"Okay."

On the way home, I stop at the floating market and buy a bowl of noodle soup for us to share, and a little plate of coconut pudding from an old man wearing a blue shirt, just for me.

Minh reaches for my full hands, but I lift the plate out of her reach. "Not for you."

"Thu . . ." she whines.

"No."

She sighs dramatically, and I glare down at her. She sighs again, and I pop the last pudding scoop into my mouth. Ha.

As soon as we start for home,

Minh falls asleep. I groan, taking off my *krama* and using it to tie her to my back. She snores loudly.

Rowing home is slower, carrying an inconvenient, 22-pound bundle like a backpack, but eventually, I get there, dumping Minh into Cha's hammock. I'm done caring for her for today.

It's been three weeks, but Minh hasn't recovered. Dr. Accola was visiting family in Laos last week, and as far as I know, she hasn't returned.

Yesterday, Minh's fever spiked. She refused to drink water, and about halfway through the night, Grandma started to cry. She begged me to bring Minh to the hospital in Battambang. I agreed. It's a chance to regain my place, to be Grandma's favorite again. Maybe she'll find the will to live longer.

Today, I slip out of the house in the dark, Minh tied to my back. Lunch and a snack lies in a wicker basket at my feet, my pockets heavy with riels that Grandma took from her purse to give me early this morning. I can't help but be a little jealous that she would spend her savings on my sister instead of me, although I know that's not really fair. Bao drew me a map, highlighting the route I should travel. Everyone is pitching in to help.

My wooden paddle traces patterns in the dark, still water, as the world slowly wakes up. I wave to Xuân as we leave, the sun just barely peeking over the horizon. Minh shifts against my back, sweat dripping into my eyes as the heat becomes uncomfortable.

By the time the docks come into

view, the sun is high in the sky and I'm sweltering. I've been rowing for many, many hours, and my arms ache terribly.

I sigh. Minh's hot forehead presses against my neck as I tie our boat to a tree beside the dock, just out of view. Má would kill me if it got stolen.

I grab my shirt from the wicker basket, dunking it in the cool water and putting it on.

"Walk about half a mile west to the nearest bus stop," Bao had told me. "Ride an hour into the city, and disembark at the closest stop to the market. There, someone can give you directions to the hospital."

Sure enough, after walking for about half a mile, the three-walled bus shelter comes into view. Written in large Khmer script is a schedule:

Morning Bus: 6:00 AM
Afternoon Bus: 3:00 PM
Night Bus: 9:00 PM

It's only 1:00 now, so we'll have to wait. I should've known that such a rural bus stop would only have three boarding times.

Minh shifts against my back, slowly waking. Sheltered from the sun, I take off my shirt and use it as a pillow, getting comfortable for the two-hour wait. Some sleep would do me good . . .

The hour-long bus ride blends into brown farmlands and chipped barn paint, and we eat our lunch on the way. Getting off with a group of noisy tourists, we slip away into the market.

"Excuse me, sir? Do you know how to get—"

He pushes past me, disappearing into the crowd.

"Ma'am? Can you give me directions to—"

She's on her cell phone, engaged in a heated argument.

I hold tight to Minh's hand, determined to find someone.

"Miss? Can you help me find my way to the nearest hospital?"

She continues to hang up acrylic paintings as if I hadn't spoken.

Someone grabs my arm. I whirl around, fist raised, but it's only an old woman, hunched over a wooden cane.

"Where is it you want to go?"

"Uh . . . the hospital."

She takes Bao's map from my hands, tracing a route with her finger. "Go to the end of the street and turn right. Walk a little ways down and the hospital will be on your left. Good luck." She smiles, turning away, letting herself be swallowed by the crowd.

"Thanks!"

I carry Minh on my hip as I shoulder my way towards the intersection. Bustling people press against me as I focus on putting one tired foot in front of the other, turning right, and watching the rough cobblestone street blend into white hospital linoleum.

A nurse greets me. "Can I help you?"

"Yeah. My sister has a fever that hasn't gone away for three weeks."

"Ah. Right this way."

"Thanks." I follow her down a clean hallway and into a spacious exam room, where she removes a little pink bottle from the shelf.

"You're welcome. I have to test her before I can give you anything, though."

The moonlight streams through the window, lighting up his tearstained face.

"Okay." I take a seat in one of the plastic chairs, resting my head in my hands.

Minh gags on the flu test, and when it comes back positive, I'm not surprised. The little pink bottle goes in the wicker basket, and Minh and I eat our snack in the hospital waiting room.

The rest of the day passes in a blur. We catch a different bus that goes all the way to the docks, saving us an extra mile. My arms are so sore I can barely move them, and it's long after dark by the time I reach Xuân's house at the edge of the village. I'm too tired to wave, anyway.

When I dock the boat at our little yellow house, Cha runs out to meet me, scooping me up just as my legs give way. I reach shakily into the wicker basket and set the little pink bottle on the table. Má whoops with joy, something I haven't seen her do in a long, long time. Bao pats me on the back and Grandma hugs me, kissing Minh's face.

I stumble back to my hammock near midnight, falling into a deep, blissful sleep.

Bao is shaking me awake, shouting.

The moonlight streams through the window, lighting up his tearstained face.

"Bao! What's going on?" He pulls me out of my hammock, dragging me to Grandma's cot.

No. Tears spring to my eyes, but I don't bother blinking them away. *No. I failed her. IfailedherIfailedherIfailedher. No.* I kneel by Grandma's side, and weakly, she reaches towards me. Almost automatically, I move aside so she can see Minh, but instead she grabs *my* hand.

"Grandma?" I whisper.

"Thu. . ." She gasps. "Thu, I—"

But then her hand goes slack, her eyes close.

"No! Grandma!" I'm yelling now, tears streaming down my face.

She's dead.

Today, I don't even want to leave my hammock. Cha covered Grandma's body with a sheet, but other than that, no one has moved. I'm exhausted anyway.

I planned on staying in my hammock again like yesterday, but then I heard a peddler outside.

"Coconut pudding! Fresh coconut pudding!" The Vietnamese words fill my head and bounce inside my skull, a twisting pain bubbling up inside my rib cage.

Guilt.

I jump out of bed, forcing myself not to look at the sheet-covered body in the corner.

"Hey, Minh, you wanna go for a boat ride?"

"Okay!"

"Shhh . . . Má's sleeping."

"Where we going, Thu?"

"You'll see."

"But I wanna know now!"

I smile, ruffling her hair. "Kiên nhẫn." Patience.

The old man is wearing a red shirt today.

"Two small pudding cups, please."

"Here you go!" He speaks in Khmer, grinning wider all the while.

"Thank you!" I hand one to Minh. She cradles it carefully, eyes wide.

"Coconut pudding!" She squeals, scooping it into her mouth at lightning speed.

"Careful," I laugh. "Don't choke!"

She beams up at me, cup empty, face covered in pudding. "Thank you!" She wraps her arms around my leg and squeezes.

A hug. I don't think Minh's ever hugged me before. It's nice. I crouch down, wrapping my arms around her shoulders. I hug her back.

Free as a Bird, *mixed media collage*

by Sage Millen, 11
Vancouver, Canada

Trenza Francesa, French Braids

by Alina Samarasan, 12
Brookline, MA

A busy morning opens a window onto Carlita's family life

"¡Ven aquí, Carlita! ¡No puedes ir a la escuela así! Tu cabello es un desastre!" *Come here, Carlita! You can not go to school like that! Your hair is a mess!* I walk into the room and sit down so Mamá can reach my hair, wishing that she spoke English. Then I wouldn't be so embarrassed at school. Then no one would tell me to go back to Mexico.

My family's from Cuba, not Mexico, and I wasn't even born there. I was born here, unlike most of the kids at school, but that doesn't really matter. *Don't be like them,* my big brother said. *Don't fall to their level. You're better than them, Carlita. And make that known.*

He used to stick up for me. We used to be two peas in a pod, me and him, him and me. *Forever,* he said. But after he got into trouble, that hasn't been true. I haven't seen him at all since he was arrested. Mamá says that's for the best, that he is *el diablo* who won't come back. But I'd be willing to forgive him. I'd forgive him if he came back.

"¡Terminé! Ve a comer tu desayuno." *Finished! Go eat your breakfast!* I walk away from Mamá toward the kitchen, where huevos rancheros awaits me on our small counter with two stools, the third tucked away in a closet somewhere. Lifting my hand up to touch my long black hair, I feel the twists and turns of a *trenza francesa,* a French braid, and think how life is like that, twisting and turning until it throws you off the fraying black hairband at the end.

Us Three

by Layla Linnard, 11
Weston, MA

I liked it a few months ago
It was just us three
There was no sharing my room
There was no screaming baby
I at least slept when
It was just us three

It was just us three
I at least slept when
There was no screaming baby
There was no sharing my room
It was just us three
I liked it a few months ago

Lost Dog

She ran away
On a walk
I want her to come back
Why did she leave
Dog
Lost

Lost
Dog
Why did she leave
I want her to come back
On a walk
She ran away

The Golden Brick Road, *mixed media collage*

by Sage Millen, 11
Vancouver, Canada

The Woolly Mammoth

by Ava Bush, 13
Baton Rouge, LA

A giant woolly mammoth and a young girl, both outcasts, become fast friends

In a small, secluded, quiet place lived a giant woolly mammoth. The mammoth was a huge, brown, fluffy thing. His tusks were big and grand. They were as white as clouds. He looked very brave, but in reality he was a big softie. Though his heart was in in the right place, his mind was in the abyss.

The mammoth lived in a petite school, where he was supposed to be raised as the guard animal. The headmaster, Mr. Krump, would try to train him, but it was useless considering he was not a smart beast. The school was an academy for the brilliant and only accepted those of high intellect. The school had no room for arts or creative thinking, just work. Inside the school, there were students who acted, talked, and did everything the same. They were bland. They only worked and never played. Their hearts were shriveled in despair.

But, as you would expect, they were smart. Every day when they came out for breaks, they would sit and study. The woolly mammoth would often come close to the children, hoping, wishing someone would want to play or talk with him, but day after day the children would pass him by.

The mammoth would ask, "Will you play with me? I am ever so lonely."

The children would always reply, "We have no time for play. We are too old for that. Leave us be!"

It would forever be the same, he thought. *Nothing would change.*

Then one day a little girl came along. She was different from the rest. Her brown hair was smooth and shiny, and she wore a smile upon her pale, enlightened face. Her eyes glimmered with the color of the sea and changed depending on her mood. She was different, he could tell. She looked around instead of at her phone or her homework.

The other students teased her as she walked toward him. She ignored them, continued on her way, and stopped in front of him.

"Hello. How do you do?" she said cheerfully.

"Fine, and you?" the mammoth replied.

"I'm feeling yellow," she exclaimed.

"Yellow? You can't feel yellow," the mammoth said, confused.

"Yellow is an adjective, so why can't I be described by it? Yellow may mean a color to you, but it means an emotion to me," she said.

"And that emotion would be . . . ?"

"Happy," she said, "very happy."

The mammoth was intrigued. He wanted to learn more about these color emotions that he had never sensed before. They chatted for a while about the different shades of colors and what they meant. On a page of the girl's notebook, they jotted down what each color was to them. Finally, as the clock struck 12:30, it was time to go to class.

"We'll meet tomorrow, yes?" she asked.

"For sure," he replied.

As the girl faded out of sight, the mammoth knew that his life meant something.

As the girl walked away, on the depressing, wilting grass, she realized that she may not be lonely anymore. As the girl walked into the building, she noticed the headmaster staring at her darkly. Then he said, "You're late. You weren't talking to that beast of a mammoth? He's very dangerous."

"No, sir I was not."

Then she shuffled to class with her head in her books. The headmaster, Mr. Krump, was a stern man with scrappy brown hair and a goatee. He wore very expensive glasses and a tuxedo. He often would stare at the young girl because he believed that, although she was smart, she could be a risk to the rest.

For the next few days, the new friends conversed during every break. They talked about the beautiful things they had seen, like the birds that played on the rooftop. The young girl impersonated her teachers and the kids who took their work way too seriously. She tried to make friends with them, but they would tell her they had no time. She would often tell the woolly mammoth jokes. There was one in particular he liked:

What smells like rotten eggs and has the hair of an 80-year-old man?

Mr. Krump.

He would laugh so hard that the ground shook as he stomped his feet.

One day, they decided to try meditation because the young girl had had a stressful day. She was being bullied by the other students for hanging out with the mammoth instead of working and studying. Also, a teacher had confiscated her headband and earrings, because of their creativeness. They started to concentrate but the girl got tired and fell asleep on his ginormous foot. When she awoke, everyone was gone. The courtyard was empty and quiet. Then she realized what must have happened. She said sleepily, "I have to go. I'm sorry. I'm going to be late."

As she silently entered the building, she saw no sign of anyone, which meant she could go into class and say she was late because she had been in the bathroom.

What she did not know was that

Mr. Krump was watching everything from his surveillance cams in his office. He had a grimace upon his face. Mr. Krump knew he had let this go too far. The headmaster had seen the way the girl did not take homework as seriously as the other students, and how she always hung out with that stupid softie of a beast. He needed to stop this at once.

The headmaster yelled through the open door to his secretary, "Call in Miss Herbert!"

Miss Herbert was known for punishing children—especially creative children. Children who were creative took time to look at things other than their work, and this was not okay in her eyes. She was a disciplinarian. She made sure every student studied hard, got good grades, and was never ever creative. She was short and stubby, with her messy gray hair in a bun and wrinkles mucking up her face. She wore huge glasses and carried a ruler around. Miss Herbert scoffed at the secretary as she trotted into the headmaster's office on her short, stubby legs.

"Miss Herbert, please sit," the headmaster ordered politely. "I think we have a problem with the mammoth."

As the two were discussing the future of the little girl's friend, she was listening. She had asked her teacher to get some water and had seen Miss Herbert entering the office, so, curious, she followed her. She slid in unnoticed and stood behind the office door. Then, after all the discussion, the final call was made. They had agreed to send the mammoth to the circus. The girl

trembled sadly because she did not want to see her friend banished.

Then the headmaster said, "Now what of the girl? Secretary, will you call the little girl in?"

At this moment she knew her fate would be worse than his. She knew she would not be in class when they called her. Everything in her mind went blank. She said to herself, *Think creatively*. Without a moment's thought, the little girl quickly launched her shoe at the headmaster while pushing open the door. She leaped out of the office, running for her life. She could hear the headmaster yelling and Miss Herbert shuffling to catch up to her. She dashed out into the courtyard and ran all the way to the mammoth.

"We have to leave now. They want to send you away and expel me," she said hurriedly. The mammoth, without a word, scooped up the girl on his back and galloped as fast as he could.

They broke through the metal gates and ran across the city. The police were on their trail. Cars were honking and sirens were screaming.

"We have to make it to the dunes! We can create a sandstorm to deter them," screamed the little girl.

They saw the dunes close ahead. Then with a mighty jump, they landed in the sand, which exploded all over the policemen and the teachers. They yelled as the sand came crashing down like waves upon the sea. Then everything was silent. The pair turned around to see the sand drowning their pursuers.

The mammoth and the girl traveled for days around the sand dunes, thirsty and hungry. Then the little girl exclaimed, "Look at that!" It was a bright gold door that shimmered in the desert sun. It was expansive and grand. It had many creative designs on it.

"Could it be a mirage?" the mammoth said. The little girl hopped off the giant woolly mammoth and opened it. The light from the interior blinded them. They walked in to see beautiful trees and blue skies. Everyone was happy, bright, and colorful. There were beautiful scenes with waterfalls and some breathtaking views. It was a town full of people, happy people. They stared in amazement. Then a young boy came up to them. His eyes were like the young girl's and shone beautifully. He looked at the two and said, "How do you do?"

The girl, still shocked, said, "Fine... how about you?"

The boy smiled and replied, "I'm feeling very yellow today."

Overcoming

by Salena Tang, 13
Lexington, MA

Awkward and shy, Ava's only happiness comes from reading dictionaries and learning new words

People are making room for me as I slither by. They are afraid to be "touched" by me. I quietly shuffle past, head down, eyes on the ground. As I enter my English classroom, someone yells, "Watch out!" Students laugh. My teacher, Mr. Gallagher, tries to quiet everyone down.

I shrink, my stomach tightening, and hurry to the very back of the room, hunkering down low inside my big, black jacket. Hiding like a baby kangaroo in its mother's pouch, I begin to feel safer. Slowly, I lug my 40-pound backpack onto my lap and relax when I feel its comforting weight. I know never to make any eye contact with the teacher because then he sometimes calls on me. And I definitely do not want that to happen. So I stare down at my feet for a minute, and then cautiously lift my head enough to look around my desk.

"Pop quiz!" my teacher announces enthusiastically. All the other students sigh and moan, but I get pumped up. A test means no talking, and silent rooms with no talking are what I like the most. Then my teacher says, "Don't worry! This isn't going to be graded. This is just a pre-assessment for our next unit: Etymology!"

I grin from ear to ear in my head, but my facial expression stays the same. It is a word test, and I love words. I love the way they look. I love the way they sound in my mouth. I even love the way they smell and taste. I don't think anyone else knows that words have an odor and flavor, but I do. To me, each word is unique. I love to pore over dictionaries, spending hours at a time learning where words come from. I can instantly memorize everything that I read or see. Can other people do this as well? From what I have read, it seems that they can't. I know my parents can't, but they are unlike me in so many ways; this is just one more way. Slowly, I take out a pencil and wait for the quiz to be passed out. Mr. Gallagher hands me the quiz and smiles kindly at me. I don't smile back. I just take the test and stare down at it. It really is all on etymology—where words come from. And even more than I love silent rooms, I love word origins.

Even under my rough jacket, I notice that many students are glancing at each other's answer sheets. But I know all the answers. I finish the quiz in five minutes flat. Then I crawl out of my chair and trudge to the front of the class to hand my paper in. When Mr. Gallagher sees me. His eyebrows rise. "Are you sure you've finished? Have you checked your work?"

I nod.

"Okay then."

I turn, slouching back into my chair, waiting for the time to pass. Staring at the clock, I wish the hour hand would move faster. Then I begin to daydream. I think about the clock and about the ancient Sumerians who gave us sexagesimal counting for time, and I begin to wonder about all the different kinds of counting and measuring we do. Our decimal system is Hindu-Arabic and we get inches and pounds from the United Kingdom, which uses the British Imperial System . . .

I glance around at the other students. They seem to be having a challenging time with those problems. I am surprised and think that I may have gotten a high score on this quiz. But then, since I am so bored, my mind wanders off again. Suddenly, the bell rings. Everyone quickly passes their quiz in and hurries out the door.

This is my last class of the day, so I go to the library and walk straight to the dictionary section. This is my daily schedule. I am so interested in learning new words that I can't even keep track of my time. My parents let me stay because it keeps me occupied. And besides, they don't really know what else to do with me.

I know that I learn differently from other kids in my school. I just cannot concentrate at all during school except on things that I'm interested in. I don't really care about school or tests in general because I'm not interested in them. I only do what I like to do.

In math class, my mind wanders to thinking about how the words "integer" and "integral" are related. When I am in history class, instead of focusing on the chapter in my textbook about the Civil War, I have a debate in my head about whether or not the word, "Yankee" comes from Cherokee or Dutch. Things that I'm not interested in, I just can't make myself do, no matter how hard I try. My grades are mostly C's, but that's only because the teachers feel bad for me. In most classes, I probably deserve F's.

I have never had friends. I don't really know how to joke around and make small talk with the people around me. My feelings are all stuck inside, with no one to interact with. When I've tried, people just tease me. By now, I have stopped trying.

The librarian has always been very kind to me. She understands my love of dictionaries and recommends good ones to me or tells me when a new dictionary has been bought.

I feel safe in the library. I get to relax from my hard day with other students bullying me. I get to taste words and smell them. I get to be me. I also love to read other kinds of books, especially nonfiction books. But dictionaries are my first love.

Some words I don't like. For example, "chair." That word tastes like cabbage to me, and I loathe cabbage. Other words that I really dislike are "window," which tastes like Brussels sprouts, and "dark," which feels like

Finding Self, *charcoal*

by Evelyn Yao, 13
Cerritos, CA

snakeskin in my mouth. On the other hand, I love the word "flower," which tastes like ice cream.

After staying in the library for a few hours, I decide to go home. No one is home. Most of the time, my parents are at work. I am alone every, single day. But I like being alone. I don't have to think about other people's feelings when I say something. I don't have to worry about sharing. I can do whatever I want, whenever I want.

After making myself a dinner of bread, yogurt, and crackers, I get ready for bed. I have no idea that tomorrow will be a turning point in my life.

It is a regular school day: students mocking me, afraid to be "touched" by me. A typical Friday morning. Everyone is planning where they will go on the weekends. I love weekends. I can be alone with my beloved books and not have to interact with anyone else at all. Counting down to each Saturday is what keeps me going Monday through Friday.

In English class, Mr. Gallagher gives us back our etymology quizzes. When he reaches me, he smiles. "Great job! You received a perfect score. In my 12 years of teaching here, I have never had a student get a perfect score on this quiz before."

The whole class can hear. They don't cheer and clap for me. Instead, they stare. I can almost feel their eyes burning holes in my face. I try to bury myself under the desk, hoping all the staring will go away. It doesn't.

Mr. Gallagher keeps on talking. "You are an amazing student. What an intelligent girl! How did you learn all these words?"

I take a deep breath. My voice comes out below a whisper. "I . . . uh . . . from reading dictionaries."

But Mr. Gallagher won't give up. He wants more details.

"I just have an interest in words and learning about where they come from and their roots," I explain, clearly annoyed. He knows I am frustrated by his interest, so, of course, he stops. But he keeps a careful eye on me.

The next day at school, Mr. Gallagher calls on me to define the word "etymology." I can't hide anymore. Every few minutes, when he catches me trying to bury myself inside my jacket, he calls on me again.

I can't escape anymore. *Why is he even taking the time to ask me questions and wait for my reply?* After the class ends, as usual, I slither out, trying not to be noticed. But Mr. Gallagher comes out from behind his desk and says, "Ava? There's a town spelling bee coming up. You should enter. You have a great gift for learning words quickly and accurately. I know that you would do well in the competition. If you do win, you would get to advance into the state competition. No one in this school has ever gone past States before, but maybe you could be the one."

I feel overwhelmed. This is the first time a teacher has ever wanted to enter me into a competition. *Why is he being so nice to me anyway?* My head spins around and around, and I hear my heart thudding loudly in my chest. I don't know what to do, so I just run. Out of the classroom. Past all the students staring at me. Past the double front doors of the entrance to the school into the parking lot.

I don't know how long I spend kneeling down next to a brown truck. All I know is that there is an overpowering aroma of avocado and peanuts in the air that disgusts me. Suddenly, I hear footsteps approaching. I duck under the car for protection, but also because I want to see who it is in safety. I see shiny, black shoes. *That could be any teacher*, I think to myself. I stay still, trying to control my breathing. Butterflies swirl around in my stomach. My eyes dart in every direction in an attempt to find out more about the person who has followed me.

A sudden voice shatters the silence: "I didn't know that such exciting news would bring so much sadness." It is a kind yet stern voice, and I know it is Mr. Gallagher. It would've been so much easier if he hadn't noticed my existence. Suddenly, I break into noisy sobs. I don't know what has gotten into me. I guess that after so many years of being alone, of keeping my emotions stuffed inside myself, with no arms to cry into when I feel miserable, my feelings are finally ready to come out. Still, I don't reply to his words. I don't know how to.

Mr. Gallagher tries to persuade me again. "Oh, I almost forgot to tell you. The winner of this school spelling bee receives a few grand prizes! These prizes include a $100 check, a brand new bookcase, and 50 different books of the winner's choice!"

Now, I am listening. I could win 50 different types of dictionaries. I have already read all the dictionaries in the school.

I realize that I want to find out more about the contest, so I squeeze out from under the truck, brushing bits of gravel off me, and stand up. Mr. Gallagher smiles peacefully, like he knows that his persuasion methods have worked. I follow him soundlessly back into school.

At the end of the day, I stop by his classroom as he asked. I have thought about the contest over and over again in my other classes. My final decision: I want to enter.

I hesitantly knock on the door and hear a "Come on in!" Mr. Gallagher is expecting me.

I look him in the eye and say, "I want to sign up for the spelling bee." I have practiced what I was going to say in my head over and over this morning.

"Okay! I will put your name on the list! You should also practice for the spelling bee. Do you have time after school every day?" he asks in an urging tone. I am not ready for that question. *What am I supposed to say?*

"Uh, yes?" I reply, unsure of what I have gotten myself into. After school is my reading time. Even though I know I will like to learn new words, reading calms me and makes me happy. I don't want to give up my reading time. Also, I don't think I want to spend every afternoon with this teacher. Learning words is fun, but not while interacting with people. I would have to do something I love while doing something else I hate. Even so, I decide to give it a try. I will do my extra reading in the mornings instead.

The next day after school, I drop my backpack into my locker and stroll over to my English classroom. Surprisingly, there is another girl inside. Eyeing her nervously, I take a seat as far away from her as possible. At first, she doesn't notice me, but when she does, she jumps up in joy. "Yay! I am not the only one practicing for the spelling bee contest!" she declares. I look at her, startled. She slides over to a desk right next to mine.

"My name is Alexa! What is yours? Have we met before?"

"Uh . . . My name is Ava. I am in your science and history classes."

"Oh! Sorry! Yes, I remember you now. You are the one in the big jacket that rarely talks at all. Oh well! We can prepare for the spelling bee together!"

Over the next few practices, I get to know Alexa better. She is very friendly, and she is also very smart. She does not have my talent for memorizing the spelling of words, but she works hard. I thought that I was the only person who had an interest in word origins, but now I know that is not true.

The next few weeks fly by. I study after school every day with Mr. Gallagher and Alexa. Alexa and I have actually become close friends. Talking with her and Mr. Gallagher is not hard anymore. I learn to openly express my feelings and concerns in front of them. When I make mistakes, I no longer hide inside my jacket or get nervous. Slowly, tentatively, I begin to develop the courage to stand up for myself.

The day of the competition is approaching. I am getting more and more nervous as each day passes. Mr. Gallagher tries to calm me down by saying, "You can do it! Don't worry! Everything will be fine!"

But I always think: *What if I mess up in front of all those people?* I am always worrying about what other people will think of me if I ruin the competition. That night, my mom tells me, "Great things never come from comfort zones." From that point on, every time I feel an anxious thought well up inside me, I whisper the phrase to myself and push the scary thought away. I know I have the ability to win first place at the competition.

The day of the competition arrives. The first few rounds go by in a blur. Most of the students are eliminated; many were just participating for fun or extra credit. Then, some students who are serious about spelling get knocked out. Finally, only one other girl and I are left on stage. She has won this spelling bee for the last five years. My cheeks are as red as freshly picked tomatoes, and my hands cannot keep still. I don't think that I have a chance against her. But I know that I have to try my best.

"Spell 'convalesce,'" the judge announces.

"C-o-n-v-a-l-e-c-e!" the girl answers proudly.

"Incorrect!" the judge declares. The girl next to me freezes for a moment like an icicle forming on a rooftop and then stomps her foot in rage. She glares in my direction, slowly looking me up and down. Her rage envelopes me like a disease. I feel scared and sick to my stomach.

That's why I am grateful when I hear the teacher say, "If you get this one right, Ava, then you win this competition. But if you get it wrong . . ." the teacher continues. I think of all the hard work I have done to reach the goal I was so afraid of before. I have my chance to win. I take a few deep breaths.

"Spell 'chauvinism,'" the judge commands. I think for one second only. I know this word well. I read it in the dictionary just last night.

"C-h-a-u-v-i-n-i-s-m!" I answer.

"Correct!" the judge bursts out. There's no clapping and no cheers. Everyone is silent. No one expected me to win. Suddenly, out of nowhere, there is a scream. "Congratulations Ava!" It is Alexa. The audience bursts suddenly into an avalanche of applause and cheering. I stand, frozen stiff for a moment, but then slowly begin to smile, like the sun shining through a window. I am given a $100 check, a brand new bookcase, and a coupon for 50 books like I was promised. But I get even more than that: I have a friend now.

Chipped

by Genesis Lee, 12
Tuscaloosa, AL

Closed casket
Never can I see her again
My heart chips
My favorite song
I will never hear again
Another piece chips
They try to take the casket to the car
My sister can't take it though
She runs to the casket
Screaming no no no
I watch
She doesn't want to let go
As they try to pry her off
I chip again
We get into the car
Silently
My heart chips
They put her in the grave
I know I won't see her for a long time
A big chip chips
The gates close
Behind the gates
My heart hides
Chipped and broken inside
Scared to be broken again
Scared to love
Scared to come out
But
I live on
Chipped
I pushed people back
Never showed love or feeling
Only power, no pain
No more love to show
This myself now
Broken in pain

Do not fear
I will be here again
Powerful with feelings
Showing myself
Chipped
And in pain
I won't care
I will be here once again
I ride back home
My home Tuscaloosa
I'm silent
Watching the trees pass
I see
Mothers and daughters having fun
I start to cry
I suck up the tears
I say to myself
It will be okay
Even though I know I won't
It's been a week since the funeral
I am home now
Lying in my bed
Repeating the poem I wrote during the funeral
I look out my window
My friend wants to hang out
I say I can't
And shut the door

Hanukkah Morning, *Panasonic Lumix DMC-FZ200*

by Leo Hiranandani, 11
Northampton, MA

Honor Roll

Welcome to the *Stone Soup* Honor Roll. Every month we receive submissions from hundreds of kids from around the world. Unfortunately, we don't have space to publish all the great work we receive. We want to commend some of these talented writers and artists and encourage them to keep creating.

Fiction

Necla Asveren, 10
Alina Kaplan, 11
Kai Kathawala, 11
Claire Klein-Borgert, 8
Haeon Lee, 12
Shihoon Lee, 11
Julia Marcus, 12
Abigail Hope Jihye Park, 13
Connor Powell, 11
Eva Sanchez, 11

Poetry

Isabella Cossaro, 10
Nora Finn, 8
Gwendolyn Gibbon, 9
Lily Jessen, 10
Carly Katzman, 12
Leah Koutal, 11
Mia Livaudais, 13
Ira Seth Morse, 8

Art

Justine Chu, 11
Isa Khan, 7
Mackenzie Reese, 11
Jaya Shankar, 10

Visit the *Stone Soup* store at Stonesoupstore.com to buy:

- Magazines—individual issues of *Stone Soup*, past and present

- Books—our collection of themed anthologies (fantasy, sport, poetry, and more), and the *Stone Soup Annual* (all the year's issues, plus a taste of the year online, in one volume)

- Art prints—high quality prints from our collection of children's art

- Journals and sketchbooks for writing and drawing

... and more!

Don't forget to visit Stonesoup.com to browse our bonus materials. There you will find:

- 20 years of back issues—around 5,000 stories, poems, and reviews

- Blog posts from our young bloggers on subjects from sports to sewing—plus ecology, reading, and book reviews

- Video interviews with *Stone Soup* authors

- Music, spoken word, and performances

StoneSoup

OCTOBER 2018 VOLUME 47 ISSUE 9

StoneSoup

*The magazine supporting
creative kids around the world*

Editor
Emma Wood

Director
William Rubel

Operations
Jane Levi

Education & Production
Sarah Ainsworth

Design
Joe Ewart

Stone Soup (ISSN 0094 579X) is published
11 times per year—monthly, with a
combined July/August summer issue.
Copyright © 2019 by the Children's
Art Foundation, a 501(c)(3) nonprofit
organization located in Santa Cruz,
California. All rights reserved.

Thirty-five percent of our subscription
price is tax-deductible. Make a donation at
Stonesoup.com/donate, and support us by
choosing Children's Art Foundation as your
Amazon Smile charity.

POSTMASTER: Send address changes to
Stone Soup, 126 Otis Street, Santa Cruz, CA
95060. Periodicals postage paid at Santa
Cruz, California, and additional offices.

Stone Soup is available in different formats
to persons who have trouble seeing or
reading the print or online editions. To
request the braille edition from the National
Library of Congress, call +1 800-424-8567.
To request access to the audio edition via
the National Federation of the Blind's NFB-
NEWSLINE®, call +1 866-504-7300, or
visit www.nfbnewsline.org.

Check us out on social media:

Editor's Note

What unites these pieces of writing and art
is their close, careful attention to the natural
world: to migrating birds, to trees we see
outside our window even if we live in a city,
to the stark beauty of a desert sunset and
the tragedy of changing weather patterns,
to snowflakes and cut flowers, and even to
the worlds we invent in our fiction. Each of
these pieces enables me to see something
I have seen thousands of times, like the
sunset, in a new way. They also serve as
necessary reminders, as the weather gets
colder and the leaves begin to fall, of the
beauty and significance of each season.
After reading this issue, I hope you will feel
inspired to look more closely at the world
you see outside your window or on your
way to school.

Letters: We love to hear from our readers. Please
post a comment on our website or write to us via
Submittable or editor@stonesoup.com. Your letter
might be published on our occasional Letters to
the Editor page.

Submissions: Our guidelines are on the Submit
page at Stonesoup.com, where you will also find a
link to our Submittable online submissions portal.

Subscriptions: To subscribe to *Stone Soup*, please
press the Subscribe button on our web page,
Stonesoup.com.

On the cover:
"Mirror Mirror"
Copic markers and pen

by Avery Multer, 12
Chicago, IL

StoneSoup
Contents

A Lonely Girl, *pencil*

by Sloka Ganne, 9
Overland Park, KS

The Ghost of the Forest

by Carmen Flax, 10
Liechhardt, Australia

A mysterious, ghostly figure wanders the forest at night

The woods glowed that mildewy night in October as the transparent, lilac-colored figure hovered eerily between dense thickets of elegant dark green pine trees, whose rich aroma curled through the forest. The lady waded through roaring black-colored rivers, tearing through the determined barriers of water. She stopped, but only to lean against an ancient, knobbly tree, and let out a choked cry that rears up in your ears only to come rolling into your heart and leave it weeping the purest and most tender of tears for the lost caller. The pale being looked up at the luminous, pearly white moon and flinched, as if something so bright and hopeful had wounded her permanently and forced her to live in such darkness and be so helpless. Suddenly, the figure stood up and slunk away into the shadows where all strange things are called.

In a Jar

by Hudson Benites, 11
Excelsior, MN

Before a long heat wave turned the Earth into a desert, one person preserved each season

I live in a tiny town. It's not on any map you'll ever see—except these days a map won't help you. Everything looks the same. There are no landmarks. Things are being destroyed as fast as they are being built. The world is barren.

I'm so old I'm the only one left who remembers why it happened. It happened because of us. The wildfires, the hurricanes, occurring one after the other, the heat wave that began when I was 12 and never stopped.

I knew something like this might happen. I was very curious in my day. 'Pensive" might have been a better word. You might say I was a scientist, or I would have been one if my parents had been able to send me to college. I studied weather patterns and read books on every topic you could im-agine. In autumn, I watched the apples fall from the trees. In spring, I watched the children jump in mud puddles. In summer, I saw the rabbits frolicking in the dancing grass. And in winter, I saw the seasons die. The seasons were transient but transcendent.

Then things began to change.

I knew it had been mentioned in books. I had not thought much of it. They said one day it would ruin Earth.

I thought it was a hoax. When the weather patterns started to change, the polar bears began to die, the biomes grew desolate, I started to believe. And then when the migratory birds stopped coming I had to believe it. The oil companies tried to suppress why this was happening, but everyone knew there was an impending doom chasing behind us. By the time the oil companies claimed that fake news was being published about them, everyone had a deep and passionate aversion toward them.

When the weather patterns start-ed to malform, I started to plan ahead. I wanted a way to remember the seasons when they were gone because this change seemed inexorable. As a way of not forgetting the seasons, I decided to put a memory of each sea-son into its own, separate jar. I collect-ed some mud from spring. And then in the summer, I scrambled through a hurricane to get a dandelion. In the fall, I raced through a flood to get the most beautiful leaf you could ever imagine. Green, orange, and red. Then when winter came, there was a snowstorm, and I collected a prism-like ice crystal. I put these all in jars. Ever since the seasons died, there was this

Magic Flowers, *pencil*

by Analise Braddock, 8
Katonah, NY

abstract feeling of dread—dread that the seasons would never come back as I remembered them.

I still have those jars—well, except for one. I have no one else left in this world who loves me as much as I love them.

There is something odd about the jars though: The dandelion hasn't wilted, and the mud hasn't dried. The ice hasn't melted, and the leaf hasn't become crinkly. Maybe it's magic, maybe there is a scientific explanation for it. I don't know.

Some people ask me why I kept the seasons in the jars. I did it because I don't want anything from before to go away. I knew I couldn't stop what was happening. It was like a train, and it wasn't going to stop. So, I did what I thought was best. I didn't pray to God for everything to stop. I didn't cry for Mama. I decided to take matters into my own hands. I said to myself *I will have these memories forever, no matter what happens*. So, I tried my hardest to make that dream come true. I meant to keep that dream to myself, but that's not how it went.

One morning I turned around to grab my tea from the kettle when I noticed the spring jar that was on the windowsill was gone, and I became very scared. I heard a crash outside. I ran to the door and saw the jar on the ground and the mud lying on the hard earth in a blob.

Then something started to happen. There was a flash of brilliant light. Then there appeared lush green grass, verdure, streams, the gleaming sun. There was a moment of silence. Not a forced silence, but completely necessary and natural. After about five seconds, my neighbors ran out in disbelief and sat down in the grass, ran their hands over the leaves, and stood with their arms outstretched toward the sun. There was tumult all around me as people experienced spring for the first time in many years. I just stared. Everything I had hoped for as a child, a teen, and an adult, memories that had once seemed remote, had just come true before my eyes. It was manifest that these children would have the same memories that I have today.

In contrast to the felicity all around me, a boy was sitting against a tree crying. I walked over to him.

"I did it," he said. "I broke your jar."

"I'm not mad at you," I said. "I'm grateful."

"Why?"

"Because I had been living off of memories of the past, but now I am really experiencing it for the first time since I was a child. So come and enjoy it."

As he went out to play with his friends, I felt the part of me that had been missing had finally returned.

The Mountain

by Rhône Galchen, 11
New York, NY

I sit alone.
The only thing I see is the mountain I always run into.
Time.
I am the only person that I know who has not seen black.

I want the waves to hit me, but they miss.
I will not force the wave,
but it shall come to me.

Because why stay in the white,
when you have no yellow to be with you.

For my white has turned black.
The black will turn white.
But the mountain will never stop.
It will always stop me,
until I am gone with the wave.

The Tree Outside My Window

by Daniel Shaw, 11
New York, NY

As he moves to a new room in a new house, a boy recalls the view from his old window

As I stood in my new room, as decided at Burger Heaven on Tuesday, I looked around and saw a blank white wall, two closets, and two windows. I looked out the window on the left and saw a beautiful tree outside my window. It was gently swaying in the wind.

I remembered the other tree outside my window in my old room. You could see the roughness of the bark, and the leaves slowly turned yellow, orange, and red as we got closer and closer to the end of the fall. The tree was wise and old. It had a posture that was relaxed but knew everything at all times, like Yoda!

One day, I asked my dad if I could go play laser tag with my friend Michael.

"You know why you can't," he said. Unfortunately, I did. My dad was against all types of guns or weapons. I understood why, but I was still frustrated.

"But all of my friends are going and I don't want to be left out because everyone will be talking about it at school," I told him.

He said: "Just because your friends do it doesn't mean you have to." I

stormed into my room. Then I looked out the window, and I thought about the tree. It couldn't do anything people did. And people didn't respect it. They even had their dogs pee on it. But it was content to just watch the world go by.

Another time, I was watching the news with my mom when they said a hurricane was going to hit New York. I asked my mom if we'd be safe. She said we would but we went to the store to stock up on canned food. At the store, I asked her, "Can a hurricane kill someone?"

"Yes, if you're not careful."

Now I was so scared I didn't go outside the house at all the next few days, and school was closed, so my parents couldn't make me.

As the storm was raging outside my window, I thought about what would happen if my building fell over. With those thoughts of destruction, I fell asleep. Hours later, I woke to an ear-splitting snap. At first I thought it was lightning, but it was sunny outside. I slid off my bed into the slippers I got for Christmas, and I walked to my window, careful not to step on the

Lego creations I had made the day before. I looked around. Something was missing, but I couldn't quite figure out what it was.

Then I realized. "No, no, no, no, no," I muttered under my breath, progressively getting louder as I went on. I look down at the ground. The tree, my true friend, always loyal, never faltering, so wise, had split in half. It was just lying there helpless, cracked in half, gone. Gone forever.

I went into my mom's room and shook my mom as I did if I'd had a nightmare. I showed her the tree and then she called the super to take the tree off the sidewalk. We watched out our window as he struggled to push it to the side of the road. It was hard to be too appreciative of the beautiful sunny day because my tree was gone.

But now, in the present, I had a new tree, even better than the old one. Elegant and graceful. And no storms are going to hit New York anytime soon, so it should be safe for at least a while. Over the years I have learned more and more that you appreciate things more when they are gone, so you should try to appreciate them as much as you can before they leave.

Then my mom walked into my room and asked me if I wanted to have lunch. I realized I was very hungry since I had spent the whole morning packing up our stuff from our old apartment. As I walked out into our new living room, I saw boxes upon boxes and even more boxes. I looked in one, and I saw the back of a picture frame. The photo was of me playing in my room in my pajamas with yellow stripes. I was playing with my train

tracks, and I was holding my favorite train, Thomas. In the back of the picture, I could just make out the tree. Suddenly, I remembered one day when I found out I hadn't made the soccer team. I had been outside my old building, and I had kicked the tree repeatedly in my anger.

I went back into my room and put the photo on the radiator next to my new tree. Then I ran back into the living room because I was very hungry, and I smelled quesadillas so I knew this would be a good lunch.

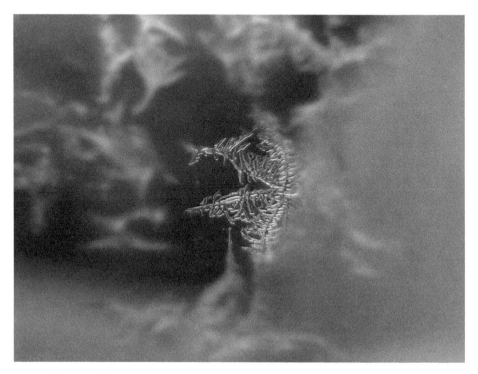

Snowflake Hiding in Blues, *Nikon Coolpix L830*

by Hannah Parker, 13
South Burlington, VT

Northern Night

by Poppy Lowenthal Walsh, 12
Minneapolis, MN

Flashlight
light
draws two silhouettes
walking side by side.
As the canvas of this heavy darkness
turns to this silent night
tonight
I gaze
into the sky sweet face
sprinkled with freckles of stars.
The crickets sing
and spread their wings.
Whose song, they ask,
is most true?
It's true
when the day fades
there's a special way
that the sky is
the brightest blue.

Migration

by Sierra Glassman, 13
Watsonville, CA

A crane braves hazardous conditions to complete his first migration

The crane cocked his head and sighted the mountains just below, the great Himalayas. They stretched into the horizon, as far as the eye could see. The sun slanted over a peak, giving an eerie green-gray glow to the crisp morning air. The wind was blustery, rushing hard against the crane's feathers. Sometimes the cold pierced his skin, and he had to shiver to keep warm. His wings were numb with cold, but at the same time were burning with the endless, tedious flapping. As the mountains grew larger, the crane in the front of the formation grew tired. It let itself drift to the back, and the next crane, hesitating at first, flew to the front.

Each crane took its turn flying in the apex. It was the crane's turn to go in the front when the lead crane tired. He stared at her tail, half awake, flapping just when needed. At the beginning of the migration, he had been boisterous while the older cranes had conserved their energy. The crane shook his head; he had heard *keee-kee-ke*, an eagle's cry. But there was nothing the flock could do. Their only defense was in numbers. The crane was drifting left too much; he flapped back into position.

Suddenly, the flock came into a dense cloud. He shivered as the cold dew clung to his feathers, soaking him to the skin. They flew through the cloud for a very long time, and eventually the exhausted crane at the apex of the V flew towards the rear. It was the crane's turn. He felt a shocking burst of cold as the wind and water droplets blasted his face. His feathers blew into his eyes, further obscuring his visibility. He flapped on. The clouds seemed endless. He closed his clear eye membrane to shield his eyes from the savage wind. He thought he saw a flash of brown feathers, but dismissed it as a shadow. He persevered through the soaking cloud. Eventually, it was too much for the crane; he started to move back to let another crane take his position.

An eagle's talons ripped the air where the crane had been flying. Realizing its mistake, the eagle dove again. Forgetting his fatigue, hunger, and thirst, the crane swooped right, and the eagle dove past him, snatching up the next crane by the neck. The eagle, clutching its prey, disappeared into the clouds.

The crane croaked quietly, in shock. Everything had happened so

fast. But the crane was tired. He drifted to the back and flew on numbly.
His toes were cold, hanging limply
behind his tail, exposed to the open air.
When eventually they broke through
the heavy cloud, the mountains were
considerably smaller.

When the crane was in the front
again, he realized it was less windy. An
older crane shrieked the stopping call:
kleu-ka-ka-kee. The crane considered
the land below. Before him lay an open
field with a few cranes already on it,
their silvery feathers shining in the
warm, golden sunlight. The crane descended, crying out in excitement. He
put on a burst of speed, landing on his
toes and flapping to keep his balance,
his primary feathers brushing against
the soft earth.

He scanned all around him. There
were plenty of plants and seeds, and
there was a stream flanking the edge
of the field. The crane hopped over
to it and gulped water, feeling the
cool, refreshing liquid flow down his
parched throat. He ruffled his feathers
in satisfaction. His instincts told him
there were no threats to them in this
place. They would have to risk the
journey back in spring; for the rest of
their lives, they would fly this dangerous route. But, for now, they were safe,
and the migration was complete.

Artist Portfolio

Sierra Glassman, 13
Watsonville, CA
Camera: Nikon Coolpix P900

Editor's Introduction

Sierra has submitted artwork to *Stone Soup* a grand total of 11 times, and nearly all the paintings, drawings, and photographs she has sent in share a single subject: birds. Birds flying, birds swimming, birds eating fish, birds protecting their chicks, even birds attacking other birds.

I have to admit that, before seeing Sierra's artwork, I had not given birds much thought. Sure, I admired hummingbirds enough to set a feeder outside my desk window, and, if I saw a hawk, I would follow it with my eyes until it drifted out of sight. But I was also somewhat afraid of birds—even of the hummingbirds, who dart out, as if it to attack me, whenever I take the feeder down for a refill. And I certainly didn't think of birds as having distinct personalities. To me, they seemed expressionless and inscrutable.

But seeing Sierra's photographs made me realize that I was wrong, that birds didn't lack personality—I simply hadn't looked at them long enough to see it. In her photographs, Sierra captures this personality. Her burrowing owl is endearingly goofy; her blue heron, pensive; her Anna's hummingbird has its tail saucily fanned out; and her silver-beaked tanager seems to stare "petulantly" at the camera, as she observes in her accompanying text.

In her cover letter to this submission, Sierra wrote, "I have loved animals for as long as I can remember. Birds fascinate me. Their evolution and behavior—how they fly and how they sing has captured my imagination. I hope to continue to help educate people about birds and make new discoveries about these awe-inspiring animals in the future."

I know she has already educated at least one person about birds (me!), and I hope that you will also learn from this portfolio—in addition to simply enjoying Sierra's beautiful, perceptive, funny photographs.

Wink

This charismatic burrowing owl winks for the camera. I noticed these owls seem to only blink one eye at a time!

Sun Worshipper

Birds are descended from reptiles and, like them, use the sun to raise their body heat. This great blue heron heats up by facing the sun with wings outspread.

A Small Tail

Hummingbirds are feisty creatures with racing metabolisms. This female Anna's hummingbird has just spotted an intruder on her territory. She prepares to take flight.

Head On

This crimson-headed silver-beaked tanager stares at me straight on and petulantly as I, the photographer, have disturbed its feeding. This swift moment passes by as the bird flutters up to the safety of the trees.

Land of the Giiants

by Alex Berman, 13
New York, NY

A description of the fantastical creature the giiant and its remote island

Once upon an hour, there was a town called Chocolate Lemon. No, not "Chocolate Lemon," but *chO-cO-laht leh-mOne*. This town only lasted for an hour in our time, but for millions of years in the time of the giiants. And no, that was not a typo: they are called giiants. Why? I'll tell you why. Unlike the giants you know, giiants not only have (had, I should say) two eyes, but also two i's.

This town was not unusual in any way you would think. It was occupied by giiants: small, wiry creatures that always floated an inch off of the ground. This town was on an island in the middle of the sea, the farthest away it could possibly be from wherever you live. From above, the island looked like a French horn, its coils wrapping in and around itself like intestines. On the kind of triangle-shaped part, the mouthpiece of the horn, lived the prime ministers, six of them to be exact. To be a prime minister, you had to be in your prime. You had to be in the prime of your career and the prime of your life. The prime of your life was hard to predict, but for most giiants it was around 30. Due to this prime predicament, the prime ministers were always changing. One

could never remember more than three of the names of the current prime ministers, let alone all of them.

Now, you may recall earlier that I said that the land of the giiants only lasted for an hour in our time. That is completely true. In fact, this story is all about how Chocolate Lemon came to an end. You might have just gasped and wiped a tear from your eye, for you think that endings are very sad indeed. If you are that kind of person, I suggest you stop reading this story right now.

Let's begin.

It all started in a children's school on the east side of the island. The students were listening to a very important safety lesson on zombie apocalypses when a young giiant raised her hand.

"What is it, Gary?" said the teacher. "Is it a question about zombie apocalypses?"

"No." Gary shook her head sadly. She was going to ask why giiants had two eyes.

"Ok," said the teacher. "Let's get back to our lesson. Let's run through the drill one more time . . . " She turned around to face the wall, and then suddenly jumped back around and yelled,

"Zombie attack!"

"Ahhh!" all the kids screamed and crawled under their desks.

"Good, good, good . . ." said the teacher, scanning the rows of huddling children. She came across a boy kneeling outside of his desk, struggling to get his rather large head under it. "Suzie . . ." she said warningly to the cowering boy. "The zombies have eaten you by now. Go sit in the time-out chair."

Suzie stood up and walked over to a wooden chair in the corner, sitting down on it with a thud.

"Wait!" he said, raising his hand. "How will I be able to get under my desk quickly when the zombies come?"

The teacher thought for a bit, processing it. She knew it would make no difference to Suzie, for it took him so long to get his head under the desk. Suddenly, she had an idea.

"Class," she said, "from now on, we'll have our whole class under our desks. You have time to get under now so that when the zombies come, you'll be ready."

The kids all groaned and crawled under their desks. They hated being under the desks because their heads always got smushed against the top. On the ground they'd be fine, but their floating inch pushed them up just enough to be squished.

One good thing about lessons under the desk is that there were no lessons. The teacher's desk was the kind of desk where the part where the chair goes is open, but the part in front of your legs is closed off. The teacher taught lessons upon lessons from under that desk, but nobody could see or hear her. To pass the time, the students talked, knowing that the teacher couldn't hear them behind the thick desk.

"Hey," said Gary to the boy next to her named Lily. "Do you know why we have two eyes?"

"Dunno," said Lily. "To see stuff I guess."

"Want one of mine?" said Gary, popping out one of her eyes. This might sound kind of gruesome to you, but for giiants it was normal. Their eyes popped on and off cleanly and painlessly, so they popped them off all of the time. They took them off to go to sleep or during a scary movie.

"Sure," said Lily, taking it and sticking it on his forehead. Now he understood what the strange blank space above his eyes was for.

Well, that sweet little classroom scene was, as they say, the beginning of the end. Gary's one-eyed fad became the look of the year. EVERYONE was doing it.

Soon, a new dump was created in the middle of town solely for throwing away unneeded eyeballs. Sadly, Lily's three-eyed statement was short-lived, and eventually, even he got rid of his two extra eyeballs.

It was three years and two days after that scene when the giiants not only took away their extra eyes, but also their extra i's.

Later that year (in giant time), the issue of having only one eye was brought up between the prime ministers. They were evenly divided on the issue, which brought up the issue of hiring another prime minister to make an odd number so that this would not happen again. This brought up the issue of whether seven or even six prime ministers were too many, which brought up the issue of the disastrously huge population of giants in Chocolate Lemon. This brought up the issue of expanding into another country, which brought up the issue of possible war. This brought up the issue of Chocolate Lemon not actually having a military, which brought up the issue of . . . well, you get the picture.

It was years (in giant time) until the prime ministers finally got back to the topic of one-eyedness. By then the prime ministers were different, and they decided that one-eyedness would become a regular part of giant culture. "Why do we need two?" they said. "One is plenty!" They also brought up the issue of foreheads being useless, but by the time they would've resolved that, the giants were long gone.

Now the extra eye was being popped out when babies were born, just like how umbilical cords are cut out when human babies are born.

In the year of the end of the giants, a huge issue came along that not even the prime ministers could solve. The number of eyeballs in the dump was so great that they had overflowed all over the town, into the streets and into the schools, and even into people's homes. Finally, there was only one thing to do.

The giants fled to places all over the world. No one would take in these strange, one-eyed creatures, so they lived in the wild. Over deserts, jungles, mountains, and plains they wandered, trying to find a place to call home.

Over the years, evolution changed the giants to fit their one-eyed preferences. To compensate for their only being one of them, their eyes grew MUCH larger and moved to the middle of their foreheads. Their bodies grew bigger and bigger to make up for their one eye. Their weight made them no longer able to float, so to compensate for both this and their width, the giants grew to be taller than anything else on Earth.

Oh, and another thing had changed. Now when humans saw them, they wouldn't say, "What a weird little one-eyed creature." They would scream, "CYCLOPS!"

Epilogue

A million years after the giants left Chocolate Lemon, the zombies invaded the little island. There were no giants, but there were millions of eyeballs for them to feast on. After they ran out of eyeballs though, they were hungry again for human flesh.

I'm not pointing any fingers, but don't you think it's funny that sailors lost at sea are always last seen right near Chocolate Lemon?

Why Frogs Croak in Wet Weather

by Malcolm Dillehay, 9
Gardiner, NY

by Bryan Lux, 9
New Paltz, NY

Once there was no rain in the rain forest and then

the cloud was being mean to god and god started

to cry and the clouds felt bad so they

turned gray and all the frogs croaked

it's okay it's ok it's ok

Lady in Red, *soft pastel*

by Alexa Zhang, 9
Los Altos, CA

Windsong

by Emma McKinny, 13
Old Fort, NC

Anticipation builds as Emma awaits her father's opening-night performance in a new opera

A sweet summer wind tore through the desert, flinging dust and small rocks into the night air. Flying over fields of cacti, across Los Alamos, and finally making it to the open back of the Santa Fe opera house, it tousled the hair of the many stagehands, all dressed in black. It breathed life into the bells on the ceremonial clothing of the three different indigenous tribes that had been invited to perform in the show, and as I stepped out of the car that my father had driven us in, it stroked a gentle hand across my face.

"It's beautiful . . ." my Grandma Laura breathed, looking up at the magnificent structure that towered above us, with its rafters, all shaped like the sails on a boat, lit up with a warm laughing glow. My face curved into a soft smile as I too gazed up at the familiar building I had used as my second home that summer.

"It is, isn't it," I mumbled.

"I have to go get into costume now," my father called to us. I nodded, a grin starting to appear on my face as I remembered the uptight suit Dad had to wear for the opera. Grandma beamed.

"Of course!" she exclaimed, hugging him. "Good luck! I'll just be at the lecture with Emma," she said, the smile never leaving her face. I gave him a one-armed hug, chuckling slightly at my overly excited grandmother.

Dad started to walk towards the stage door, but before he got out of earshot, I called out my own good luck: "*In bocca al lupo!*" His face lit up at the familiar phrase, a bit of secret code between opera singers that means "in the mouth of the wolf," and he replied in the way he had thousands of times before:

"*Crepi il lupo!*" ("Bite the wolf!")

And with that, he turned to the waiting door and disappeared from sight.

Grandma and I hiked up the steep hill the opera house was built on and into the plaza. We walked straight past the iron gates, welcoming to me, but intimidating to the strangers all gathered at its feet, and to the employee entrance that was guarded by two junior ushers.

"Hello, Emma!" the boy greeted, smiling as he opened the gate. "Here to see your Dad?" I nodded, grinning.

"Julia and Dan too," I said, waving as Grandma Laura and I walked right on through. There were a few people there for the lecture by Peter Sellars, all of them in a large blob of a line, an air of excitement and impatience at the prospect of being able to meet the director of the show.

"Are you coming too?" Grandma asked as she joined the line. I smirked.

"Nah, I already know everything there is to know about Dr. Atomic," I said, smiling. "I'll probably just walk around a bit, and meet back up with you afterward, okay?" I asked, looking at her face, glowing with anticipation, for confirmation. She nodded quickly, slightly too eager to pay attention to a word I was saying.

I giggled and waved goodbye to her as I strode over to the terrace, my shoes making a soft clicking noise on the stone courtyard. A few employees glanced at me, sizing me up, as if deciding if they should tell me that this place was only for adults, but all of them quickly decided otherwise. My mother had taught me the art of looking like you belong. Chin up, shoulders back, back straight. I leaned on the wall, its rough and bumpy surface scratching my hands, but I didn't care. I gazed out at the sunset, its colors lighting a fire on the desert sand, arcing over the few clouds that coated the light-blue and lilac sky. Orange, pink, and red flames danced across the sailboat roof for the last time as the sun gave way to a dark blanket of navy blue, littered with tiny glittering gems sprinkled across the night sky. I tilted my head up to the wind, breathing in the smell of rain and lavender that seemed to be an ever-present scent here, in this magical place.

I was gently reminded that I was here, not out on the open plains painted dark blue with the lights of Los Alamos in the distance, as the orchestra started to tune itself. The sweet melodies of the violins, the flutes sounding like a choir of songbirds, and the strong embracing arms of the percussion welcoming me home. I smiled as the friendly wind nudged me toward the main entrance where Grandma Laura and Mister Verm would be waiting. I strolled past the families of both young and old, and laughed internally at their excitement to see a performance like this, perhaps for the first time. I didn't actually know which show was my first, or where the houses first welcomed me into their never-ending hearts. I didn't know when I first became a daughter of the opera.

"Emma! Over here!" The voice of a baritone singer pulled me out of my musings. Mister Verm was waving at me from the front steps, his green-and-blue eyes shining with amusement and laughter. I grinned and made myself a path toward him, my eyes still sweeping across the large crowd, searching for Gram. I finally found her, waiting not too far from the Verms. I pulled the Verms over to her, and they were just getting introduced when the chime of the 10 minute bells rang over the chattering crowd.

"We should get going," I said, grinning at the ever-growing impatience. "Can you get to your seat alright?" I asked Grandma Laura. She nodded

Orange, pink, and red flames danced across the sailboat roof for the last time

quickly, her movements becoming fidgety.

"Yes, of course!" she exclaimed. "You go on, have fun!" She gave me a quick hug and tottered off. I giggled and made my way to the VIP lounge with Mister Verm. When we got there, I once again recognized the ushers and smiled at them.

"Here," Mister Verm muttered, showing the girls his ID. "And the young lady is with me."

"Of course." The one on the right smiled. "Enjoy the show!"

We walked in, and I looked around, grimacing at the very obvious absence of anyone under the age of 18. I shook my head and made my way up the stairs onto the upper level of the lounge. I pulled a chair over to the wall and positioned myself so that I could see the show. The lights went down, and a hush fell over the crowd. The only set the entire show used was a gigantic metal sphere hanging from the ceiling. It had a mirrored surface, and it sparked the interest of everyone in the vicinity, except for me. I had spent all summer seeing the rehearsals of Dr. Atomic. My dad was playing the lead role, Oppenheimer, after all.

But as the show went on, even I became captured by the story. The people it spoke of were not yet gone, the effects of the testing had not yet ended. People from the Santa Clara, San Ildefonso, and Tesuque Pueblo were still dying because of the radioactive energy emanating from the

test site, and a group of people called the Downwinders were suffering the same fate. Intermission came and went, and at the very end of the show, a young woman's voice sounded across the audience, bringing tears to my eyes. She was speaking in Japanese, and she was speaking from Hiroshima. She was asking where her son was, she was begging for water, she was praying for help.

Then, as she fell silent, a terrible scream of a hundred children sounded over the loudspeaker. It rang through the night, flying on the wind, angry, scared, sad. It made its way to the lights of Los Alamos, to the ancestors of the people responsible for their pain, and it shook me to my core. Others in the audience had tears of wonder in their eyes as they leaped to their feet to applaud the singers, the tribes, and the Downwinders, but as I clapped, the tears I forced away were not of joy, or wonder. They were born of anger so deep, I didn't recognize my own emotions. The anger screamed for recognition: it didn't want to be shut away, it didn't want to be channeled into something else. It wanted to be set free, and then it wanted to force my country to take responsibility for all the harm it had done.

I locked it in a chest and saved it for later. I put on my best smile and waltzed out of the lounge as if I were simply intrigued by the show. I didn't say anything about it when Grandma or Mr. Verm asked me what I had thought of the show. I just smiled and said I had loved the performance, just as I had during rehearsals. When Dad came over to us and offered to show us backstage, I beamed and acted just like my usual happy self. He showed us the stage and introduced Gram to our friends and two of the other main performers in the show, Julia and Dan. We also got to meet some of the dancers, but we, of course, had to leave eventually. So we made our way to the car, and Dad waved goodbye to his colleagues, still blind to the turmoil boiling in the pit of my stomach.

The wind felt it, and so did the house. They wrapped me in their embrace, reminding me I wasn't alone in my anger. The wind wanted its people back, and the house did too. And so I got into the car without complaint, and as the wind hugged me for one last time, I looked back at Los Alamos and smirked, knowing what would eventually come.

"*In bocca al lupo*," I whispered to the wind and got into the car.

A sweet summer wind is tearing through the desert, throwing rocks and sand into the night air. It's angry for its people, and when the wind is angry, all of the world feels it. The wind has never been alone in its anger, and it never will be. It has an ally, who is lying in wait, searching for the perfect moment to bring all the secrets to light. Until that day, the wind will hold onto its anger and keep its best friend, the opera house.

Honor Roll

Welcome to the *Stone Soup* Honor Roll. Every month we receive submissions from hundreds of kids from around the world. Unfortunately, we don't have space to publish all the great workthat comes our way. We want to commend some of these talented writers and artists and encourage them to keep creating.

Fiction
Tristan Hui, 13
Akshara Kambam, 10
Lindsey Liu, 11
Adam Smith, 12
Aayati Vijayakar, 8
Sasha B. Wang, 13

Poetry
Nora Finn, 6
Addy Lee, 11
Beatrice Lundberg, 10
Grace McAllister, 4
Annabelle Pugh, 12
Kathleen Werth, 9

Art
Anaya Ajmera, 6
Claire Jiang, 12
Tara Prakash, 12
Shanaya Saraiya, 6
Rocky Wang, 12

Visit the *Stone Soup* store at Stonesoupstore.com to buy:

● Magazines—individual issues of *Stone Soup*, past and present

● Books—our collection of themed anthologies (fantasy, sport, poetry, and more), and the *Stone Soup Annual* (all the year's issues, plus a taste of the year online, in one volume)

● Art prints—high quality prints from our collection of children's art

● Journals and sketchbooks for writing and drawing
. . . and more!

Don't forget to visit Stonesoup.com to browse our bonus materials. There you will find:

● 20 years of back issues—around 5,000 stories, poems, and reviews

● Blog posts from our young bloggers on subjects from sports to sewing—plus ecology, reading, and book reviews

● Video interviews with *Stone Soup* authors

● Music, spoken word, and performances

Stone Soup

NOVEMBER 2019   VOLUME 47 / ISSUE 10

StoneSoup

The magazine supporting creative kids around the world

Editor
Emma Wood

Director
William Rubel

Operations
Jane Levi

Education & Production
Sarah Ainsworth

Design
Joe Ewart

Check us out on social media:

Editor's Note

What is home to you? Is it a specific place—a whole country, state, or city? Is it a whole house or just a room? Is it being with certain family or friends? Or is it simply a feeling you get—of comfort and belonging—regardless of where you are? For me, home is not just one of these things: it is all of them. It is my childhood bedroom in my parents' New York City apartment *and* New York City *and* the U.S. *and* my family, my dogs, and my closest friends *and* a feeling I sometimes get, even when I'm far from all of these places and alone. The pieces in the issue all explore different ideas of home—as well as what it means to leave home, how one can make a home, and even what happens when someone enters that home uninvited.

I hope you will feel "at home" in this issue!

Letters: We love to hear from our readers. Please post a comment on our website or write to us via Submittable or editor@stonesoup.com. Your letter might be published on our occasional Letters to the Editor page.

Submissions: Our guidelines are on the Submit page at Stonesoup.com, where you will also find a link to our Submittable online submissions portal.

Subscriptions: To subscribe to *Stone Soup*, please press the Subscribe button on our web page, Stonesoup.com.

On the cover:
"Water Droplets"
Canon G9 X

**by Anya Geist, 12
Worcester, MA**

StoneSoup
Contents

Contrast, *Nikon D3400*

by Delaney Slote, 12
Missoula, MT

Grateful

by Vandana Ravi, 12
Palo Alto, CA

*A simple bike ride to school occasions a complex
meditation on life*

7:35 a.m. My mind is still heavy with sleep, barely woken up by my hurried breakfast. It only allows one thought in at a time, so two words are looping through my head: *get ready*. I take a last gulp of lukewarm tea and place my lunchbox in the basket on the side of my bicycle. I try to get my thoughts in order as I strap on my helmet and roll the bike out of the garage. I tie my sneakers, the laces chafing my cold fingers, and pull two layers of warm mittens onto my hands. I pause for a moment to look back at my house. It is the smallest on my street, painted a dull brown. I can see warm golden light flooding the rooms inside, illuminating the furniture, each piece of which seems to be having a friendly conversation with the others. I glimpse my younger brother's face inside. He is smiling. The contented spirit of the house seems to reach out of the dusty windows and embrace me. I carry an image of it in my heart. My talisman.

7:40 a.m. I pedal out onto the street. The crisp, chilly morning air wraps around me like a cloak, blowing the wisps of sleepiness out of my hair and eyelids. Somewhere, I can hear the cheerful fluting of an early songbird. I blink and lean forward in the saddle. I

am ready.

7:43 a.m. After a couple of minutes, I take a sudden turn onto the main road. The change hits me like a slap—the formerly empty streets are filled with rushing, honking cars, the peace of the morning cut to pieces with sound and motion. But both environments are so familiar to me that I take a strange pleasure in the new leg of my route.

7:46 a.m. My bike grinds to a halt in front of the main intersection. It is filled with early morning traffic. I walk my bike to a pole and press the walk button, then lean back in my seat to wait.

Gradually, a crowd of children appears behind me, filling up the sidewalk. They wait on their bikes, some chattering quietly. Others sit and stare ahead, breathless from their ride. They all have the same look in their eyes—that expression of blank determination. It is the only expression to have when the cold is biting through two layers of mittens and numbing your cheeks. Scarves and conversation are the thawing agents for those kids. The thing that thaws my fingers is the thought that there are some things that are gifted only to me—the sight of my tiny, welcoming house, my muddy-but-strong Goodwill sneakers, the texture of tattered cloth in my fingers. That knowledge is as much a part of my body as my arms and legs, throbbing slowly in the chilly air. I can see this knowledge flickering in their determined-yet-carefree faces, but it is more than a flicker in me. It is a flame, keeping me alive.

7:48 a.m. The cars are facing each other like bulls rearing for a fight, engines growling softly. It takes me a moment to register the faint, ghostly white form flickering ahead: the walk sign. A second later, the group of bicycles is whooshing across the road. We are like a single form, the colors of the bikes blending and blurring together as we ride. We reach the sidewalk and disperse like colorful butterflies, many remaining in tight groups of two or three. I ride alone, as always, savoring the scent of the apple blossoms, which have fallen over the bike path like a carpet.

7:55 a.m. I take a turn into a wooded, shady trail. The trees arch over me. Red and gold ivy climbs over the walls on either side of me, spiraling and curling over the peeling paint. With satisfaction, I think about how the trail will look coming home from school: sun-dappled, the green-gold shadows dancing on the path before me. Only a few riders accompany me on this leg of the route, going and coming: I will enjoy the beauty alone. That is the moment I look forward to all day, the thought sustaining me through seven hours of misery and happiness, dappling the hallways of the school like sunlight on the road.

8:00 a.m. The few bikers remaining with me turn right at the intersection, their flashy wheels glinting as they move. I pause and watch them for a few moments. The road ahead of them is smooth and nearly shiny, the spotless streets lined with green ginkgo trees, immaculate bushes, and sprawling, pastel-hued houses. Their colorful coats dot the landscape, and I gaze at the picturesque sight with the same bittersweet pleasure I feel every morning. Finally, I take a quick glance at my cracked pink watch and ride precipitately in the opposite direction.

8:02 a.m. I ride in the middle of the road—there is no bike path here. The path becomes increasingly cracked and dusty as I move forward, and I watch the ground carefully, avoiding a fall. The houses, packed together like sardines, line the streets. The idea crosses my mind, as it does every morning, that the grimy-yet-sunshiny yellow walls look suffocated, like caged tigers. But the simile, however impressive, does not fit. The houses are more like the stray cats that sometimes sleep on the road in this part of town— bedraggled and tired, yet strangely contented. The thought leaves my mind as quickly as it came, and I wave to an acquaintance standing on her

I gaze at the picturesque sight with the same bittersweet pleasure I feel every morning

doorstep. The time to linger and dream is gone.

8:05 a.m. My school, from the outside, looks much like the identical yellow houses that captured my imagination a few streets down. It has a bed of flowers growing in the front. Just daisies, nothing more—yet they tug at my heart every morning as I pass their dusty, begrimed container. Their surroundings seem to have no effect on the delicate rosy petals, a testimony to the resilience of the least flashy blooms.

I park my bike and undo my ponytail. The dingy walls of my school make something taste bitter in my mouth as I walk past them in the morning. Images flash through my head. The smooth, painted walls of the school on the other side of town. The sparkling, decorated bicycles of my fellow bikers alongside my own scratched black one, a picture I always try to forget. The expensive backpacks stuffed carelessly into bike bags.

Something aches in my chest. The word darts through my mind, the color of earthbound spring weeds: envy.

And then I think of the splendid wooded trail, the roads filled with apple blossoms, the colorful whoosh of the bicycles crossing the road. I think of the cheerful yellow houses packed along the sides of the street. I think of my brother's smiling face in the window. My heart feels light. Winged. There are some things that are gifted only to me.

In the Playroom

by William Chui, 12
Mill Valley, CA

The silver and bronze chessmen
wait to be set against one another,
next to Lego soldiers who defend their base
from giant robots while starfighters stage dog fights.
Facing themselves in an otherworldly mirror
like an alien monument to primitive gods.
While the slow whirr of the foot massager
comforts my mother as she texts her friends.
A big centerpiece, a shiny, often-out-of-tune piano
on which "Für Elise" was mastered in a month.
Opposite, a huge window with sunsets galore
and at night, I can make a game of
finding how many moths plaster the window.

When I am down, I can always escape over here,
away from all the excitement and hubbub of outside
and indulge in dear playtime and my own fantasies.
Ah, the sweet smell of fond memories,
of earthy, waxy incense candles burning,
fit for meditations at a Buddhist monastery.
And the moist lemon and herb tea,
as savory as a summer salad.
The spicy jalapeño chips contrasting
with the clean air of the heater
warming me while I type this on the Mac.
When stuck on writing, I chew on my comfort food,
cheesy, nutty, spiced crackers,
and feel the hairy fuzziness of the piano sheepskin cover for inspiration.
My favorite sound: Lego pieces falling onto
the smooth, polished hardwood, little souls
trapped inside and unable to help themselves.

Spirit to Healthy Living, *Prismacolor pencils*

by Parinita Chandrashekar, 12
Bridgewater, NJ

The Missing Hair

by Oliver Giller, 10
Providence, RI

Oliver employs a detective to find his missing hair

Once, when I was counting the hairs on my head, I noticed that one hair was missing. You see, usually, I had 2,476 hairs on my head, but when I counted them this time, there were only 2,475 hairs on my head. Someone had stolen my hair. I went to the police station for help, but they said that I was crazy. Then I went to the FBI, but they said that they had much more important cases on their hands. Personally, I don't understand how vandalism in the White House could be more important than my missing hair, but it wasn't my choice. Finally, I realized that the best way to handle any situation was to take care of it at home.

I went to the private detective on my street. No one ever went to him to solve their cases. I wondered why. I walked into his room, where I found him holding a magnifying glass to my face.

"Do you have poor eyesight?" I asked.

"No," he said. "But I could never be a proper detective if I didn't always hold a magnifying glass to people's faces when they enter this room."

I was impressed. This was clearly a man I could trust.

"What's your name?" I asked.

"My name is Detective DaVinci."

"That name sounds French," I said.

"It's actually Spanish," Detective DaVinci said.

"My name is Olivier Ruthe."

"That name is also Spanish," the detective noted. "What trouble do you bear?"

So, I told him about how I lost my hair and about how no one would take me seriously.

"This is a difficult case," Detective DaVinci told me. "I will need $100."

I hesitated. One hundred dollars was a lot of money. But my hair was worth a lot of money.

"Of course," I said. "Anything for my hair."

"You should give me the money before I solve the case. Just so I know you aren't a crook."

"OK," I replied. I met his price. Then I went back to my house, feeling satisfied and tired after a long day's work.

That night, I had a hard time sleeping. I kept hearing shuffling noises at the window. Once, I felt a sharp pain on my scalp. I kept my eyes closed the whole time, hoping I might fall asleep. Eventually, the noises stopped.

The next day, I went straight to my detective.

"I found your hair!" he exclaimed. He showed me the hair in a glass bottle. I immediately started counting my hair. It took about an hour and a half. When I was finished, I found that I was missing another hair.

"Don't worry," the detective said. "I'll find it."

That night, I had trouble sleeping again. The same thing happened as had happened the night before. I heard noises at the window, felt a pain on my head, heard more noises, then silence. First thing in the morning, I counted my hair. I was missing another hair. I told my detective. He had, however, found another hair.

"You probably counted wrong." He started counting my hair. "There. I counted the same number of hairs you started with . . . whatever that number was."

"Oh," I said simply.

Again, that night, I heard a noise. I rolled over.

"Ahhhhhhhhhh!"

The voice of the scream sounded familiar. Then I went to sleep. When I arrived back at Detective DaVinci's house to thank him, he was frantically packing. He was bruised, covered in dirt, and his hair was sticking out in different directions.

"You look like you fell out of a window," I said.

"Something like that happened. No one will steal your hair again." He started toward the door.

I tried to say something. "But—"

"Bye." Then he slammed the door.

I lived quite happily after that, except for the time I stepped on a broken magnifying glass right below my bedroom window and ruined my shoe.

I wonder how it got there.

Dandelions, *acrylics*

by Alicia Xin, 13
Scarsdale, NY

The Cedar Bracelet

by Ella Martinez Nocito, 12
Mount Vernon, ME

A girl needs the courage to face a new home and a new school all the way across the country

I only felt like myself when I was listening to stories.

It was no surprise, really. Words were my sanctuary. I had never been good at making real friends, but those in books had always welcomed me with open arms. I had lived in the same town my whole life, and the friend I had had since preschool had moved away the previous summer. We hadn't seen each other since.

Books were different. They never moved away. They always stood beside me.

My cousin was my only real friend. She was six years older than I was, the kind of person to whom words come as easily as breath. She always told me stories.

We used to sit outside on the porch, which wrapped around the back of my house, in the sky-blue hammock that hung between two of the posts. When I was smaller and too young to get into it on my own, my cousin would lift me onto it, nearly tossing me off again when she got on herself, causing the hammock to sway back and forth like a ship on a stormy sea. We sometimes took ice-cream sandwiches outside, or bags of pretzels, or carrot sticks, and we'd munch on them and watch the butterflies and bees dart among the brightly colored flowers of the garden. On windy days, we'd bring a kite and watch the breeze play with the kite tails as it dipped and dived through the air.

She used to tell me stories: fantastical tales of other worlds which could only be reached through mirrors, of lands of eternal snow and ice and sun. She would describe the blaze of a sunset over a restless sea and the patterns of the stars seen from the highest tower of a castle perched on the tip of the world.

Sometimes, she read to me from books with bright illustrations painted on the covers. But usually, she would tell stories that didn't come from a book. These were the ones that spun images of fantasy in my mind—of a princess in an azure gown with a bronze-plumed bird perched on her hand, or a forest-green dragon reclining on a vast horde of treasure, or a wizard in starry robes watching a phoenix circle in the sky.

There was a land among the clouds where only fairies lived, one story began.

An elven girl once floated on a raft down a river of light that ended in the stars, went another.

The daughter of the king did not plan on being trapped in the tower for long, began a third.

These days were perfect. They were the times I savored, the moments I wished could last forever.

But nothing can.

It was June. I had turned 12 a few days before. We were moving, my parents said, to the other side of the country. They said I would make new friends, that our new home would be even better than where we lived now. But my cousin was different. I knew no friend could ever replace her.

We sat in the hammock as we had so many times, with the wind swaying us back and forth and sunlight playing on butterfly wings as they fluttered through the flowers. My cousin told me that she'd be going to college soon. She said she'd write. I knew she would. But no words could change the miles that would stretch between us, a void wider than the sea.

She seemed to sense my thoughts, because she said, "Penelope, have I ever told you about the girl who went on a quest to find a feather but found something much more important?"

I shook my head.

"No? Well, in a far-off land where trees speak in the language of wind, where magic is more natural than earth and sea and sky, there was an elven girl with moon-black hair who was afraid of change, of the shifting future and the uncertainty of what would come next. There was loneliness and fear in that world as much

as in this one, and for her, she had a name to lay upon it. For all the elves go on a quest when they turn 13, and she knew hers would change her life forever.

"Her 13th birthday dawned on a sunny day, with bluebirds and orioles singing sweetly in the trees. And she learned her quest would be to find the silver feather that the phoenix Avis left when she was reborn from fire on the top of Blue Mountain, whose cliffs reared high above the clouds.

"The elven girl embarked on her journey, as tradition decreed. She scaled Blue Mountain by way of a forgotten road. She faced ancient monsters, outwitted cruel thieves, and went long days without food or drink. After the sun had risen and set more times than she could count, she reached the fabled place. She looked high and low, but she found no silver feather, nor any sign that it had ever been. All there was, was a bracelet made of cedar beads, one of which was shaped in the form of a dragon. She took it back with her, but she knew she had failed.

"When she returned home, ashamed and uncertain, she was greeted by the sage of her village. The girl told him of her failure, expecting to be rebuked or worse, but the old man simply smiled.

"'Why do you cry, child?' he asked, and to the elven girl's dismay, she realized tears were indeed running down her cheeks. She bit her lip and tried to keep her voice from trembling.

"'Because I have failed my family.'

"The sage laughed, a low, husky sound, like the rustle of dry rushes on a riverbank. 'You have found what you needed most,' he said. 'Your goal is simply a destination. Your journey is what is important.'

"He laughed again, and suddenly the girl understood. Her quest had never truly been for any material thing. For along the way, while facing more adversity than she ever had before, she had found courage and resilience inside her that she had never known she had. Her quest had never truly been what she needed most. What she sought had been found in the journey.

"She showed the sage the bracelet, and said, 'So this is nothing, then.'

"'Far from it,' said the sage. 'Think of it as a way of remembering your quest. A thing of your quest—and your journey.'"

My cousin fell silent with the end of the story.

"Is courage my quest?" I asked.

My cousin smiled then, the breeze playing with her hair so that it danced around her face. "No. Courage is your journey."

———————————————

The day before I left, my cousin gave me a bracelet. Each of the beads was crafted out of a rich red wood.

"They're cedar," she told me.

"Like in your story?" I asked, remembering the tale she'd told me.

"Yes," my cousin said. "Do you see that bead?" She pointed to one larger one, which I realized was a different shape from the others. "It's a dragon. Just like in the story."

I peered closer and saw she was right. It made me smile. "Thank you,"

I said.

My cousin smiled at me. "Use it to remember—and to make—your journey, just like the elf girl. When you wear it, it will give you the courage to make new friends. You can look at it and think of me."

I always wore the cedar bracelet after that day.

———————————————

My cousin was right, of course. The bracelet gave me courage to do new things, to make new friends, to make myself a new home. I knew I missed her, but it was easier than I had expected. We wrote every week, and we both knew we'd see each other again.

And when we did, we would find some far-off, secluded spot. We'd sit together as we did in old times. I would feel the warm reassurance of my cedar bracelet, and she'd tell me a story.

A Monarch's Way Through

by Alexa Rivera Rockwood, 12
Potomac, MD

A monarch butterfly encounters many obstacles —pollution, cars, and predatory birds—on her migration route

Silver buildings gleamed in the distance. They rose high into the sky, blocking the view of it. Shorter buildings puffed out too much smoke, making it impossible for birds to fly over the area. Cars honked almost every second of the day, filling the city with sounds of car horns. Around the perimeter of the city was a row of trees too perfect to be anywhere near the new city. The sun looked like it was ready to cough out its sunlight through the smoke in the sky.

A small monarch looked out at the new city, afraid of the new obstacles in her way. She had not seen this city before and didn't like how it was right in her migration path.

No other monarchs had made it this far yet, and she had been told by a ladybug that the only ones who had tried had gone in groups and come back with broken wings or had lost almost everyone in their group. This information scared the monarch, but she was determined to migrate to Mexico, only led by her instinctive compass and the warmth coming from the south.

The trees surrounding the perimeter of the city look safest at the moment for the monarch, so she makes her way over. From far away, there seem to be no animals perched in the tree. *That's strange*, the monarch thinks. *A tree like this is perfect for most animals who dwell near the city.*

She lands on one of these trees and almost passes out from a strong smell that burns her small trachea. Now she understands clearly why not one creature dares use this tree. It is covered in a pesticide meant to repel only a few select insects. Humans thought they were warding off termites. They had really just made this tree uninhabitable for all creatures.

The monarch coughs and glides down to the smooth marble walkway. Her small feet slip on the floor because there's no friction on the walkway. To get around, she must use her wings.

The monarch is in front of the first house and stops to take in the view. She has never seen a place so clean, so organized.

The house is modern, with three levels and a flat roof. The yard is filled

Which Way Car Wash, *Canon Rebel T4i*

by Nicholas Taplitz, 13
Los Angeles, CA

with completely fake plants, with the exception of one small tree covered in pesticide. Children are playing inside, and they appear to be alone.

Then there is a light visible from one of the rooms. The monarch finds herself inching toward the light, entranced by the amazing creations of humanity. Then a small child runs up to the window, staring down at the monarch. He yells something to someone and disappears.

The monarch flutters to an upper room and can't see anyone anymore. She hears a slight sliding sound, like wood against marble. Four children burst out of the door, yelling into the street that there is a butterfly.

The monarch disappears around the next corner, knowing that staying in that area would only mean death or a short life in a glass jar.

The buildings are beginning to get shorter. There is no longer a chemical scent in the air. Here, it smells musty, and slightly of rotten things. Everything is covered in a thick layer of multicolored grime. A few starlings are poking at trash near a fast food restaurant. Not that many people are in sight. The walkway has also turned into gritty concrete, and the monarch guesses that this is part of a cheaper side of the city. All sorts of bad things happen in places like this. She doesn't want to stay long but wants to visit the only animal she has seen since she started her journey through the city.

The monarch swoops down to the starlings, hoping to know what happened to the monarchs who did not come back from their migration. She also wants someone to talk to.

When she lands in the middle of a group of starlings, all of them turn to look at her.

"What is a monarch doin' around here?"

The monarch is startled, and turns around quickly to see a big starling looking down at her. He cocks his head and puts his face very close to hers.

"I'm migrating through the city," she answers confidently.

"Well, monarch, I wouldn't keep on goin'. Most of your friends died when they got to that main road," he said with a strange accent. The bird sounded British but the way that he slurred his words slightly led the monarch to believe he was from the city.

"Goodbye, bird," the monarch said as she began to flutter off. They looked uninterested in her.

The bird said nothing and went back to picking at trash.

The majority of her journey along the walkway had been uneventful, with only the occasional distraction or stomping feet to interrupt the journey. It was noon now, and what would have been a relaxing evening of cricket chirps is now the loud honk of cars not that far away.

As the walkway continues, the honks get louder. Everything seems to be tainted with car oil, and the stink is beginning to make the monarch lightheaded. The monarch is coming near to the main road, which sits right at the edge of the city. It stretches on for miles, reaching seven main cities along the way. The road is four lanes wide. Each lane is large enough to fit an 18-wheel truck comfortably.

The monarch reaches the edge of the road, and all of the determination drains out of her as fast as water going down a drain. She shudders, afraid that one car going too fast could be the end of her dream to be the first monarch to reach Mexico.

Even though there is no pattern of any type to the traffic, she does need to time when she will enter the road and plan how long to stay in certain areas. Most cars are high enough off the ground for her to fit underneath and maneuver her way past. But if one car has some wire sticking out, then it could catch on the monarch's wings and drag her so fast that her legs would be shredded away.

Going above the cars could work, but if a truck comes, she will have to go high enough that the air could become poisonous from the amount of smoke. Trucks pass by often because of the rest stop that comes right before the monarch's section of the road. *I could walk to the truck stop and fly overhead*, the monarch thinks. *There has to be some way for me to go above.*

Once she has observed the sky carefully, the monarch decides she wants to see for herself how bad the pollution in the air is. She cautiously flies up into the sky. The monarch stops below a cloud of smoke. From here, she can feel herself burning. There's no way she would be able to survive that for more than a few seconds.

Deciding it's the safest option, the monarch begins her journey underneath the cars. Sirens wail; the cars are forced to stop. Something has gone wrong up ahead. Everything is still, but it won't stay this way for long. She flutters underneath one of the cars, a sleek white thing with no roof covering the driver's head. The monarch doesn't know why humans tend to do things this way. The car won't be fully functional if rain comes.

Humans have always been strange, the monarch thinks. *Maybe we have to be strange to understand them.*

While the monarch is lost in thought, the cars begin to move again. The monarch flattens her wings down to the ground, hoping nothing will catch and tear them. Things come dangerously close to her head. Nothing has touched her yet, though. She inches toward the safe stretch of white paint separating the two lanes. The next car passing above the monarch seems to be going slightly slower than the others. The monarch hurls herself toward the white paint and just makes it as two monstrous wheels almost crush her.

There is a loud swooping sound, and then it stops. The monarch stops in her tracks. She's unsure what the sound is. It's there again, but closer now. A feeling of uneasiness fills the monarch.

"If it isn't a monarch! Your friends were a rare treat. They tasted real nice."

A small bird with a yellow stomach descends from above. He swoops the rest of the way down, landing close to the monarch. The monarch can tell that it's the sound she heard before. The bird has a heavy Spanish accent, and that is enough information for the monarch to know what it is.

"You're a black-backed oriole. One of the few animals that will eat monarchs," she says back. This oriole is alone, but they are still dangerous. Other birds won't eat monarchs because of the poison they carry. But two types of birds and one species of mouse are more immune than others. Since no other animals will eat monarchs, the species is an easy target as millions pass through to migrate.

"That is right, dear monarch. To make this easier, I would suggest that you stay still." The oriole advances on the monarch, flaring his wings and pecking at the ground.

The monarch flies up into the sky, flapping as hard as she can. The oriole follows, then suddenly stops. He starts to choke and lets himself drop to the ground. The bird is overcome by wracking coughs.

The monarch feels safe and breathes in. Smoke fills her trachea instead of air. The monarch tries to breathe in again and again as she falls to the ground. She chokes on her own tongue and begins to lose consciousness. The world is spinning and continues to spin the more she tries to breathe.

From their cars, people see a small orange paper-like thing fall to the ground. No one takes much notice.

Hhhuuuuuuaahhhhh

The sound is strange, but it escapes the monarch's throat when she breathes in. Breathing in is a challenge, taking every ounce of strength from the monarch to get air into her body. Her mind is wandering, not aware that around her, cars are beginning to move. Not noticing that she is sprawled across the windshield of a car.

The windshield of a car of someone who cares nothing for wildlife.

"Eww, gross."

"What is it this time?!"

"A bug died on our car. That's bad karma, if you ask me."

"Oh, just use the wipers! They invented them for a reason, you know ..."

"Help!" she screams, grabbing onto the car's license plate.

Big, black sticks push the monarch to the bottom of the car. Not enough air has reached her brain yet. She flops her head to one side, feeling exhausted after that simple movement.

"Hello?" she whispers into the air.

"Oh, monarch. Don't waste your breath."

"Who is it?" she demands, with a stronger tone.

The voice doesn't answer. The monarch feels alone now, even wishing the oriole could be here as company. Everything seemed so easy at first—just get through the city and fly to Mexico. But this whole trip, she has seen nothing but humans being cruel. Even now they don't notice that a monarch is trying to make her way through. The monarch curls up at the bottom of the windshield, wishing that her journey could be over. A feeling of dread takes over. She is left with no fight in her, none of the fiery determination that got her this far.

"Don't give up now, monarch."

There is the voice again. It seems like someone who wants to help. The monarch extends her wings, filled with a new need to not let the mystery voice down. Whoever this is talking to the monarch, they want her to get through to Mexico.

So, she will get through to Mexico.

The monarch is far past the city. Cars travel fast, and the smoke from a new city is now in view. Things tend to be slower around cities. This city is set up differently from the other one. The main road crosses directly through the center of the city, not near the perimeter. Due to this set-up, there will be a small amount of city to cross before the monarch gets to the suburbs. But it will be easier to cross the main road.

The car the monarch is riding stops to let people through, and the monarch takes her chance. The two lanes ahead of her seem easy enough to get through, so she flutters past the car bumpers. The monarch makes it past the first lane easily. But at the second lane, the street empties of people. None of the other cars go yet except the one in front of the monarch.

The monarch freezes, stuck in place. She isn't able to move up or down out of sheer terror: a car is about to hit her. The car is coming fast, and the monarch has nearly run out of time to move. She lets herself drop, but not before there is a sickening ripping sound, and a cry of pain only she can hear.

"Help!" she screams, grabbing onto the car's license plate. Her wing is torn, and the excruciating pain from the small tear is already too much to bear.

The car is speeding fast, going so fast that the wind is keeping the monarch stuck to the car. The pressure is becoming too great. The city is gone now, leaving a big open road for cars to go as fast as they please. The wind presses the monarch into the car, flattening her wings so much they almost rip. The monarch is growing cold from the constant flow of wind. Her wings are numb, and she takes the few seconds she has to rip free the rest of her wing that's stuck to the car. The pain makes her vision start to go black, but not before she tosses herself off of the main road. The monarch feels the sun warm her up before she goes to sleep.

Waking up is hard. The monarch wants neither to leave nor stay. The warmth of the sun and the soft grass remind her of her cocoon. But the pull of her migration instincts are enough to get the monarch on her feet again. Flying is impossible now that the monarch has only half a wing, but walking will do just fine. The monarch takes a second to go over the last few events.

She made it past the city. Maybe she will be the first monarch to reach Mexico. The monarch is filled with grief that future generations will have to go through the same experience as her. And that her friends will have to, too. But if one monarch can make it, then so can the rest.

The monarch looks into the horizon, thinking of what else she will have to undergo to get to Mexico. There is still a long way, and without half a wing, it will be hard. But she has passed the city. If she can do that, she can do anything.

Days

by Analise Braddock, 8
Katonah, NY

The nights are long
The days are short
A breeze is blown
A day is a day.
It can't be reliven
Make today today
Tomorrow is tomorrow
The gray is space or a planet.
A cold breeze sweeps by
It is time to return

The Mountains Are Calling, *chalk and acrylic*

by Marco Lu, 12
Champaign, IL

Seanella's Magical House

as dictated to a parent
by Sean O'Connor, 3
Bishop, CA

A generous, imaginative turtle dreams of building a house for her friends

Seanella was an unusual turtle. She could use her shell as a boat.

As she flowed down the Owen River near her home, she felt the breeze grow more powerful.

Seanella thought the breezes were kisses coming from the friends she loved most. Seanella believed that what you thought of was real.

When she imagined a rainbow glistening on the river, she could see the strong colors, and she was never bored.

One day, Seanella dreamed she met a kitten. The kitten was shiny brown with purple eyes and a lollipop in her mouth.

The kitten introduced herself as Mouse. The kitten did the cutest dance whenever she spoke. Seanella was so happy to meet such a special cat that she wanted to give the kitten the perfect place to live.

She continued to dream up a place for the kitten with all her favorite foods, like spaghetti and burnt broccoli.

This place was always the right temperature, not too hot and not too cold. She then realized, in order for her friend to be really happy, she would have to stay there, too, or Mouse would be too sad.

Out of the blue, a very real dog came to talk with Seanella. "What are you doing floating down the river?" he barked.

"I am building my friend Mouse, who is really a kitten, the perfect place to live."

"How can you build houses for kittens when you are just a turtle?"

"When I think of it, it is there," she proudly said.

"Can you think of a place for me to live too?" asked the dog, Weevle.

"Yes, I can!" The turtle proudly glowed.

She then imagined the dog in a very beautiful doghouse made of swirling rainbow glass and obsidian roof tiles.

She didn't stop there. She also thought of the bowls he would drink out of, which were studded with gems and nested in colorfully woven grass.

As she thought, the dog got impatient. "Well, are you going to do anything?" he asked.

"Don't you see all the obsidian I used for your roof and the bowls I have knitted with grass?" she cried.

"No!" he sputtered. "I can't see anything!"

"It is sad no one can see what I can," the turtle lamented.

At this, the dog thought about the house and bowls the turtle had described.

"What an idea!" He realized he could make a house using obsidian and bowls made of gems and grass! "While I collect the obsidian, who can knit the grass?" he asked. "My paws are too clumsy."

And with that, the turtle quickly knew the answer, for she was friends with many a creative bird. "My friend Lil will help you—she makes the most exquisite nests!"

In the end, the imagination of Seanella and the practical work of the dog helped create a magnificent home for the two of them, with tree houses equally beautiful for the visiting birds.

Two Poems

by Griffin Romandetta, 10
Apex, NC

Wobbly Teeth

Wobbly teeth are like
broken legs on
an old creaking white
chair.

My Secret Dream

My secret dream is to
soar high like a soccer ball
flying into a net
and be sort of like
the tip of a paint
brush.

Lighthouse, *watercolor*

by Oishee Sinharay, 11
Pennington, NJ

Green

by Sascha Farmer, 12
Northampton, MA

After moving from a small town in Canada to a big U.S. city, Gale struggles to adapt

Gale was a late sleeper. She had always been. It was just her way of responding to the weekend. But for some reason, she felt as if she wanted to get up now. And what made it odder was that it was the last day of summer vacation. Typically, she would have crammed as much late-sleeping into the day as she could, but no. She was getting up right now.

Gale rolled out of bed (getting her blankets tangled around herself in the process) and fell to the floor, letting out an involuntary groan. She sat up and looked around. Her room was clean and tidy as always. On one side of the room there were two windows, both of them a quarter of the way open, and beside her bed was a green crate that served as a bedside table. A few feet away from the foot of the bed, mounted on the wall, was an ugly white wire shelf. On it were all sorts of things, from kindergarten artwork to baseball trophies.

Gale turned on her fan. Summers in Houston could be hot. She then pulled on a T-shirt and jeans and yanked her long black hair into a ponytail.

Gale thumped down the stairs, clearing the last four in a massive leap and checked the breadbox for sliced bread. It was the only kind she would willingly digest.

"Gay-o," yelled Violet, Gale's two-year-old sister, as she charged into the kitchen. She wrapped her arms around Gale's legs, preventing her from moving. Gale, ignoring her human barnacle, pivoted and grabbed a jar of peanut butter.

Early on, she had learned that it was no use asking her sister to stop. Violet would just laugh maniacally like a tiny Disney villain and hold tighter. Siblings were odd that way.

Gale layered her peanut butter about an inch thick on her toast. She had a bit of a peanut butter problem. She bit into her toast and instantly found her teeth stuck together. After finishing her toast, she licked the peanut butter off of her fingers to make sure they were clean.

Gale pried her sister off her legs and dashed outside to enjoy the warm summer air and flopped down onto the grass. She missed her old home. Gale hated living in Houston. She just wasn't a city person.

They used to live in British Columbia, Canada. "They" being Gale, her mom, and her dad. Violet hadn't been born yet.

Her home had been in a small town by the sea. It rained all through the year and never snowed. But she loved her old home. She remembered the chipped brown paint of the house, the front door with the big silver knocker, and most of all, the big balcony where she used to imagine that she was a wildlife photographer. She had always been more secure with animals than her friends. She was different from them in that. While they all dreamed of being astronauts and police officers when they grew up, all she wanted to do was to be romping through the woods with her friends, the animals.

They had lived on the outskirts of town. Their house had been surrounded by pines. Back on the west coast, conifers were everywhere. They were lush green due to all the rain. Green, the color of the docks with all the boats moored to them. Green, the color of the sea. Green, the color of the grass on their lawn after a rainstorm. Green was everything back there.

She needed to be walking through the woods, rain pattering on her hood, legs soaked.

She remembered her friends, the gray jays. Whenever she went outside, she would bring a couple of nuts in her pocket in case she saw one. Then, she would hold out her hand; they would land on it and start poking around. They would pick up the nut and fly away.

Fly away. They would fly away just like she flew away to Houston.

She had always preferred sailing. Gale's family had owned a small canoe. By the time she was eight, she knew all the strokes and could paddle effectively. By the time she was 10, she was allowed to go out on the ocean by herself. She would bring her fishing rod, but always spincast with it. She refused to learn any other technique.

Back then she had a routine. Mondays, Tuesdays, and Wednesdays were for homework. Thursdays were free. Fridays were for baseball practice and Saturdays were the games. But her favorite days of all were Sundays. Fishing days. In the morning, Gale and her family would go to church. Afterward, she would dash outdoors, untie the boat from the dock, and paddle out as far as she could. Then she would start fishing.

She could almost *smell* the salty air, *feel* the paddle in her hands, *see* the fish swimming in the murky water. *That* was her old life.

"Gay-o"! yelled the unmistakable voice of Violet. She stopped when she saw the expression on Gale's face. "Miss home?" asked Violet, wrapping her pudgy arms around her.

"Yeah," said Gale. "Yeah, I do."

Honor Roll

Welcome to the *Stone Soup* Honor Roll. Every month, we receive submissions from hundreds of kids from around the world. Unfortunately, we don't have space to publish all the great work that comes our way. We want to commend some of these talented writers and artists and encourage them to keep creating.

Fiction
Josie Ervin, 12
Alice Greene, 8
Sam Hanson, 13
Kris Li, 11
Maya McDaniel, 13
Matthew Miller, 11
Valerie Song, 11
Jacky Xue, 11

Poetry
Edward Biggins, 8
Aspen Clayton, 9
Oskar Hockmann, 11
Fiona Mikita, 10
Bo-Violet Vig, 13
Amy Yan, 7

Art
Talia Chin, 8
Ludivine Martin, 9
Ignacio Moyano, 10
Grace Williams, 12

Visit the *Stone Soup* store at Stonesoupstore.com to buy:

- Magazines—individual issues of *Stone Soup*, past and present

- Books—our collection of themed anthologies (fantasy, sport, poetry, and more), and the *Stone Soup Annual* (all the year's issues, plus a taste of the year online, in one volume)

- Art prints—high quality prints from our collection of children's art

- Journals and sketchbooks for writing and drawing
  ... and more!

Don't forget to visit Stonesoup.com to browse our bonus materials. There you will find:

- 20 years of back issues—around 5,000 stories, poems, and reviews

- Blog posts from our young bloggers on subjects from sports to sewing—plus ecology, reading, and book reviews

- Video interviews with *Stone Soup* authors

- Music, spoken word, and performances

StoneSoup

DECEMBER 2019 · ISSUE 11

StoneSoup

*The magazine supporting
creative kids around the world*

Editor
Emma Wood

Director
William Rubel

Operations
Jane Levi

Education & Production
Sarah Ainsworth

Design
Joe Ewart

Stone Soup (ISSN 0094 579X) is published
11 times per year—monthly, with a
combined July/August summer issue.
Copyright © 2019 by the Children's
Art Foundation, a 501(c)(3) nonprofit
organization located in Santa Cruz,
California. All rights reserved.

Thirty-five percent of our subscription
price is tax-deductible. Make a donation at
Stonesoup.com/donate, and support us by
choosing Children's Art Foundation as your
Amazon Smile charity.

POSTMASTER: Send address changes to
Stone Soup, 126 Otis Street, Santa Cruz, CA
95060. Periodicals postage paid at Santa
Cruz, California, and additional offices.

Stone Soup is available in different formats
to persons who have trouble seeing or
reading the print or online editions. To
request the braille edition from the National
Library of Congress, call +1 800-424-8567.
To request access to the audio edition via
the National Federation of the Blind's NFB-
NEWSLINE®, call +1 866-504-7300, or
visit www.nfbnewsline.org.

Check us out on social media:

Editor's Note

Sometimes not a lot happens in the stories
we publish. This is not the case in this issue!
In these stories, a young boy, still reeling
from his father's death, fights to save the
world; a journalist travels to a refugee
camp in war-ridden Syria; a Parisian street
orphan befriends an old woman who has
many crazy stories; and a Spanish nobleman
finds an ancient fossil. The poems and
the art we've included have a similarly
lively energy—from the snow falling in
Hannah Parker's "A Glimpse of Winter" to
Santa Claus making his rounds in Gianna
Guerrero's "A Christmas Poem."

We hope this action-packed issue will keep
you entertained during the long December
nights!

Letters: We love to hear from our readers. Please
post a comment on our website or write to us via
Submittable or editor@stonesoup.com. Your letter
might be published on our occasional Letters to
the Editor page.

Submissions: Our guidelines are on the Submit
page at Stonesoup.com, where you will also find a
link to our Submittable online submissions portal.

Subscriptions: To subscribe to *Stone Soup*, please
press the Subscribe button on our web page,
Stonesoup.com.

On the cover:
"Summer is All About
Nature," *Acrylic*

by Nataly Ann Vekker, 12
Towson, MD

StoneSoup
Contents

A Glimpse of Winter, *Nikon Coolpix L830*

by Hannah Parker, 13
South Burlington, VT

There Goes the Sun

by Phoebe Donovan, 11
Boulder, CO

A strange man appears in Robin's house one day and attempts to enlist him in the battle to save the Infinity Realm

Robin stared at the orange plaid subway seat across from him, thinking about his father. How he always liked listening to "Yellow Submarine." How after all that Robin had been through, his dad's favorite song was still played all across the world.

The subway seats went fuzzy as visions and voices swam into focus. It was as if he'd been transported somewhere else entirely without moving an inch, somewhere strange and unpleasant, yet oddly familiar. And as quickly as it came, it left, and he found himself staring at the empty seat cushion, where he saw only fabric and thread and heard only the grinding of the subway wheels.

Robin almost fell out of his seat. His head was spinning. He felt like he was going to be sick.

As the car took a long lurch, his trumpet case nearly slid away from the grasp of his feet. He lifted it to his lap and went over the notes to a C Major scale in his mind until the speaker called out the stop for Ms. Merry's neighborhood.

Robin collected his things (and with them his thoughts) and readied himself. He had decided not to mention what had just happened to Mrs. Merry. He didn't think she would believe him. He wasn't sure he believed it himself.

He wobbled off the subway and into daylight. The sun against his skin felt like an electrical shock. How was it that he felt so weak and vulnerable?

Robin climbed Ms. Merry's marble steps and passed the colorful flowers lining them. Birds chittered in the trees. He felt more at home here than anywhere else.

The front door was never locked, so Robin stepped into the foyer and listened as the boy before him finished his lesson in the study. He smirked; it was nice to hear someone who was worse at trumpet, even though that wasn't the nicest thing to think.

Ms. Merry welcomed him into the study. Her kind eyes smiled warmly as she offered him a plate of freshly baked cookies.

"What did you think about your homework?" she asked. "Was it hard? Was it easy? Do you think you practiced enough?"

Robin's voice felt higher than usual as he replied that he had done his homework and was quite satisfied with his efforts. Ms. Merry's eyes peered, and her smile was just a little too tight. *She always knew things*, he thought.

"How's life been lately, Robin?" she asked.

"Dim," Robin answered, suddenly taking a profound interest in the patterned rug.

"Oh," answered Ms. Merry, her tone flat. She tried to catch his eyes but found he couldn't look at her.

"How was the subway today?" she asked.

Robin didn't like lying, but he liked his trumpet lessons with Ms. Merry. So he lied.

"Boring."

The lesson was wonderful, as always: his favorite diversion (and perhaps the only one that worked) from all that had happened in the past year. If he concentrated on the flow of air through his tightened lips, the notes on the page in front of him, and Ms. Merry's sweet, sturdy voice in his ear, the knot in his heart loosened. Only to return, of course, on his train ride home.

Home. It was a funny word, home. The place, the people who made up home were no longer all there. Home was no longer home without the missing piece of the puzzle.

Washed away by the aching in his heart, he nearly missed his stop. He brushed the gathering tears from his eyes and jumped over the gap between the train and the platform and ran to his front door in the bright daylight.

He let the front door swing shut behind him, and he listened to the silence of the house. His mother was still at work, he knew, but he listened, anyhow, just in case a footstep fell or a faucet ran. And then he did hear something; it was so striking and alien his body jerked backward and his heart pounded.

The upstairs shower was running, splashing down the drain. Horrifyingly, a booming voice rang out, singing slightly off-key to "Yellow Submarine." There was something about the voice that made Robin not reach for the phone.

Robin felt his legs drift toward the stairs as if he weren't really in control of them. As if his curiosity had shoved his fear out of the car door and taken hold of the wheel.

The shower was switched off, and the singing got louder. Holding a chair high above his head, Robin kicked open the door. The outline of a dark figure with a large stomach in a towel shone through the opaque curtain.

"Yellow Submarine" kicked into its chorus once more, and Robin wondered if it would be the last song he'd ever hear.

"Who are you, and what are you doing in my house?" Robin shouted and found his voice was steady.

The song came to an abrupt halt.

"Robin?" the man in the shower questioned.

"Dad?"

Robin was confused. He couldn't be here, could he?

"No. General X is my name. I am the leader of the Infinity Army."

"The what?"

"If you'll step outside for just a minute whilst I change, I'll show you."

Robin waited in the hallway as shivers passed through him.

"I'd like to be, under the sea, in an octopus's garden, in the shade!" echoed from within the bathroom. Somehow, having this strange guy in his house felt familiar.

A couple of verses later, General X emerged from the bathroom. He had a glistening round face and set into it were a pair of baby-blue watery eyes. He wore a navy blue uniform with numerous badges pinned to the front. This attire made him look very official.

"So, what is it?" Robin asked.

"Oh, yes, the Infinity Army."

General X put his hands together and then spread them apart. With the most satisfying sucking noise, a video screen spread to fill the space between his hands. Robin's eyes were fixed . . .

At the front of an enormous army stood a man he recognized from their brief meeting as General X.

"Let us be united and stand as one!" General X shouted. He raised his fist in the air and bellowed, "For the Infinity Realm!"

The entire army raised their fists and echoed, "For the Infinity Realm!"

He slapped his hands together just as before, and the video closed.

"Was that you who showed me that thing?"

"Mmm?" General X fidgeted with one of his badges.

"The transmission I had earlier on the train, did you give it to me? I was there—in that place that you just showed me."

"The Infinity Realm?"

"Yes."

"Oh yes. Yes, I did."

"Why?"

"Because you, Robin, are special."

Robin swelled with hope, though he couldn't pinpoint why.

"Do you mean that I'll matter? That my life matters?"

General X tugged at Robin's cheek. He hated when grown-ups did this, but he didn't really mind General X doing it.

"Very much so, my Robbie. You already do."

Robin would never admit it, but at that moment, he practically glowed with pride.

"Let's get ice-creams!"

This had been Robin's way of expressing his overflowing joy whenever his father made him happy, and it just felt right to use it now.

General X agreed, saying, "I'll explain more on the walk over."

They put on their shoes, and General X collected his hat. It was navy. It looked very stiff and had a few more badges hanging officially from the front.

"Let us walk," General X said briskly, and off they went.

People stared as they walked past. General X ignored them.

"Tell me more about the Infinity Realm!" Robin pleaded.

"Well, as you know, I am the General of the Infinity Army."

"Yes! The Infinity Army."

"The Infinity Army is fighting in the Withering War, against the Purple Witherers—"

"Who are the Purple Witherers?" Robin interrupted as they plodded along together in the glaring heat.

"The Purple Witherers are purple baby dragons. They are nicknamed 'Witherers' because once they are killed, three more spawn from their withering skin."

> ### "If we lose, Queen Elementa is going to lock all of the Infinity Realm's citizens in a dungeon for all of eternity."

"Wow," said Robin, "So, you're fighting them in the Withering War?"

"Yes, and they are incredibly difficult opponents, even with the Infinity Army at the height of its power. But the worst part is the possibility of losing."

"What happens if you lose?" Robin asked, wrapped in the General's words.

"If we lose, Queen Elementa, the leader of the Purple Witherers and a very powerful witch, is going to lock all of the Infinity Realm's citizens in a dungeon for all of eternity."

How horrible it would be to be locked away in a dungeon until your skin shriveled and your bones decayed, Robin thought. He tried to imagine his new friend General X in that dungeon, but the result was too upsetting.

They arrived at Moolicious and studied the flavors. At the top of the bulleted list was his dad's all-time favorite flavor, mint chocolate chip.

"What can I help you with?" asked a smiling teenage girl behind the counter.

"May I please have a single scoop of salted caramel in a cup?" Robin asked.

"Sure thing," she replied.

The girl handed him a see-through cup, packed to the brim with pale, toffee-colored ice cream.

"Anything else for you today?" she asked, still only looking directly at Robin. Robin turned to General X.

"Robin, can you order me a single scoop of mint chocolate chip in a cup, please," he whispered.

"Good choice," Robin said, approvingly.

"It's my favorite and always has been," General X said.

They sat outside, eating their ice creams in silence. Robin scraped his spoon across the wall of the cup, collecting every last drop.

General X turned to face him. "The Infinity Army needs you, Robin. We need you as a fighter and as a comrade."

"I'll help in any way I can," replied Robin solemnly, thinking back to the awful dungeon. The pitch-black walls dripped with the stench of decay. Human bones crunched underfoot. It was not a place in which he would like to spend any amount of time.

"That a boy, Robbie!" General X delighted, plopping his hat on Robin's head. It fell over his eyes.

That night, Robin sat in bed, re-reading one of his dad's old letters:

Dear Robbie,

I miss you and your mother dearly. I wish I could be there with you. I feel the war is almost at an end and I hope I will be back from deployment shortly. When I do get back, be ready for The Beatles, twenty-four seven. There is no decent radio here at camp and I am going crazy with the lack of good music! Make sure your mischievous mother doesn't (and hasn't) changed the color of our navy walls in the few weeks that I have been away—ha-ha!

Please don't have too much fun without me, save the fun until I get back—tell your mother not to plot anything!

I love you so much.

Forever and always yours,

Dad

P.S. continue practicing with your trumpet, you're getting really good! I expect a high-level concert the minute I get home!

Robin waved goodbye to Ms. Merry as he exited her studio—half-heartedly, Ms. Merry established. She slipped into her silver Subaru, turned the key, and drove homeward.

Ms. Merry switched on the radio, hoping for some music.

"Excuse me, Ted, but who do you think is going to be this month's winner of our hot-dog eating contest?" issued from the speaker in her door.

"Well Joe," came the reply, "the odds are . . ."

Blah, blah, blah, Ms. Merry thought as she switched it off again.

She swung the car around and pulled it into a yellow-marked space in the parking lot and took the elevator up to her floor.

Ms. Merry let the front door of her apartment swing shut behind her before dropping her keys on the worn grey bench in the mudroom.

"I'm home!" she called, all of a sudden considerably tired.

"Hi, honey!"

Arthur came to greet her, his salt-and-pepper hair ruffled, a wide grin across his face. Rain or shine, he always greeted her with a smile.

They sat down to supper at their little table and ate microwave mac-and-cheese with a freshly cut salad.

"Oh, Arthur, Robin is an amazing student, but lately there's been something wrong with him. It's like something is controlling him from the inside."

"Monica, dear, you have such a big heart. I'm sure he'll be fine."

Arthur squeezed her hand.

Ms. Merry lay in bed as wave after wave of worry hit her. *What if Robin was sick? Or crazy? What if no one knew anything was wrong?* She was drenched.

Robin's dreams were filled with pictures of horrible monsters bearing down on General X and locking him in a musty dungeon as high-pitched cackles filled his ears.

Robin felt the sun through his closed eyelids as he was shoved back into the normal world. *Though the normal world isn't so normal at the moment,* Robin thought. His thoughts were confirmed by a message scrawled across his mind:

Just letting you know how the war is going, we're winning!

General X

Robin was so surprised that he banged his head on his outer-space headboard. *General X is very unusual,* Robin thought to himself as he massaged his head through his carrot-colored hair.

His mum appeared in the doorway. She looked tired.

"Sorry I had to work so late last night, honey," she said, sitting down on the end of his bed where his sheets were twisted into knots. His mum had been working extra lately, and when she was away, Robin felt like he was on a different planet, a not altogether pleasant one.

"Do you have to stay late at work again today?" he asked.

"You got your wish. It's Friday."

His mum never worked at all on Fridays. She gave him a big hug to start the morning. An image of a Purple Witherer, horrible and scaly, lingered in the center of his mind, and he hugged his mum tighter, his fingers against her silky hair, her wonderful flowery scent flooding around him.

At recess, Robin sat behind a bush, his back resting against the wall of the school. The bush's leafy branches were less dense up close. Many small twigs, each with six or so leaves, grew out of a curvy central stick in intersections. His observation was interrupted by General X's face, staring at him out of the bush.

"Hello Robbie!" the General's head said.

Robin stifled a scream.

"You look down," General X's head spoke again. "In need of something sweet, I think."

An arm protruded from the bush, quite a hairy one in fact. The arm handed Robin a chocolate bar.

"Just making sure you're happy," General X said as he faded back into the bush.

The bell rang and Robin walked inside eating his chocolate. Robin noticed people giving him funny looks as he walked down the hall. What did they think he was doing, eating an earwig?

Robin's mum was waiting for him when he got home.

"I was thinking we could spend the rest of the afternoon at the pool. What do you say?"

"I think that's a great idea," Robin said, relieved to spend some time with his mum.

"Okay, then go and collect your swimming things, and I'll get ready as well," she said as the phone rang behind her. Robin walked to his bedroom, taking the short flight of stairs two at a time. From his bedroom, he could still hear his mum downstairs.

"Hello?" there was a short pause and then, "Oh, Ms. Merry, I'm about to go swimming with Robin, can we talk later?"

After that, his mum sounded worried as she said, "Urgent?" There was a long gap before his mum finally replied.

"Don't be silly. There's nothing wrong."

His mum put the phone down.

The pool was busy, but they spotted a quiet corner where they were not in the chaos of the shouting teenagers and the little kids splashing in. The two of them slipped into the cool water. Robin had a bubble in his mouth as he sank down, down, down. He pushed off from the bottom lightly and surfaced, his face breaking the water slowly.

As he arose from the depth of the water, his mum was there, her comforting face pleased. She held an orange ball in her hands. They spread apart, and she tossed it to him.

The orange squishy ball felt good as it sank into his cupped hands. Robin jumped as he tossed it back. The ball arced in the air before reaching its mark with his smiling mother. She laughed, and her wet hair glimmered, as she again threw it to him.

The pool was extremely noisy, but Robin couldn't hear any little bit of it. It was like he and his mum were in their own shared bubble, where everything was absolutely and completely perfect, and nothing would ever go wrong.

Their space was bombarded with toddlers in floaties, so they hopped out to dry. They both spread towels on the warm concrete and lay on their backs, absorbing the heat. Robin's mum rested her hand on top of his and gently squeezed it three times: I - Love - You. It was a moment Robin wished would never end.

On the subway, Robin stared at the people across from him. There was an over-large woman, dressed in all pink, who looked fussy. She stared at her cell phone with her nose wrinkled.

Next to her sat a scruffy male teenager with thick-rimmed glasses; they circled his magnified hazel eyes, which stared at the ceiling, not focused.

In the middle of the row sat a tall, skinny Asian woman, with her hair cut to her chin. She conversed in rapid Mandarin with her small-looking son, who sat in the seat next to her and doodled with crayons in a sketchbook.

The man sitting next to the Asian boy caught his eye. He had a glistening round face with a set of baby-blue watery eyes, fixed steadily on Robin's. Robin jumped in his seat and forced his eyes elsewhere, though he could feel the man's steady gaze boring into him. It was as if the man knew Robin, and though Robin recognized him, he couldn't think where from.

The direction Robin was looking was overcome by Purple Witherers, plodding in a charge down the subway.

It was like he and his mum were in their own shared bubble, where everything was absolutely and completely perfect.

Each Purple Witherer had two spectacular silver horns protruding from its purple scalp.

All of the people he had observed earlier, and others, got up to fight them. Some used backpacks, cameras, pencils, and cutlery. Others brandished swords, clubs, and other weapons to slay the beasts.

The lady in pink fell over on her enormous backside. One of the Purple Witherers snorted fire and singed her frizzy hair.

The Purple Witherers were reducing the numbers of the human army, and very quickly. More and more people were being thrown back, burnt, pushed to the ground, or skewered. One of the Witherers withdrew one of his horns from the Asian lady's leg, his magnificent horn shimmering with blood.

Robin pressed his back against his seat. In the middle of the battle, Robin spotted General X. The General held one of the Purple Witherers at bay with a handsome sabre.

From somewhere over the din, Robin heard the announcement for Ms. Merry's stop. He ran off the subway, away from the battle with his arms over his head. He uncovered his head when he reached the open streets but still ran to Ms. Merry's studio, his trumpet case hitting against his knees.

Ms. Merry greeted him with a smile (a rather forced one, though Robin didn't notice).

"Your homework was to practice the second part of the 'Knitted Cap' duet, did you do it?"

"Yep."

This was a lie, though Robin thought he knew it pretty well.

"Good then. I go first."

She touched the trumpet to her lips and blew the melody. Robin joined in on the second verse and played the harmony.

A message twisted into life in familiar handwriting: **We lost**.

Robin stopped playing.

Something deep inside him snapped. He fell to the ground.

Robin could almost see it.

General X stood in his cage, his face pressed against the bars, pleading for release to a woman with a stony face in a long white dress. The woman laughed and General X screamed.

Robin screamed too.

He opened his eyes to see Queen Elementa standing over him.

"Get away from me, you beast!" Robin yelled, sliding backward. She laughed. Robin was trapped. His back hit a wall. Everything went black.

When he awakened, his mum was standing over him.

"Watch out for Queen Elementa!" he warned her, "She's dangerous! She put General X in an Infinity Dungeon!"

His mum nodded at Queen Elementa.

Robin's mum steered him out to her car. She placed him in the backseat. The sun shone through the front windscreen, making it hard to see.

It felt as though this were his own prison, hot and sticky. As though he was sharing the same fate as his beloved friend.

Robin's mother typed "Bluebird Children's Hospital" into the GPS system. Then she drove off.

Sky Blue Hijab

by Seoyon Kim, 12
East Greenwich, RI

A journalist travels to a refugee camp to report on the Syrian Civil War

I twist the fake wedding ring on my finger nervously. It's a cheap copper ring that I superglued a rhinestone to. Back and forth. Back and forth. It's supposed to arouse sympathy if someone tries to kill me. It'll convince them that I have someone back home I love and need to get back to, my colleagues had assured. Though it's likely that I won't be killed by an assassin. If I do get killed, it's more likely to be by a bomb or a missile. I'm pretty sure my ring won't convince anyone to refrain from blowing up everything in a five-mile radius.

Unless it's a magical shield ring. You never know.

The countryside spreads outside the window. I peek outside, but the dizzying height quickly gets me sick, and I close the window blind. I don't have time to get sick. Plus, the airline doesn't seem to have any barf bags.

Syria. Syria. I have to get to Syria. To the war. To the story.

I grip my saddlebag so that my knuckles turn white. I go over the plan in my head. I will land in Lebanon. I will go to the Sweet Tooth Cafe where I will meet my unnamed accomplice. She will sneak me into Syria (I wasn't able to procure a visa to Syria; Leba-non was the best I could do), where I will get a hotel room and spend the night. Then, I will begin to investigate and write.

It's 2018. I'm a freelance war reporter, on my way to report on the Syrian Civil War. The conflict began a long way back, in 2011, when demonstrations escalated into a full-blown war against the government. I'm still not sure what to think of this entire messy situation.

I sigh as a voice over the speakers announces that we will be landing soon. I check my dull grey hijab one more time. I'm not quite sure if it's necessary, but it's better to be overdressed than the opposite. It's horribly messy and has been tied without technique, but this will have to do. I organize the coarse cloth one more time, then turn my attention to the task ahead.

Two hours later, I finally arrive at the Sweet Tooth Cafe. I see a young woman in all black at the corner table. She has to be the one. I'm slightly shocked that she's so young. The girl couldn't be over the age of 22. I join her and show my identification. She gives me a slight nod.

We buy cupcakes. My mysterious accomplice gets vanilla, and I get chocolate. Both have strawberry-flavored frosting. Then she leads me to her car. The moments from then on are unmemorable and fleeting; I'm so caught up in my nervousness and adrenaline, I can barely remember anything. I fall asleep within 30 minutes (all that worrying is tiring!), and she wakes me after 30 more.

"اننا هنا," she says. *We're here.*

I look around. I thought it would be harder to cross the border, seeing that it's illegal and all. Either border control is very lax here, or my guide is an expert.

"شكرا جزيلا," I say. *Thank you.* She leads me out of the car, and I find myself in an alley behind a hotel. I grab my saddlebag and suitcase, and my guide drives off. I take a good look around. Dusty street. Tin trash cans. I make my way to the front of the hotel, the wheels of my suitcase making loud *clunk!* noises as they roll over pebbles that line the street.

The hotel is admittedly shabby. The war has taken its toll. The fluorescent lights flicker periodically. Dust has settled on the furniture. The rug is worn, and the man behind the counter looks like he has been to hell and back. Scraggly beard, glasses askew, clothes that may as well have been worn for years. The war has made it hard for ends to meet.

"أهلا بك," he mutters tiredly. *Welcome.* "كيف يمكنني مساعدتك" *How can I help you?*

I ask for a hotel room. He complies. After five minutes of paperwork, I get my keys and make my way down the hall. I open the creaky door to a dusty room. The beige wallpaper is peeling, and the curtains and bedsheets are threadbare. I sigh. I change, wash up, strip the bed, then pull out a blanket I packed. Exhausted, I slump onto the bed, and five minutes later, I'm out cold.

The next day is overcast, with the scent of rain in the air. It's cold, and I am reluctant to leave my warm cocoon of blankets. I sigh as I get up. Back on goes the hijab . . . and jacket . . .

My first stop is the refugee camp. Hundreds of people are huddled inside thin blue tents, stationed in the dusty, barren valley because they have nowhere to go. The stench of the poor living conditions pervades the still air and bodies that surround me. Wailing babies, infected wounds, dehydration, hunger, and fear fill the scene. The list goes on and on.

I approach a young woman caring for a screaming baby. She hushes and sings to him, but to no avail. The woman's chocolate-brown hair sticks to her face in the perspiration and humidity. In sadness, I look at the baby's ribs poking out. I begin to ask her if she'd be comfortable with being interviewed, but then I see her face. She is already taxed with caring for her family, and she is afraid of me. Her brown eyes widen, and she quickly looks away. She is not the one. I thank her and walk away.

Next, I walk up to a teenager looking at the camp blankly, as if in disbelief that he is actually there. The cold

Fighter Jet, *colored pencils*

by Ethan Hu, 8
San Diego, CA

air slices us, but he barely notices it or my voice. I speak several times before he acknowledges my presence.

"Would you be willing to be interviewed?" I ask him timidly. He looks at me warily, seeing me as a prying foreigner. I ask again, pressing for an answer. "Please. Your voice needs to be heard."

He gives in, and I am delighted. Whipping out my pen and trusty notebook, I skim the list of pre-written questions.

"How has the war affected you and your family?"

"Can't you see?" he says impatiently. "Can you not see the suffering of those around me?" I move on.

"What are your plans for the future?"

"Depends on how long this war lasts."

"Do you have any hopes for the future?"

"I did." He gives no further explanation.

"What was your life like before the war?"

"We were the average middle-class family. My father managed a small grocery store."

"How are your family and friends?"

The teen looks away sharply. It is clear I am prying too deeply. I thank him. He hasn't given much information, and the answers he gave are very general, but he is clearly uncomfortable saying more. I leave.

Next, I approach an elderly woman chatting with friends. Unlike the faces that surround me, hers is smiling. She wears a sky blue robe and hijab, fading from years of use, simple yet beautiful. Wisps of salt-and-pepper hair escape, surrounding her tan face. Wrinkles spread from her eyes like rays of the sun. Her eyes are misty, but the pupils are bright and clear, like a young girl's.

She gives me a warm smile and gestures towards a wooden crate on the left.

"Come! Come!" She laughs. I slowly sit down.

"Would you be willing to answer some questions?"

"Why not? Are you from those newspapers? Ask away."

"Where are you from?"

"Me? I'm from the beautiful city of Aleppo, right along the Silk Road." She sighes. "It was supposed to be a safe haven. No fighting."

"Both parties are accused of war crimes. How do you feel about that?"

"I cannot make assumptions. But I'm greatly disappointed. What happened to dignity?"

I scribble down words. My pen can barely keep up.

"What are your hopes for your future?"

"My future? Well, I would like to see rocking chairs and tea in my future. But I can only hope that the war will end well before my grandchildren grow up." She smiles.

I ask more questions, each digging up old memories. As the minutes tick by, my elation increases. This is *exactly* what I need.

"What are you doing now?"

The woman looks delighted to show her work to me.

"Ah! I am weaving a rug. It is a most wonderful thing, is it not? It will be sold, and the income will help us. A wonderful organization suggested it!"

"How beautiful." I glance over my notes. This should be enough. I yearn to stay and learn more, but I have a deadline. "Thank you so much for the interview!" I say, genuinely meaning it.

"Of course."

I leave for the dreary hotel, caught up in my thoughts.

Back in my room, I skim through the notes, lying on my bed. The woman had the most exquisite memories in such vivid detail. She also had a lot to offer, opinion-wise.

"Nothing justifies war," she had said. Those words kept circling my head. "Whatever the rebel groups wanted, this was not the way. However the government wanted to retaliate, this was not the way. Thousands of people are driven out of their homes, out of the places that were supposed to be safe. All for what? At the end of the day, what did anyone gain? Nothing, dear. There is always another way." Her speech went through my head in an endless loop.

___

A few weeks later, I am safe at my apartment in New York, the reassuring cacophony of cars outside the windows. My article has been written and published. There was the customary praise and critics, and the article had been forgotten.

I didn't forget.

The sky blue hijab the woman had been wearing will not let go of me. My dreams are constantly centered around it. I didn't forget what she said, either.

Nothing justifies war.

I'll be waiting for the day we can announce the war is over, that the destruction and causing of suffering will end. I'll be waiting, and I'll be ready. But until then, I won't be standing around. People need to know, and people need to step up to stop it.

I take my pen and move to my desk. People need to know, and I will be the one telling them.

Halloween Moon, *Nikon Coolpix L830*

by Hannah Parker, 13
South Burlington, VT

Cafe Terrace at Night

by Aoife O'Connell, 11
Los Angeles, CA

One cold, hopeless night in Paris, a homeless orphan girl meets a mysterious woman

The only noise that night in Paris was the soft tapping of my flats against the cobblestones. It got louder at some parts of the road and softer at others. Sometimes it was fast: a short, discreet sound; other times, slow, like a grandfather clock ticking away the hours.

My hair flew out behind me like a blonde sail, as did my frayed white dress. It wasn't quite white, though. Years of living on the streets of Paris had turned it a light, caramel-colored brown. My hands, smeared with soot and sweat, clutched a handful of stolen coins. I ran my fingers over the words and pictures, reading them without seeing them. Faster and faster I ran, with no real destination in mind. I was feral, desperate, untamable.

I looked up at the sky as I scampered through the dark alleyways. The bright stars stared back at me, their beautiful luminescence stunning my eyes. They were the only light in my life, the only light to guide me. Suddenly, a wave of sorrow passed over me, so strong I cried out. Images of my mother, draped in red robes and mink-fur scarves, filled my mind, as sharp and clear as the cinema. I didn't care how deplorable she was, how deplorable my past might have been. I remem-

bered looking up to her; she was the only thing I'd had. She had been my life. Until she died.

I felt a glut of tears well up in my eyes and didn't stop them from pouring out onto my flushed cheeks. Rubbing them away with dirty hands, I crumbled to the cobblestone street. I felt the cold hardness of it through my dress. As I curled in a tiny ball on the street, a hollow clunk thudded down the road, sounding like a rusty cowbell. Without looking up, I envisioned a man with a large bushy mustache, graying on the edges, his stomach bulging from a black suit. Right now, he would be reaching up and checking the time on a gold pocket watch engraved with his name, Henri. The soft light of the lamp above him shone down, turning him into a ghostly figure.

"Mademoiselle."

I looked up, startled by the high, nasal voice. When I saw the woman standing above me with a smirk plastered on her face, I jumped up. She wore a tattered gown that must have once been beautiful, but now the jagged hem was stained red. Here, my imagination got the better of me; I pictured the woman smearing her dress in a child's blood. I shivered, though the humid air made my sweat trickle down my back in rivulets. The woman's eyes stared at me, willing my mouth to say something. I could not utter a word. I just took in this lady from head to toe. Her face was wrinkled and old like the pages of a well-loved book, her eyes shone, and her silvery hair coruscated in the moonlight.

"Can ya talk?" she asked with a glint of confusion in her eyes. She had an aura of faded beauty around her. I could tell she had once been a figure of stature, of honor. But now she was an unsightly old lady. Her silvery hair was ugly and full of split-ends, her boxy hands stretching out the fabric of her silky white gloves. She had hideous black boots that were muddy and slick with rainwater, boots that must have been three sizes too big. Nevertheless, I was a naïve child, and I loved her almost immediately.

"Yes, Madame, I can talk," I told her. Brushing my blonde hair from my face, I tried to smooth my dress and seem as formal as possible. I doubt I did, though, for my shoeless feet were dirtier than her boots, and my skin had a layer of grime that made it darker.

"Good," the woman announced firmly. "I was beginning to think ya couldn't." She extended a hand to me, and I was surprised to see it only had four fingers. There was a small stump where the ring finger should have been. Alarmed, I shot my hand back, staring into her deep eyes. She laughed heartily. "Lost in a scrimmage with some pirates. Long story. Anyway, I'm Clementine. Call me Clem."

Clem smiled, rotten teeth stuck in her mouth like tombstones. I smiled too, my flushed cheeks lifting. I nodded my head, my mind slowly processing what I had heard. Before I could ask anything, Clem inquired, "What are you doin' out here on a night like this? And what's yer name?"

I frowned. "I'm Alice," I told her sharply. My life was like that cactus in William & Son's Apothecary. It had seemed so beautiful and sublime that I had stumbled into the store to touch this unique specimen—but when I did, one of the hidden, protruding spikes stabbed my finger, drawing a small drop of blood. When my few and short-lived friends got to know me, they got to know my spikes, my sharp, prickly spikes that I tried so hard to keep hidden.

Clem raised one perfect eyebrow but didn't ask anything else. Inside, I thanked her for not being like the gendarmes who always had a million questions at their disposal.

"Well, Miss Alice," Clem pondered aloud. "I am wonderin' if you'd like to come with me just down the street to Café de Minuit. They have great coffee if yer old enough." My stomach flooded with joy, always enticed by the thought of free food.

"Yes, Madame Clementine, I mean, Madame Clem. Yes. Please. Merci." I spoke that last word louder, for my stomach growled, and I could not let this kindly old woman hear it. How kind, I thought to myself, admiring the one golden ring on her thumb. It was perfectly smooth and surprisingly dull. It wasn't the solid gold I noticed, though, it was the sparkling diamond on the top. It was clear and shiny and reflected light like a lamp. Absolutely beautiful.

Clem began to saunter down the street, talking all the while.

"My mother used to work at Café de Minuit. She worked every day from six to midnight, scrubbin' dishes, servin' coffee, takin' orders. But she told me, every day when she left for work, 'Good coffee is worth the work.' I follow 'em same rules every day too." Clem smiled at me again, her bright face lighting up mine. We talked all the way up to Café de Minuit.

When we arrived, Clem pushed open the door, and a soft chiming of golden bells filled my ears. A lonely bartender sat, peering at us with hawk-like eyes. It was silent, other than the crackling of the radio mounted on a table. A muffled song sank into my ears—it was "Ma Pensée Vous Suit Partout," my mother's favorite. Memories of sitting together, listening to the radio, made me choke back sobs.

Clem stopped at a small table in the corner of the room, where there was hardly any light except for a flickering candle. I shivered and closed an open window. Clem sat down on a brittle chair and gestured to another. As I sat, carefully placing my hands on my lap, Clem yelled across the room, "Two coffees!" The bartender nodded solemnly and scratched his slicked black hair.

The two of us chit-chatted for a while, talking about everything. Yet I noticed Clem seemed much more open. She was like a shop window in a fancy, well-known mall where normal passersby can view the little, happy scenes. Clem let the world see her and judge her; she didn't care.

As I drifted into my realms of thought, my hold on the present slipped, and I tumbled into an abyss of boredom.

"So," Clem addressed me softly after many minutes, "Alice. Ya look bored. Why don't I tell ya a story?"

I perked up, my wispy hair floating around my face like a halo. Mother used to tell me stories. Lots. I remembered sitting on a green satin couch adorned with pillows, hungry for tales. My mother would sit next to me, her verbena perfume filling my nose. She would tell me a story, a new one every day. One day it would be about a girl in a red coat visiting her grandma, the next day it would be a cat in boots.

"Oh, yes, please!" I gasped. My hands grasped the edge of the smooth wooden table. "I would adore that, Madame Clem!"

Clem laughed, the noise filling up the entire room. "Sure, hon. But just call me Clem. I never liked them fancy names. 'Madame! Mademoiselle!'" Clem rolled her eyes. I began to see her as an independent-minded woman: she didn't care what anyone else thought. Clem just did whatever she wanted.

The bartender arrived, placing a steaming cup of coffee in front of us both. The hot liquid sloshed over the cup and onto the table, but the man didn't seem to mind. He walked off, his shiny black boots clicking on the wood floor. I daintily picked up my cup and sipped it. The bitterness surprised me, and I coughed it up.

Clem burst into laughter. "Not many people like it!" She gasped between cackles. "Anyway. I oughta tell ya a story." She cleared her throat. "Before I begin, I need to tell ya this: I'm a pirate. I ride on the *Dusty Bones* with my seven-man crew. We spend our days robbin' merchant ships and on the run. I love it." As Clem continued to tell her tale, my eyes kept drifting back to the ring. The sheer beauty of it made me almost salivate. *Think of all the money I could get with that,* my greedy mind thought. And so, as Clem got faster and faster, I slyly slid my hand over to hers. My hand flew out and snatched it off her finger, so fast I could barely see it happening. In just a split second, her priceless diamond ring was mine. Now that I had it, I began actually assimilating the pirate's story.

"Now, one day, when I was 'bout yer age—I started bein' a pirate when I was 'round nine—I woke up to a crazy bearded man with a hook staring into my young eyes. We began an epic scrimmage, but not before I lost that finger. After I tied him up nice and tight in some rope, me and my buds threw him overboard. It was a blast!

"Bein' a pirate ain't just 'bout fighting, though," Clem whispered darkly, suddenly serious. "We steal a lot too. I'm proud to say I'm one of the best thieves in all of France." I bit my lip to keep from laughing. If only she knew that her stolen diamond ring was now clutched in my sweaty palms. Clem resumed spinning her tale, whispering at some parts, yelling at others. I think the bartender got interested too, but I was too hooked to Clem's stories to tell. By the time the grandfather clock struck six, my coffee was cold, Clem looked as raggedy as an old doll, and the bartender was asleep on the bar.

Clem stood up. So did I, eager to leave and sell my ring. Clem peered around, making sure no one was around—or awake. Then she looked joyfully at me and whispered, "Can I have my ring back?" I stood, stunned. "Look, hon, that was some pretty fine stealing you just did there. And I was wondering," Clem put her face so close to mine I could smell her bitter breath, "if you'd like to join our crew?"

My Hand

by Devon Mann, 11
San Anselmo, CA

My hand moves endlessly
On the piece of paper.
I am writing on and on.
Words spread across the paper rapidly,
Floating like puffy clouds
Pushed by wind
Towards San Francisco.
My thoughts race high and low,
My hand struggles to keep up.
My story is coming to life.

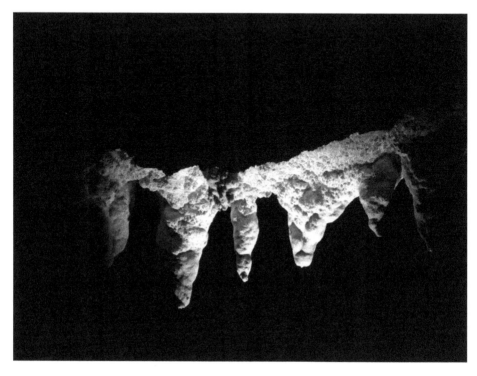

Black and White, *Canon PowerShot XS600*

by Sage Millen, 11
Vancouver, Canada

The Fossil

by Marlena Kilian, 11
Vancouver, WA

A young Spanish nobleman makes an astonishing discovery

Corian Monseur lounged on a couch with lace trimmings, gazing lazily through the window. His father was a nobleman and an architect busy designing the King of Spain's chambers. His family lived in a mansion with servants and rich bedrooms with halls leading to each one. Their backyard was a courtyard made up of rows of flower beds and perfect oaks rising as high as the mansion's roof. The pride of Corian's family was the lake beyond the courtyard, which flowed into many brooks and creeks behind and along the sides of the mansion.

Corian yearned for the tempting freedom he could enjoy not under the mansion's roof, but under the blue sky. Although he was permitted to go outside, he could only go along the endless flower beds, but they were not of any fascination to Corian.

Ceon, his younger brother, darted into the room with pleading eyes and said, "Corian, please come with me outside. Mother tells you not to idle."

Corian's gleaming eyes glanced at his brother, and he spoke solemnly, "I am 12 years old, yet we always seem to have an adventure together." Then he gave an awkward smile as Ceon happily went to get their moccasins

and their light coats.

Molly, a servant who was like an aunt to them, sternly said, "Tsch, tsch, boys. Be sure not to get dirty or walk into one of these chambers with a frog like last time."

Ceon chuckled but Corian remained silent in his deep thoughts. They went out of the wooden door and ran through the flower beds. As much as Corian wanted to carry out his brother's desire, he also got exasperated at having to leave his desirable chamber. Suddenly Ceon halted, greatly surprised. When Corian caught up with Ceon, he could not take in what lay before him: a creek ran between the last two rows of the flower beds, and where the creek flowed, the lilacs lay wilted with the front side of the wooden bed crushing their stems and petals. Ceon burst into tears: lilacs were his mother's favorite flower; she made certain they received extra water from the barrels each day.

As Corian was attempting to console his weeping brother, his eye caught hold of a shiny object lying untouched in the water. Corian tried to avoid looking at the object, which he knew would only be a rock, yet he felt his hopes rise quickly. So, he took off his moccasins and wool socks as he edged near the creek to take a look at the object. The spring breeze whirled through the air, and the cold water came up to Corian's heels. By now, Ceon was wiping his eyes just in time to see Corian turning the object over and over again in the palms of his hands. Corian was about to throw the object back into the water carelessly when he saw that white had begun to show through where he had rubbed it. The strong feeling that it couldn't possibly be a rock was growing. Corian finally said, "Ceon, we must get Molly, for I think in my hand is an animal's tooth," and they ran hastily to the patio, where servants were brushing the dusty furniture.

Corian yelled for Molly, forgetting his manners, bringing his older brother, sisters, Molly, and even Mother bustling down the stairs with curls flying. Corian could hardly believe that perhaps he held in his hands a great discovery that would be marked down in history.

Servants led the family to a large resting chamber where everyone sat excitedly upon the narrow sofas. "Speak! Speak!" They cried at once as Corian gave the fossil to Molly with shaking hands. A young servant gave her a pair of spectacles. Molly looked intently at the object, and with Corian constantly inquiring if it might be an animal's tooth, she replied, "Well it proves to not be a rock." She paused briefly. "What I am getting to is that I don't know if it's an animal's tooth."

Philip, Corian's eldest brother, suggested cheerfully, "Surely this is a discovery after all; there is no report of a tooth finding in all of Spain!"

Ronara, his eldest sister, said, "Let us send a telegram to some experts in Russia, for surely they would know."

All the other sisters gasped with surprise, but Philip clapped as Mrs. Monseur got up and proceeded to prepare the curious discovery for travel. They sent the fossil in a mini-box with an expensive telegram, and afterward, Corian and Ceon explained where the object had been found, and they also explained about the half-crushed lilac beds.

For the next few days, Corian was impatient to receive the telegram from the experts, and the days were hard to endure. Finally, after waiting a long month, a letter arrived. Mr. Monseur was going to return the next day, after spending six months at the King of Spain's palace, and Corian decided to wait before opening the letter so that all the Monseur family could be present.

Mr. Monseur was greeted warmly by his family the next day, and he was given the information about the discovery, which he enjoyed hearing, as they gathered in the second fanciest chamber in the mansion. Corian's eyes opened wide when he was to do the honors. Usually, his father did the honors of opening the letters the Monseur family received, but his father said Corian deserved to do the honors this time. Corian opened the flap of the letter, pulled it out, and eagerly started to read:

To the Monseur Family,

This discovery was a new study for us, and in answer to your question, "Is it a fossil?" Yes, indeed: it is an animal's tooth. The tooth is believed to be an ancient baby dragon's tooth. Dearest friends, you have made a fantastic discovery. The fossil is being sent to other scientific experts who will study the fossil more, and soon perhaps the fossil will be in a prehistoric animal museum. Please keep on sending letters not to us but to the building in London, England.

Signed: Workers of the Scientific Animal Culture in Russia

The Monseur family applauded Corian for such a discovery.

By the time Corian was 17, five years later, he had almost forgotten about the fossil he had discovered when he was 12. He had not received a letter since—nothing but the reassurance that it would come. On the day that Corian was getting ready to go to his great-uncle's mansion, a letter arrived at last. Corian was thrilled to open it, but this time his family was not present to hear its words. Corian read aloud as if he were in front of an audience:

Dear Corian,

These past five years have gone by so quickly that we were caught up in examining the fossil very closely, delaying our writing to you, and we beg your pardon. We are proud to say that this discovery is a real one, and we do believe that it is the tooth of a baby dragon. We hope to have another good year of examining the fossil. I gladly write that you,

son of the designer of the King of Spain's chambers, are granted with our permission to display this fossil in the Baton Museum in Spain with your name as the sole discoverer! We congratulate and thank you for this discovery that we hope may go down in animal history!

Signed: The Society of the Museum of Spain's Discoveries

Sam Peters and Carson Coom

Corian was amazed.

Another year went slowly by as the scientists continued to study the fossil. That it was a dragon's tooth was confirmed, and the fossil was put in the Baton Museum, where it was placed in a large glass container and was viewed by many. After 10 years, the fossil was transported to England and Italy, where skilled scientists studied it more. After another decade passed, it was known all over Europe, Russia, China, India, and North America.

Corian's discovery was put down in history, and when he died at the age of 92, his story, along with his background, was recorded in more detail. Corian Monseur's actual life was of little account aside from this famous discovery; however, he did follow his father as the architect for the chambers of the Kings of Spain.

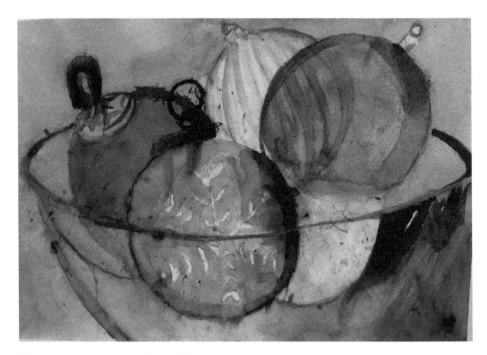

Bowl of Joy, *colored pencils*

by Ethan Hu, 8
San Diego, CA

A Christmas Poem

by Gianna Guerrero, 7
Ontario, NY

Santa Claus is always on schedule
If he misses, a piece of snow
The wind will blow, blow, blow!
That sled of his will set a trail
Of a wish and a blow through the wind
Those rooftops are
The ones that clickety tock
Some have branches tall and wide
Others have so many thunks and clunks of presents
Down, down, down the clattering

News from Stonesoup.com

First Place
Three Days Till EOC by Abhimanyu Sukhdial, 11 (Novel)

Second Place
The Golden Elephant by Analise Braddock, 8 (Poetry)
Searching for Bow and Arrows by Tatiana Rebecca Shrayer, 11 (Poetry)

Third Place
Elana by Hannah Nami Gajcowski, 9 (Novel)

Honorable Mentions
Leather Journal, Abhainn Bajus, 14 (Poetry)
The Hidden Key, Peri Gordon, 9 (Novel)
Frozen Nocturne, Sabrina Guo, 13 (Poetry)
The Demisers, Zoe Keith, 11 (Novel)
Last Birthday Boy, Olivia Ladell, 13 (Novel)
Family of Spies, Micah Lim, 10 (Novel)
Escape the War, Priyanka Nambiar, 13 (Novel)
A Brief Encounter with Chaos, Anyi Sharma, 11 (Stories)

New Contest: Personal Essays

Stone Soup is partnering with **The Society of Young Inklings** in our very first nonfiction contest. Their team of professional writers has designed a mentorship experience for both the youth and the educators who take part in this contest. The first 150 submitters will receive a personalized note from SYI. These notes will highlight a strength in your piece and offer guidance about how to build on that strength in future writing. We are so excited to be partnering with such a wonderful organization and thrilled to be able to offer personalized feedback to many of our writers! Find more details on our website under "Current Contests" or the SYI website: www.younginklings.org

Fundraisers: The Refugee Issue and Reaching Marginalized Communities

We have two fundraisers currently underway, and we're so grateful for the support we've already received! In 2020, we plan to publish an issue of *Stone Soup* consisting of art and writing by refugee children, or children of refugees. We also hope to create an initiative to help reach marginalized communities, as we believe all children should be able to enjoy reading and writing. You can find more information about both projects on our website under "Donate" on the main menu.

For the latest news and current material, visit Stonesoup.com

Honor Roll

Welcome to the *Stone Soup* Honor Roll. Every month, we receive submissions from hundreds of kids from around the world. Unfortunately, we don't have space to publish all the great work that comes our way. We want to commend some of these talented writers and artists and encourage them to keep creating.

Fiction
Hyunjin An, 8
Ava Chen, 13
Ava Evak, 8
Michael Hoffen, 12
Hadley Horton, 11
Lucy Shin, 9

Poetry
Panagiotis Apatsidis Gunaratnam, 9
Mackenzie Duan, 13
Teddy Klein, 8
Ignacio Moyano, 10
Daniel Shorten, 8
Michael Zhou, 12

Art
Benicio Moyano, 8
Adele Stamenov, 10

Visit the *Stone Soup* store at Stonesoupstore.com to buy:

- Magazines—individual issues of *Stone Soup*, past and present

- Books—our collection of themed anthologies (fantasy, sport, poetry, and more), and the *Stone Soup Annual* (all the year's issues, plus a taste of the year online, in one volume)

- Art prints—high quality prints from our collection of children's art

- Journals and sketchbooks for writing and drawing

 ... and more!

Don't forget to visit Stonesoup.com to browse our bonus materials. There you will find:

- 20 years of back issues—around 5,000 stories, poems, and reviews

- Blog posts from our young bloggers on subjects from sports to sewing—plus ecology, reading, and book reviews

- Video interviews with *Stone Soup* authors

- Music, spoken word, and performances

This Year on the Blog

Have you been following our blog? We post new work by *Stone Soup* bloggers every week, and they are constantly coming up with something new to tell the world about! We have published music, reviews of books and movies, sports analysis, opinion pieces on important topics from climate and nature to refugee crises, and lots of fun stuff too. Here is a selection of some of our favorites since last year's *Annual*.

Young Bloggers

Alien Serenity
by Lukas Cooke, 12
Posted January 21, 2019

Image from the author.

A gust of wind blew, but not a thing seemed to stir. *How odd*, I thought to myself, shivering as the gale sent spikes of cold into the depths of my body. As if to spite the fact that I wore three sweaters, every swirling movement of the air seemed determined to make me freeze. But where I was made all the discomfort go away.

I have traveled to many places, from the towering beauty of the German Alps to the vibrant colors that make up the reefs of Fiji. However, I have found that there is something unique to every place I go, something that makes every trip worthwhile. Often when I think about it, I find the varieties of the Earth we live on stunning. And that is more fact than opinion.

The desert was not new to me; I take trips with my family to the high desert of Nevada twice a year. Each year we have a great time, and I have learned that, if you look hard enough, the desert is not such a bland place after all. But the desert I found myself in now was different. Every part of it seemed to scream, "I am not dull in the slightest! And if I have to show that to you by sprouting the weirdest trees you have ever seen, I will!"

Yes, I was in Joshua Tree National Park. I had an odd sensation, my brain knowing that I was on Earth but all of my senses saying I wasn't, that I was on Mars, with giant rock formations jutting out of the landscape all around me to accompany the trees from another world. The deathly stillness didn't help my perplexity either.

And yet, it was wondrous. It didn't matter that none of it seemed to make sense; it just was. There were so many different hues of yellow, green, and brown, all intermingling to form an extraterrestrial landscape. Stacked boulders told tales of the earliest days of existence, the trees a constant chorus of agreement.

We spent the day driving to different trailheads in the park, hiking a little ways up them, and climbing boulders until our hands were raw. We walked through valleys, canyons, and washed our dusty faces in a crystal-clear pond that sat in a small oasis. It was an experience I will never forget.

As the sun began to disappear behind the horizon, I climbed one last boulder, the largest one I could find. Once at the top, I sat down and closed my eyes. The wind whirled around me, blowing my hair over my eyelids, but at that moment, it couldn't make me cold. I was immersed in the full glory of the Earth, and the only sense I had was one of deep understanding and peace. A feeling of serenity.

Later that evening we were sitting by the fireside of the cabin we were staying in. I looked outside the window and found myself gazing upon an endless expanse of stars. Among them was Orion, the full constellation. I thought back on the calm I had felt as I sat on top of the rock, and I thought to myself, *How odd.*

There is something in nature that can only be accessed through a search, a search in which one must ignore the stress of the world and delve deeper into the connection between man and Mother Nature. It is a feeling of peace, of calm, of understanding. It is a feeling of serenity.

Writing My Own Path
by Sabrina Guo, 13
Posted March 11, 2019

Detail of illustration by Joanne Cai, 13. Published in *Stone Soup* March/April 2016.

As a child, I loved the smell of libraries. I would flip through the pages of any book and take a good, long sniff. My favorite scent was sweet—a bit of lemon and coffee, mixed with paper, of course. However, other books had a bitter smell and were covered with all kinds of food stains, which I hated because it reminded me of how books were sometimes treated just as paper and nothing more. I thought of each book as a life—a key to a specific person's brain.

At the same time, I hated books. I respected them and liked their smells, yes, but I absolutely loathed words. Every time I tried to read something as minor as a news headline, words would swarm around me like taunting wasps. While other kids talked about their new favorite books, I was the wallflower, standing away from the crowd and nibbling slowly on my sandwich.

A memory: when I was five, I learned that *To Kill a Mockingbird* was a book loved all around the world. I decided to read it—after all, if there were so many positive reviews, how could I not love it? In addition, I was determined to open myself up and conquer my fear of words. I asked my father to check it out at the library. When he walked through our door with it, I was giddy with excitement. I flipped through it, smelling it like a perfume tester. It was unique and unlike any other book I'd smelled before—like moss drenched in rain, bittersweet and mature. Greedily, I started reading the first page. But almost immediately, dark words started to choke the air around me. The enlarged first letter pounced on top of me, and the rest of the words quickly followed, swimming around me. I tried to push my fears away, telling myself I wasn't going to be engulfed this time. My fear of reading was going to end right there, right then, that second, with that very book. But because of its advanced language, I had no idea what was happening in the story. It was boring and tiring . . . and I was only halfway down the first page. I exhaled, telling myself there would be a next time. Then I slammed the book shut in frustration.

Although I had a complicated relationship with books, I did love writing song lyrics. After school, I would transform my tangled thoughts into strings of words, which I wrote down in a tiny notebook about the size of my hand. Little did I know that these song lyrics were actually poems; later I would take a risk and reshape my lyrics into a more literary form. And that was how I took my first step into writing. From there, I decided to experiment with reading again. I borrowed many types of library books, but it was fantasy that finally hooked me. Fantasy made me feel like I was soaring above moonlit clouds, plucking shimmering stars from the sky and collecting them inside of my heart. These stories gave me an amazing sense of freedom, adventure, and suspense. And after a while, my interests expanded to other genres; I even started to read some news articles, which had intimidated me so much before.

My father and I like to watch the news together, and last year, as coverage of the refugee crisis increased, he encouraged me to dig deeper into the topic. It can sometimes sound like it's a simple, fast process to immigrate to the United States; but as I read up on the issue, I discovered that it's far from easy or quick. It can actually take up to several years to go through all the necessary steps! Even after reaching the US, refugees can still face economic and emotional difficulties, along with discrimination. After learning all of this, I decided to write a blog about it, as I am a blogger and contributing writer to the children's magazine, *Stone*

Soup. I was also inspired to write a poem addressed to refugee children, welcoming them to their new home in the US. I tried to explain some of the things that they might encounter in their new country, from academic pressures to peer pressure. Writing the poem enabled me to think more deeply about what a refugee child might experience after leaving their home country. It challenged me to think outside of my own life and circumstances, and this poem was one of the first works I'd written truly from my heart.

Around that time, William Rubel, the founder of *Stone Soup*, mentioned in his weekly newsletter that he hoped to create a platform to showcase refugee children's art and writing. Due to my interest in the refugee crisis, I immediately volunteered to help. He suggested that I begin researching organizations, photographers, and artists who were working with refugee children. Through doing this, I found many amazing organizations. One in particular, Another Kind of Girl Collective (AKGC), really struck me. This organization, founded by Laura Doggett, holds photography and film workshops for Syrian refugee girls living in Jordan. AKGC aims to give refugee girls the deeply necessary space, training, and equipment to develop their preferred art forms, along with providing them a platform to share their own stories and experiences. The girls prove themselves not to be passive and tragic beings, which is sometimes how the media portrays them, but rather hardworking, creative, smart, and motivated visionaries.

Because of how much I admired Laura's work, I reached out to her through email, asking if I could interview her. I had doubts about whether she would respond. After all, I was just a 12-year-old girl, and she was surely busy with her extremely important work. So you can imagine my elation when I did hear back from her! She told me she would be happy to give me an interview. She was heading to Jordan and even invited me to interview two young female Syrian filmmakers, Marah Al Hassan and Khaldiya Jibawi. These filmmakers live in Za'atari refugee camp and have participated in the AKGC workshops; their work has been shown in places as renowned as the Sundance Film Festival and *The New York Times*.

Before interviewing the girls, I did not know what to expect. After all, they lived in refugee camps, had very different life circumstances, and came from another culture. However, when we spoke to each other on Skype, it was as if we were friends at summer camp! Even though they were already young wives and mothers, they didn't talk down to me because I was younger than them. They answered my questions warmly and expanded on them, giving me more information and insight. I felt respected and embraced by these incredible girls. Before getting to know Laura and the girls, my only exposure to refugees was what I saw in the news, which is often one-dimensional. But because of my conversations with Marah and Khaldiya and how they welcomed me into their lives by talking about personal subjects, I learned that they weren't as different from me as I expected. We all shared the same desire: to be heard. And after speaking to them and the AKGC facilitators, I grew more aware of the many obstacles, from gender discrimination to loss of family members and violence, that the Syrian women had to overcome to achieve their goals. This shifted my perspective on my own life. I began to see how many advantages and benefits I'd previously taken for granted.

I already had a high level of respect for the refugee girls, but after seeing them on Skype, my admiration soared. Through their creativity and bravery, these young women change our world for the better. I had to spread the word about my new friends and their vital work, and so I wrote a blog about AKGC on the *Stone Soup* website. Inspired by this, Mr. Rubel announced the launch of a new refugee issue of *Stone Soup*, which will feature the creative work of children caught up in the Syrian war. I am so happy that this important information will be shared with a larger audience of kids my age, and I am proud of the work I did to contribute to the effort.

Without words and writing, my world would be much narrower with fewer opportunities to meet inspiring women. For example, I am now a member of the Grow, Inspire, Reach, Lead (G.I.R.L.) Talk Committee in my school district. Our goal is to empower girls and encourage them to pursue careers in STEM. Recently, I wrote a letter to Michelle Obama, telling her how she consistently inspires me to be a strong and capable young woman, how much she's affected my life, and how she inspired the G.I.R.L. Talk Committee. To my excitement, she replied, thanking us and providing tickets to a talk on her new book, *Becoming*. We learned so much listening to her talk about her life: her obstacles, haters, writing process, and even how she met Barack Obama. It was a motivational and energizing experience for all of us.

It took time for me to welcome words into my life. But after I stepped out of my comfort zone by writing lyrics and poems, it was not long before I was avidly reading books and finally conquering my fear of newspapers. Words became an essential part of my life. And by educating myself on current events, I became more connected to the outside world, which led to my discovery of AKGC and the formation of my relationships with Laura, Marah, and Khaldiya. I will carry these new friendships with me for the rest of my life, along with my love of words and writing. And for this, I will be forever grateful to the power and beauty of words.

Why Animation Is Important
by Dylan Gibson, 13
Posted March 13, 2019

Animation, while often thought of as a more or less modern medium, has been used in different forms since 1906! Throughout the last century, we have used it to entertain, as propaganda, and to tell stories that evoke emotion.

Title frame of *Humorous Phases of Funny Faces* (public domain).

The earliest known animated film was made in France in 1906, titled *Humorous Phases of Funny Faces*, and was made from chalk pictures. Since then, other small animations were made, but the first animated cartoon with synchronized sound was made by Walt Disney in 1928, called *Steamboat Willie*. Many cartoons like this followed, and they were used to entertain viewers with gags and charades of drawn characters. Nine years later, Disney released the first full-length future film, *Snow White*. And in 1993, software for 3-D animation was created.

All of these events led up to the animation and films we see today. From *Spiderman: Into the Spiderverse* to live-action movies with CGI to popular YouTube animators like Jaiden Animations, animation has become a popular form of storytelling that has helped shape the modern world.

Animation is important because it makes us able to tell stories and communicate emotions and ideas in a unique, easy-to-perceive way that both small children and adults can understand. Animation has helped connect people throughout the world in a way that sometimes writing and live-action films cannot. Today, anyone can pick up a drawing tablet and show their ideas to the world. Drawn figures can be funny or make something sad or serious have a playful, less intimidating feel to it to make the viewer feel more comfortable. Other times, it allows people to be united by a single passion, such as a fandom, and work on huge projects (called MAPs, which stands for "multi-animator project") about their interest and make something as high-quality as a professional film, such as *The Five Giants [COMPLETE Warrior Cats M.A.P.]*, regardless of different beliefs and opinions. Often, animation has simply served as a way to make a heartwarming story that makes you think. Through live-action movies, people can form biases based on the appearance and real-life personality of an actor playing a character. But as an animated character, the character feels like their own being.

No matter what the exact use, animation is one of the most powerful creative tools we have, and we should continue to use it as a form of uniting people, no matter their beliefs, biases, or interests.

A Day in the Life of the Amazon Rainforest

by Rizwan Thorne-Lyman, 11
Posted April 2, 2019

Detail from *Green Envy* by Delaney Slote, 12. Published in *Stone Soup* June 2018.

The rainforest is one of the most complex and interesting places on Earth. It is also full of energy. This energy comes from the plants, which are eaten by other organisms known as primary consumers, which in turn are eaten by secondary consumers. The energy continues to travel up the food chain until it reaches the apex predator; at this point there is not much energy left.

As the sun rises, consumers like macaws and harpy eagles begin chirping and screeching. Meanwhile, the jaguar sets out to the swamp in search of caiman, a reptile like the crocodile. However, another predator is already there. The green anaconda. The conflict between the green anaconda and the jaguar is an example of competition. This mighty snake can weigh up to 550 pounds and can swallow a pig easily. When this massive snake comes into conflict with the third largest big cat, who will come out alive? The jaguar tries an ambush attack, but the anaconda shakes the jaguar off and begins wrapping around the jaguar's chest. The jaguar begins scratching and kicking at the anaconda, drawing blood. The hurt and exhausted snake recoils and tries to flee. However, the jaguar grabs the anaconda and performs a skull bite, killing the snake instantly. Then, it begins to hunt caiman . . .

Not so far away, a colony of leafcutter ants is gathering leaves from producers like a jackfruit tree. The ants are doing this so they can obtain some of the energy the leaf got from the sun. In other words, eating it. However, the journey back to their nest is dangerous, as 10 feet away lies an anteater. The anteater immediately starts trotting to the line of ants. It then proceeds to eat, that is until a harpy eagle begins chasing it. Still, the dangers are not over yet. The phorid fly is a tiny insect that attacks the leafcutter ants and lays its eggs on the ant's head. When the larva matures, the head of the ant detaches. This is an example of parasitism. The ant will soon be consumed by decomposers, such as worms, fungi, and bacteria.

It is midday when a macaw is out searching for food. Suddenly it spies a banana tree. It starts flying toward it when suddenly a puma lunges out. The macaw barely dodges. The puma aims another swipe at the macaw. This time the puma's paw slightly cuts the macaw's wing. The puma is about to deliver the killing blow when suddenly it spots another predator. The jaguar. The jaguar doesn't normally eat macaws, but it takes opportunities for a chance to eat. These two animals normally stay out of each other's way. However, both animals are hungry, and they are ready to fight. Perhaps this will give the macaw a chance to escape from predation. Indeed, it does. While the cats fight, the bird escapes. Whatever cat dies shall feed the scavengers such as millipedes and phorid flies, although a fight will take place. The interesting things in a rainforest are not limited to the bugs and animals. The tall trees in a rainforest mean that the other plants can't get enough sunlight. However, the orchid has evolved to solve this problem. The orchid has evolved so that it can grow on a tree. This helps the orchid get sunlight, and the tree does not care at all. This known as commensalism.

As the sun sets, a lone capuchin monkey wanders about looking for bananas or flowering trees. When it spots one, the monkey begins climbing toward it. The monkey quickly devours the pollen. In the process the monkey spreads seeds everywhere (annoying a caiman while doing that). The plant gives the monkey food and the monkey spreads its seeds around. Both benefit, so this is a mutual relationship. Perhaps more of the seeds would have been scattered had it not been for a harpy eagle snatching the monkey away.

Being a Fan
by Thomas Steytler, 11
Posted April 4, 2019

Detail from illustration by Erin Wolf, 12. Published in *Stone Soup* March/April 2009.

I was 8, just a third-grader. It was June 2016. I had my mind full because the Copa America Centenario was happening and my team, Argentina, was doing well and had a good chance of making it to the final. When I got home one afternoon, my dad said, "We're going to the Copa America final at MetLife! I have tickets!" I couldn't believe my ears. I could be watching Argentina play in the final, live!

That weekend, I watched Argentina vs. USA—the semi-final—with anticipation. After 90 minutes of waiting, I knew I was going to see my favorite international soccer team play, with my favorite player: Lionel Messi! The next week was the longest week I could remember. I went from counting the days, to hours, to minutes. Finally, the big night arrived!

As we arrived at the MetLife Stadium,

I heard the announcer talking about how you should drink Pepsi and how they sponsored the game. I stepped into the stadium. Many smells filled my nostrils: hot dogs, burgers, chicken, and so many other things. But I didn't want any of it. I was too nervous to eat. I looked around. The stadium was huge! Each floor was packed with vendors that were selling all of these delicious things, and hundreds of people trying to find their seats. All of the Argentinian and Chilean fans were chanting in Spanish, the Argentinians in blue, the Chileans in red. Even though I couldn't understand what they were saying, I could feel the strength in their singing, the passion.

I was one of those fans. A few years before, my dad's friend from work had given me my first Argentina shirt, with Messi's name on the back. When I got that shirt, I didn't know who Messi really was, but since that day, I had followed his career and watched Argentina play many times. Now Messi was my idol, and Argentina was my team. I had to pinch myself to believe that I was actually going to see him play in less than an hour!

After a completely excruciating 40 minutes of waiting, while the two teams warmed up and my nerves took over, the game began. The first 10 minutes of the game were very even, and then Argentina took control of the ball and I started to relax. I was about to ask my dad for something to eat when an Argentinian, Marcos Rojo, fouled a Chilean player and got a red card! My heart sank. How could Argentina win

the final when they had one less player than Chile? That thought got stuck in my head until a Chilean player also got a red card and the teams were even once again.

The rest of the first half went by with little action, and so did the second half. Because the score was still 0-0 and the teams couldn't share the trophy, they played another 30 minutes of soccer. For the first time that day, that week, the reality dawned on me that Argentina might not win, but I pushed that thought away. I believed too much in this team for them to let me down. I sat on the edge of my seat until extra time was over. There was still no score. It was down to a penalty shootout.

Messi was going to take the first penalty for Argentina, but it was Chile's turn first. Everyone in the crowd in front of me was standing up, blocking my view, so I had to listen to the crowd to know whether or not the Chilean player had scored. Penalty shootouts are usually a 50-50 battle, so there was no way of knowing who would win. Suddenly, a roar from the Chilean fans filled the stadium. He had scored. A sinking feeling tried to penetrate my confidence, but I wouldn't let it. I had believed in this team for too long for them to let me down now. Then it was Argentina's turn. "Piece of cake," I muttered to myself as Messi got ready to take the penalty. The whole crowd became silent, just like they were holding their breath. Out of nowhere, everyone gasped, and I saw the best player in the world bury his face in his hands and walk away to his team. He had missed! Tears started to pool in my eyes. He was the player that I'd wanted to see play more than anyone. And he'd let me down. I didn't even care if Argentina won anymore.

"He missed," my dad said breathlessly.

"I . . . I know," I stuttered back. My dad and I stood and watched as Chile won the penalty shootout and the tournament.

My eyes became two faucets and poured and poured. I got up from the slippery plastic seat and cried, "I don't want to see them lift it!" (the trophy). "Okay, okay. We'll go then," said my dad. The train ride went by very quickly because I slept like a baby. It was, after all, 1:00 am. As we pulled into Penn Station, my eyes popped open, and I was removed from dreamland. After the taxi ride home, just as my dad and I walked into the apartment, my mom said, "I'm sorry." I felt like throwing my Copa America scarf against the wall and storming into my room. I felt like giving up on Messi and Argentina for good. I wanted to do so many things because of the way I was feeling. But I didn't do any of them. Instead, I walked over to my mom and gave her a hug . . .

As I laid my head on my pillow, I thought about what had happened at the MetLife Stadium. Messi was probably feeling way worse than I was. I thought of all the amazing goals I had seen him score before on TV. I couldn't stop liking him because of one bad penalty. I knew I'd be cheering for Argentina again the next time they played. "This is the first time I have actually experienced being a real fan," I thought to myself. "I now know what it is like to experience defeat, and I know that I will always stick with my team, no matter what." My eyes then closed, and I plunged into a world of penalties and Argentine fans chanting in Spanish.

Galaxies
by Ishhayu Jha, 10
Posted April 15, 2019

Detail from illustration by John P. Anson, 7. Published in *Stone Soup* April 2019.

Galaxies are one of the most interesting things in space. They are all filled up with stars, planets, and dust. Did you know that you are made of star dust because our galaxy is filled with dust? Comets are falling on Earth all the time, spreading this dust.

Galaxies, as you know, are made of stars, planets, and dust. They flood the universe together. Every few light-years, galaxies are seen. NASA has found a other solar systems in the Milky Way, but they have not seen water yet. Even if there was water, most stars are much too young and dim to live on. All galaxies keep their stars, planets, and star dust together with gravity. Gravity is a galaxy's best friend. Galaxies are huge and seem endless! Even after so much research and space travel, we still do not know where our galaxy ends.

As you know, we live in the Milky Way galaxy. Do you know that the Milky Way is a spiral galaxy? A spiral galaxy looks like an octopus, with its "arms" swinging around. We live on one of the outer parts of an "arm" in the Milky Way. There are three main kinds of galaxies. Spiral, irregular, and elliptical. An irregular galaxy is a galaxy with no proper shape. Hence the word irregular. An elliptical galaxy looks oval shaped, like an egg except flatter. It is important to classify galaxies' features from each other.

There are millions of galaxies in the universe, but we can only see so many without a telescope, specifically three galaxies. People who are north of the equator see the Andromeda Galaxy. This galaxy will crash into our galaxy in a few million years. The Andromeda Galaxy has a weird gravitational force. South of the equator people can see the large and small Magellanic Clouds. Although not much is known about them, scientists think these galaxies are two of the brightest galaxies in our universe. You can't exactly see these three galaxies properly. They look like small, hazy patches of light. We need to research more about these galaxies and see if we find intelligent life.

Galaxies have so many interesting facts about them. People have learned more about galaxies since 2015 than ever before! Galaxies are or one the most intriguing puzzle pieces to the biggest puzzle of all, the universe.

My Fancy Cake
by Maya Viswanathan, 12
Posted May 23, 2019

Photo from the author.

Do you care about style? I do. I like things that are fancy and colorful with a lot of patterns and designs. My mom thinks that I just try to make things look crazy. But I don't. It might seem crazy to other people, but it is just what I think is pretty. I think it looks boring otherwise. When it was time to choose the cake for my bat mitzvah, I made sure that it looked the way I wanted it, with many colors and patterns. Let me tell you what happened.

The sliding door slid open and my mom and I walked into the store. My bat mitzvah was next week and we were going to order a fancy, three-tiered cake for the party. I was super excited because a fancy cake was one of the things that I really wanted. I first decided that I wanted a fancy cake when I saw one at my friend's bar mitzvah. It really grabbed my attention. It was beautiful, and I knew I wanted mine to be just as spectacular. We weren't going to make everything in my party fancy, but my mom said I could choose to make one thing fancy. The cake would be my thing to have however I liked it. I thought it was a crucial element to make the celebration really festive. I could just picture it. It would be dazzling and magnificent and exquisite. It would sit in the center of the table. Everyone would love it. It would be just as I hoped. I knew what it would look like too. I had a vision from the beginning. My family and I discussed it to make sure they liked the design too. We planned it all out before we went to the store. Planning it out took a long time, since my mom disagreed with me on many things. The design I wanted was going to have three different colors for each layer and flowers cascading over it. My mom thought that flowers were nice, but she wanted three shades of one color instead of three different colors. "Mom, I want it to be colorful," I said over and over.

"How about three shades of yellow?" she asked. "You want yellow, so let's do three shades of yellow. It will look much more elegant."

"Mom, I don't want it to be elegant. I want it to be colorful," I kept repeating. She kept saying that it was my cake, but I still had to convince her. "Look," she said, showing me a picture of a cake online. "Here is a picture of a cake with three shades of yellow. Isn't it pretty?"

"How about this picture?" I asked. "These are the colors I want." When my mom saw the picture, she admitted it looked nice and agreed to go with my way.

Then we talked about many other things. The leaves would be light green, not dark green. The flowers would be red. The yellow layer would be on top, followed by coral, and then gold. My mom and I had discussed every tiny little detail. We had talked and talked until we came up with the perfect cake. But now we were done. My mom had agreed to go with the cake I wanted. Placing the order at the store would be easy.

I followed my mom to the bakery section of the store. We looked at the book of designs and quickly flipped through the options. The exact design we were going to have wasn't there. But it wasn't a problem. We quickly found a similar one. We then started looking at the colors to make sure they had what we wanted. They had everything. We were having yellow, coral, and gold layers with red roses and light-green leaves. Everything was set. We were about to fill out the form when we noticed something. This cake also had dots piped around each layer and we had never talked about their color. I flipped through the colors again.

"How about teal?" I asked. I thought that teal would add one more pretty color to the design.

My mom frowned. "Teal?" she asked. "How about orange, or something that matches?"

"I don't want it to be too monochromatic," I replied.

"Fine," my mom said. "It is your cake. Choose whatever you want. I am staying out of it."

I could tell she was not pleased. I thought teal would look nice. But I was not sure. It is hard to pick something when I feel like no one else thinks it is nice. Then again, orange would be boring. My mom did say I could choose. I stared at the colors and tried to imagine the cake and decide.

"Mom, what do you think?" I asked her again.

"Whatever you want," she said again in an exasperated tone.

"Fine," I decided. "Then teal." I was not sure, but I decided to go with my instinct. I wanted the cake to be colorful, not boring. It would make my party

much more festive. The dots would be teal.

The next Friday, I was super excited as I got into the car after school. "Give me your phone," I told my mom. She had picked up the cake and delivered it to the synagogue for the next day while I was in school, and I had reminded her 10,000 times to take a picture so that I could get to see it immediately. As she handed me the phone, she said, "It is even nicer than you could have imagined." As I looked at the picture, I saw that she was right. It was beautiful. Even my mom admitted that the teal was a good choice and that she was glad we went with it.

I was glad too. I was really pleased with how the cake came out. Everyone at the party liked it. It was gorgeous. It was colorful and flowery and bright. It was the centerpiece of the dessert table. But I was happy not only because the cake was a success but also because it was my creation, the way it had been in my imagination. It might seem silly. Why should I care who came up with the design? What matters is that it came out well, right? But I did care. Because it was my design, I felt proud of how it came out. I am glad that I stood my ground.

The Blue Chair
by David Jacobs, 7
Posted January 31, 2019

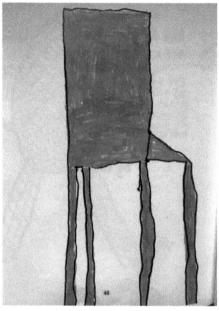

Image from the author.

One blue chair in the
middle of the world Just
waiting for Someone to
Sit on it.
In a house that nobody
Lives in
It's waited and waited
And waited . . .

Author Interview: Alexis Farjado, author of *Kid Beowulf* talks to *Stone Soup* blogger Mirembe Mubanda, 12
Posted April 10, 2019

Mirembe Mubanda, one of our young bloggers, read Alexis E. Fajardo's graphic novel Kid Beowulf: The Rise of El Cid, *and talked to the author about his inspirations, his process, and writing multiple storylines.*

Mirembe Mubanda: As a child, what were some of your favorite stories? Did they play a part in your inspiration to write *Kid Beowulf: The Rise of El Cid?*

Alexis Fajardo: I've always loved mythology, in particular the Greek and Norse myths. One of my favorite books growing up was the D'Aulaires' editions of Greek and Norse mythology; they were wonderfully written and illustrated. As a young reader I was particularly drawn to the Norse myths because they were always a little bloodier than the more refined Greek myths. Those stories were a gateway to epics like *Beowulf* and *El Cid*.

MM: If you were to host a dinner party where you invited characters from different comics and graphic novels, whom would you invite, and why would you invite them?

AF: This is a hard question! Hmm . . . I suppose first off we would need someone to cook the meal, and I think Phoney Bone (from the graphic novel *BONE*) is a pretty good cook. Then of course we need some good conversation, so I would invite Delilah Dirk (from the graphic novel series *Delilah Dirk*), Tintin and Asterix to tell me about all their adventures (and we'll need plenty of food if Obelix and Captain Haddock come along too). Finally, I don't want to do any dishes, so I think we'll probably need Smiley Bone in the kitchen to help Phoney clean up.

MM: What was it like when the idea of writing *The Rise of El Cid* came to mind?

AF: When I started the *Kid Beowulf* series, I knew I wanted Beowulf and Grendel to interact with epic heroes from other countries. Spain was always on the list because of *El Cid*. I was also looking forward to writing *The Rise of El Cid* because part of my family is from Spain, so to weave in some of that history was important to me. One of my favorite parts of creating new stories is doing all the research. I love reading the source material (in this case, the epic poem *El Cid*), as well as histories and other stories related to the topic. The research is fun because it means all ideas are on

the table. Eventually, the hard part of writing begins when I have to whittle away at the story until it takes shape. I knew for *The Rise of El Cid*, I wanted to tell the story of how one Rodrigo Díaz becomes the great knight known as "El Cid" but must stay true to himself to achieve that title.

MM: While creating *Kid Beowulf: The Rise of El Cid*, did you have a favorite character? If so, who and why?

AF: There are a lot of fun characters in this book, but one of my favorites is Rodrigo's friend Pedro the Mute. He is small, feisty, but never says a word! He has a slate board that he communicates with by drawing pictures on it; it was fun to come up with the different things he would have to say. I am also fond of Rodrigo's horse, Babieca, and especially enjoyed creating the part of the story where the two first meet. Horses are very hard to draw though, so Babieca was a challenge.

MM: On a scale of 1 through 10, how much is *Kid Beowulf: The Rise of El Cid* based on the poem *El Cid*? Why is it this number?

AF: In the book there is a prologue in which I retell the original epic poem, and that is a solid "10." The rest of the book is inspired by events in the epic poem, other stories about El Cid, as well as the history of the time. My story is intended to be a prequel to the events depicted in the epic poem. The research is pretty detailed and thorough, and the history is mostly accurate. At the same time it's an origi-

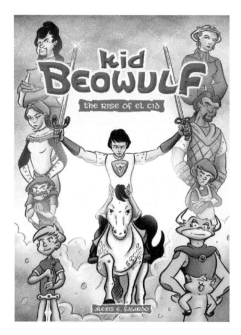

nal story, especially the parts involving Beowulf and Grendel!

MM: *Kid Beowulf: The Rise of El Cid* is the third graphic novel in the *Kid Beowulf* series. Which comic book did you enjoy writing the most?

AF: Even though they are all part of the same series and we follow Beowulf and Grendel from one book to the next, each book is very different from the other. Book 1 is very much a fantasy that has elements of magic in it. Book 2 is a swashbuckling adventure story with some comedy thrown in. And Book 3 is a more serious adventure with some romance and political intrigue. Each one has its own challenges, and when I'm creating them I am fully invested in that adventure; it's only after I'm finished when I can begin to judge them. That said, Book 2, *The Song of Roland*, has

some of my favorite characters and sequences in it, and I always like coming back to that setting.

MM: In *Kid Beowulf: The Rise of El Cid*, there are three different story lines. Did you ever think of making only one?

AF: Ha! There are multiple story lines in all my books! I think that's because I try to create three-dimensional characters who have lives and stories of their own . . . which can sometimes complicate plots. Ideally all the different story lines come together by the end of the big story; so in the case of *El Cid*, we have the story of Rodrigo Díaz, which is very separate from what Beowulf and Grendel are doing; however, by the climax of the book all their story lines intersect and (hopefully) pay off.

MM: Were any of the characters' personalities based on yours or someone you know well? If so, which characters and people?

AF: I have a few friends who sometimes become the inspiration for characters. Rodrigo's close friend Martín is inspired by a good friend of mine—in looks, personality, and facial hair.

MM: What was your process for writing the story line and making the art?

AF: There are lots of different ways to make comics, and each cartoonist has their own method. For me, I like to write out full scripts that I then draw out. There are several stages to creating the art: pencils, inks, color, and letters. I pencil and ink on paper, after which I scan the artwork into the computer and color and letter digitally. I also have a colorist who helps me color the book. Comics are deceptively complex to make, sort of like putting together a giant puzzle.

MM: *Kid Beowulf: The Rise of El Cid* has many different types of scenes, some happy, others action-packed. Which type of scene do you like to write the most?

AF: Every scene has its own challenges. Action scenes and fight scenes can take a long time because I have to choreograph the action and make sure it reads clearly on the page. At the same time, the slower, more emotional scenes are the glue that keeps the story interesting, so it's important to make those resonate too. I love writing stories, and the thing I want to do most is create a good story that keeps the reader excited, engaged, and entertained. I want my reader to race to finish a book because they are invested, and then I want them to read it all over again because they enjoyed it so much the first time.

Thank you to Alexis E. Fajardo for doing the interview with Stone Soup, *and to Mirembe for asking great questions! Check out the* Kid Beowulf *website to read more about the books.*

The Lifecycle of Clothes
by Mahati Kashyap, 7
Posted May 25, 2019

Detail from illustration by Laney Haskell, 12. Published in *Stone Soup* March/April 2009.

Have you ever wondered about the clothes you wear? Where they come from and what happens to them when you no longer need them? Recently, I got very interested in learning more about clothes. It all started when I went with my mother to a clothing-donation box in the parking lot of a small mall near our home. Every few months, she collects all our unwanted clothes in a bag and drops them off into a big box. During this trip, for the first time, I wondered what happens to all the clothes that are deposited into the box. I asked a lot of questions and found many interesting answers. Read on to find out more about the lifecycle of clothes and why unwanted clothes never belong in the trash!

Clothes are made from two main sources: natural and artificial. Natural sources are plant fibers like cotton, jute, bamboo, and rubber; and animal sources including silk, hide, wool, feathers, and fur. Human researchers have also invented fibers such as nylon and polyester using chemicals in the lab. These are artificial fibers and are often used to make light, waterproof clothing such as sportswear and bathing suits. All these fibers require plenty of water, land, and other natural resources to make. Clothing is usually made in developing countries because it is cheaper to make there. Once the clothes are made, they get shipped all over the world. This is how clothes get to stores near you!

Once you buy a piece of clothing, several things to happen to it:

- You may not like it.
- It could become well worn and even raggedy.
- You could outgrow it.
- It could get out of season, for example, shorts in winter and jackets in summer.
- You wash it the wrong way and it shrinks!

Once you no longer need a piece of clothing:

- If it is in a good condition, it could be handed down.
- You could drop it off in a donation or charity box.
- You could sell it at a second-hand store.
- You could throw it in the garbage can.

Every year, each one of us throws about 70 lbs of clothing in the trash. One pound is equal to about three T-shirts, nine pieces of kid's clothes, or one pair of shoes. These trashed clothes end up in landfill, which is a large area where trash is buried.

Throwing old clothes in the trash pollutes the environment, and it is a waste of the natural resources that went into making them. So, it is better to recycle clothes, even if they are torn and raggedy. But when we think of recycling, we only think of bottles, paper and cans. Not clothes! Clothes cannot even be thrown in the regular recycling bin! So, what do we do? Even with our clothes, we can practice "reduce, reuse, recycle."

If clothes become too worn out to be handed down or sold, they can get dropped off at a donation box. Companies that recycle clothes provide these boxes at many convenient locations, such as parking lots, malls, etc. From here, the clothes get sorted according to their condition. Many clothes are sold back to developing countries. A city called Panipat in India is nicknamed the "cast-off capital" of the world. In these places:

- Ships and trucks bring in recycled clothes from all over the world.
- They are sorted into reds, blues, greens, and blacks, and also according to their fiber.
- Workers remove zippers and buttons with small knives.
- Machines shred the clothes into smaller pieces and remove the fibers to make yarn. Some of the pieces are used to stuff couches and cushions.
- The yarn is used to make blankets that are sold at a very low cost.

After big disasters like tsunamis, earthquakes or hurricanes, families lose everything of theirs. These blankets are given to keep them safe and warm. This is a much better use of our torn clothes.

Now, I have learned that the lifecycle of clothes does not end in a trash can. They can continue to live as a warm blanket for someone in a faraway place who has lost everything. So next time I buy a new piece of clothing, I will first ask myself if it looks good on me. Then, "How can I make it look good on my planet?" This is called sustainability, and we can do this as kids too!

Japanese Traditions for Spring
by Abigail Herrington, 13
Posted May 29, 2019

Illustration by Stanislav Nedzelskyi, 13. Published in *Stone Soup* May/June 2009.

Spring is a time for new life. Japan demonstrates this through their Hanami festival and their story of Amaterasu and Ame-no-Uzume.

Hanami
Hanami in Japan is a festival celebrating the blooming of cherry blossoms, harkening the arrival of spring. The festival is a time for people to assemble and picnic under the trees. They eat *wagashi*, traditional Japanese sweets. Some of these sweets are *daifuku*, which is made from sweet rice flour that surrounds red bean paste, and *yokan*, a jellied confectionery made from red or white beans, sugar, and agar, which is a type of gelatin. A traditional beverage is *sakura* tea, which is tea made from cherry blossoms. Seasonally decorated teaware is also used.

The festivities usually last all day and into the night. The festival dates vary by location and year because the trees blossom at different rates. Ueno Park and Yoyogi Park in Tokyo are popular spots for cherry blossom viewing. Washington, DC, is also famous for its cherry blossom festivities. You can search online for the National Park Service's webpage on cherry blossom festivals.

Ever since the Heian Period, which lasted from 794-1185, the Japanese aristocracy has given parties to view blossoming flowers. In the Azuchi Momoyama Period, which lasted from 1568-1600, viewing parties spread in popularity to the remaining population. Short plays were performed, and women would wear brightly colored kimonos. With the dawn of the age of technology, "Sakura Forecasts" were broadcast online and on television. Today, pink dots cover maps of Japan showing where the cherry blossoms are. These forecasts are usually followed by information on finding the best viewing points, the areas where the seasons have finished, and where the seasons have begun.

Amaterasu and Ame-no-Uzume
Ame-no-Uzume or Uzume is the Shinto goddess of joy, happiness, and good health. She danced to bring the goddess of the sun, Amaterasu, back from where she was grieving. Amaterasu was hiding because her brutish brother grew jealous of her beauty and popularity and went on a rampage, killing one of Amaterasu's sacred animals. Amaterasu felt so violated and betrayed that she ran away and hid. However, Uzume's dancing filled Amaterasu with revelry and good humor, dissipating her grief and ensuring the return of spring and sunshine, bringing life and fertility. This myth is said to be symbolism for the return of spring after a long, cold winter.

I highly encourage checking out cherry blossom festivals. Who knows? You might have one near you!

Rats
by Louis Spindler, 9
Posted July 9, 2019

When you think of rats, you probably think of them as just a filthy animal living in the sewer and searching for food. But rats aren't quite what you think.

First of all, rats are in the family of rodents along with mice, gerbils, porcupines, chipmunks, beavers, muskrats, woodchucks, and squirrels. Capybaras are the largest rodent, and they can weigh up to 110 pounds.

The point is, there are many different species of rodents. In fact, there are 4,000 types of mammals and 1,500 of them are rodents.

Rats have managed to reproduce and survive for many years because they are the champions at survival. Rats can scale straight up a wall, and drop from a five-story building and live. They can also be flushed down a toilet and survive, and they can even climb straight up a drain pipe. Another amazing feat of rats is that they can stand on their hind legs and box with their front.

Also, unlike us humans, rats' teeth won't stop growing. If their teeth grow too large, the rat will die. They stop this by gnawing, which wears down their teeth. Gnawing is very easy for rats because they can gnaw through almost anything, and this is because they have teeth as sharp as chisels. They can bite down at a force of 7,000 pounds. That is as powerful as a fully grown crocodile's jaw force. By com-

Illustration by Indra Boving, 13. Published in *Stone Soup* September/October 2009.

parison, humans can only bite down at 270 pounds. This means rats can chew through steel and even concrete.

Humans and rats have constantly been at war with each other, mostly because we eat the same food and rats steal it. So over the years humans have learned to hate rats. The word rat (which was originated in Asia) even means evil. Also in Asia, rats stole a massive amount of food. They stole enough grain to fill a freight train as long as the US. Overall, rats have stolen a fourth of the human food supply. This has caused humans to hate most rodents as we tend to generalize or stereotype rats, or rodents, as evil creatures. Because of this, people have been cruel to rats. For example, there was a very popular sport called rat baiting which took place in America and Europe. People would gather in a large room where there were rows of benches set around a pit. Workers emptied bags full of rats into the pit. Then a fierce dog called a ratter would be tossed among them. People from the audience bet on how many rats the ratter could kill in a certain amount of time. Some breeders would breed albino rats so the audience could see the blood better. In 1895, Jenny Lind killed 500 rats in just over an hour. Around the same time, Joco The Wonder Dog earned the world record for killing 100 rats in five minutes. Of course this cruel sport is now illegal, and nowadays breeders breed rats for pets not for killing. In fact, more than 550,000 American families own pet rats and mice. From hearing this, you probably want to hear a less gross story, so

that's what I'm going to do. Rats and humans have also befriended each other. For example, during the Vietnam War there was an American prisoner who was very lonely and he could only talk to the guard. But one day a rat came in and the prisoner fed the rat. Very soon the rat and the prisoner became very close.

Later, the prisoner said, "The rat seemed to understand me when I talked."

Also, rats have proven themselves very useful. For example, there are landmine problems in many places because in war nearly every army uses landmines. In fact, the world has about 100 million bombs that have been buried, causing the death of many innocent people. Thankfully, the African giant pouched rat can detect a landmine more easily than a human's technology ever could. Because of this, people use these rats to detect bombs, and every time they find one they get a treat from a trainer. Weighing just three pounds, these rats are too light to set off any landmines. Another example is recently, scientists have used the rats' marvelous sense of smell to cure TB, a disease that killed two million people in 2005. Because of rats' amazing sense of smell, they can smell out TB in saliva samples from suspected victims. Laboratory workers can only analyze 20 saliva samples a day with microscopes, but a trained rat can analyze 120 to 150 an hour.

In many places, people eat rats and other rodents. Roman emperors used to serve their guests rodents dipped in honey. Another place where they serve rats is a restaurant in China that has a menu which mentions rat many times. Their menu includes rat with chestnut and duck, lotus seed rat stew, black bean rat, deep-fried lemon rat, rat soup (with potatoes and onions on the top). Also, there are many other rat-related foods. Some nutritionists think that rats are a solution for solving world hunger because there are so many rats and rat meat is rich in protein. Most people would think it is gross to eat rat, but a rat raised for eating isn't any more harmful to eat than a cow or chicken raised for the same purpose.

In conclusion, there are good things about rats and there are bad things about rats, and I think we should focus more on the good things.

Sources

Marrin, Albert (2006) *Oh, Rats!* New York: Puffin Books.

How the NBA Season Works
by Himank Chhaya, 11
Posted July 23, 2019

Detail of illustration by Spencer Hanson, 11. Published in *Stone Soup* July/August 2011.

A lot of people don't know how the NBA season works. Those people might be die-hard NBA fans, but they still are oblivious as to why their team made the playoffs and why they didn't. So, here it goes.

The season begins with preseason; those are kind of warm-up games, getting the teams ready for the rigors of the NBA season. After the eight games of the preseason end, the real fun begins.

The first game of the season is called the opener. That one game can decide a season, or do nothing at all. If Team A wins the game, they go to 1-0 in the standings, and Team B goes to 0-1. This keeps on going for all 82 games until the playoffs. There are multiple things in the standings, however, that I should bring to your attention. The first is a column that shows the amount of wins the teams are behind the first-seed team. The second column is an average of the wins and losses of the seasons. If a team won 60/82 games, then their average would be 0.77 percent. A perfect 1 percent would occur if a team won all 82 games. That's never happened—a 1 percent has never happened.

In the middle of the season, you get All-Star Weekend, which showcases the best talents in the NBA. Contests include the Dunk Contest, the Rising Stars Challenge, the Skills Challenge, and the game itself. Captains are selected and choose their players in a draft.

Let's go to the playoffs. Unlike football, where one game decides your season, the NBA uses a best-of-seven series. The teams are decided like this: the top eight teams in both conferences, the East and the West. The matchups are sorted by pitting the first seed v. the last seed, second v. seventh, third v. sixth, and fourth v. fifth. If Team A has a better record (i.e., 67/82 games), then they would get to have the first two games on their home floor, and then Team B would get the next two games on their home court. After that, it alternates. The winners of those matchups advance to the second round. The winners of those matchups reach the conference finals, and then the top team from the West and the East square off in the NBA Finals.

The latest winners (late July, 2019):

NBA Finals and Eastern Conference Finals	Toronto Raptors, 4-2, 4-2
Runner-up and Western Conference Finals	Golden State Warriors, 2-4, 4-0
Runner-up (East)	Milwaukee Bucks, 2-4
Runner-up (West)	Portland Trailblazers, 0-4
Second-round winners (East)	Toronto, Philadelphia, Milwaukee, Boston
Second-round winners (West)	Golden State, Houston, Portland, Denver
First round (East)	Milwaukee, Detroit, Toronto, Orlando, Boston, Indiana, Philadelphia, Brooklyn
First round (West)	Golden State Warriors, Los Angeles (Clippers), Portland, Oklahoma City, Denver, San Antonio, Houston, Utah

Can You See the Stars?
by Lucinda Chu, 12
Posted August 13, 2019

Detail of illustration by Leigh McNeil-Taboika, 13. Published in *Stone Soup* November/December 2011.

Stars have long been an important part of human culture and science, from astronomy to fiction to "Twinkle, Twinkle Little Star." However, one-third of humanity may never be able to see the cosmos, according to certain studies.

On June 10, 2016, Italian and American scientists published a global atlas on light pollution. According to the report, one-third of humanity, including 80% of Americans, will never be able to see the Milky Way! (Gasp!)

According to the online global atlas, most of the major cities in the USA, Europe, and the southeastern part of Asia are affected by this problem.

Light pollution is a little-known environmental issue caused by artificial lights in developed countries that swamp the night sky with a luminous fog, covering the many beautiful constellations and stars that many kids hope to see. (You can't exactly wish upon a shooting star to see them either, 'cause they're covered too.) And not only we are affected. Unnatural light confuses and exposes wild animals such as insects, birds, and sea turtles, often with fatal consequences. Moths keep swarming the porch light, night birds can't navigate properly, and the poor sea turtles are misled by all those bright bulbs you put at your beach houses.

Of course, we caused all this, so we reap what we sow. But if we don't stop this, soon nobody will ever see the stars again. So take a few simple steps to reduce light pollution and spread awareness about this problem. Turn off the lights when you're not using them. Shield your garden lights to the immediate area, reducing the amount of light to the minimum needed. You don't need to light up your whole house with a ridiculous amount of bulbs—even if you are afraid of the dark. Talk about this with your local town committee. Host fundraisers. And just wish upon a star.

The Cold Winter
by Lauren Giglia, 11
Posted September 16, 2019

It is Saturday morning, and Nellie yawns as she wakes up from her bed. The air feels crisp and cold in her room. It hurts to breathe. Hopefully dad just turned off the heater last night and can turn it back on again today. Last time, the power company shut off our heat, and it took a long time to get it turned back on. Those were very cold days.

Quickly dressing in long pants, a warm shirt, sweater, and socks, Nellie walks down the short hallway from her bedroom to the living area. "Momma, why is it so cold?" Nellie asks her mom, who is sitting at the kitchen table. "Nellie, good, you're bundled up. The power company turned off our heat. They turned the heat off for everyone on our block. I've been trying to figure out who still has heat at the Rosebud Reservation all morning. I haven't found anyone yet."

Nellie is cold all weekend, and worried. It's November, and the weather is only going to get worse in South Dakota. Would everyone on the entire Rosebud Native American Reservation freeze to death this winter? The power company turned off power for over 100 houses on the Rosebud Reservation, and they won't turn it back on until all bills are completely paid off. With no jobs and no extra money, Nellie didn't know what her family would do.

Nellie is always excited for school on Monday morning because her teacher, Ms. Smith, is so smart and inspiring, and really seems to care about her students. "Good morning, class!" sings Ms. Smith as they get seated. "Good morning, Ms. Smith!" the class sings back. The students all look around and seem relieved.

Ms. Smith asks the class, "Did any-

Photograph by Hanna Gustafson, 12. Published in *Stone Soup* January 2018.

thing exciting happen this weekend?" Nobody speaks. Ms. Smith asks again, "Nothing? Nothing interesting happened this weekend? If not, then let's get started on our math lesson." Nellie cautiously raises her hand, "Excuse me, Ms. Smith?"

"Yes Nellie. Did something interesting happen this weekend?"

"Ms. Smith, they turned the heat off again."

Ms. Smith looked confused. "What do you mean, Nellie? The heat is on, thankfully. It's going to be cold today!"

"No, Ms. Smith. The power company turned off our heat at home. They won't turn it back on until we pay off our bill."

Ms. Smith replied, "Oh. Nellie, I'm sorry to hear that. Let's talk about it after class."

"Ms. Smith? It's not just at my house."

"Oh? What do you mean?" asked Ms. Smith.

Nellie said quietly, "They turned off the power at all of our houses."

Nellie's classmates all started talking excitedly amongst themselves. They all confirmed that they'd been without heat since Friday, and that they all got the same message from the power company. They wouldn't get any power again until they paid their bills in full.

Ms. Victoria Smith watched her students talk about the power company, the lack of heat, and the coming winter. She needed to get to a quiet place so she could think of a way to help these children, but that couldn't happen until school let out. She needed to get through today's lessons first, and then she would try to think of a solution.

"OK, kids. We will try to figure out what to do about the heat problem later. For now, let's enjoy the heat in the classroom and get started on our lessons. Today we are going to start with working on our multiplication tables."

Victoria Smith is a young teacher at a school on the Rosebud Reservation. She is 26 years old, and recently graduated from Wellesley College near Boston, Massachusetts. Wellesley is a college for women, and it has a special motto, "Non Ministrari sed Ministrare." That means, "Not to be ministered unto, but to minister." Wellesley College's goal is to educate women who will make a difference in the world. That's why Victoria chose to become a teacher on the Rosebud Native American Reservation in South Dakota. Most of the families here live in poverty. They don't have access to education, jobs, money, or anything else to help improve their lives. Victoria hoped she could make a difference for her students.

Victoria had been thinking about her students' power problem all day. She corrected assignments after school let out, and now she was reading through Facebook before bed. She enjoys keeping up with her friends on Facebook, especially now that she's living in South Dakota, far away from her friends and family. As Victoria read through some posts, she came across some Wellesley message boards. Suddenly, Victoria had an idea. Since Wellesley is known for women who make a difference, the Wellesley graduates are an unusually helpful group. Maybe they would like to help Victoria's students get their heat back? It was worth a try.

Victoria quickly posted a message of her own on a Wellesley Facebook message board explaining the problem and asking for ideas. Then she turned her computer off and went to sleep.

Victoria woke up the next morning to her phone ringing loudly on her nightstand. She answered the phone, "Hello?" A voice replied, "VICTORIA. It's Keisha." Keisha was Victoria's roommate at Wellesley during her first year. "Hi Keisha! It's so early here. Is everything ok?" Keisha replied, "Have you checked Facebook this morning? A bunch of people responded to your post last night. You have hundreds of women asking if they can donate money to help your students!" "Really?" asked Victoria. "I'll check it out right now!"

The next few weeks are a whirlwind for Victoria, Nellie, and the rest of the students. A handful of Wellesley graduates took charge of organizing payments from hundreds of other Wellesley graduates. Those women paid off the families' power bills one by one. It was thousands of dollars, and it took a lot of their time. They had to get each account number, and the power company did not make the process easy, but they did it.

This is based on a true story about my mom's friends and how they helped the families on the Rosebud Reservation in South Dakota last winter. Her Wellesley College classmates are my heroes. I have seen my mom and her Wellesley friends do acts like this one many times, for many different people. They collect money, clothes, food, and anything else that's needed as soon as they're asked. Just two weeks ago, we filled two big boxes with my books and mailed them to the children at Rosebud because they did not have enough books to read.

The Wellesley graduates don't even know the people they help most of the time, but they help anyway, just because someone asks. They learn about a problem, and they try to solve

it. They often succeed. I want to be like them—a woman who makes a difference in the world—in big ways and small.

Thoughts on Jewish Refugees in Shanghai
by Alicia Xin, 13
Posted September 23, 2019

Divided Island by Sofia Kakoulli. Published in *Stone Soup* March/April 1993.

When people think about the Holocaust and Jewish refugees during WWII, they rarely think about Shanghai. For a long time, I didn't even know Shanghai was open to Jewish refugees at that time. Recently, I watched the documentary *Survival in Shanghai*. That documentary featured many Holocaust survivors who told of their escape to Shanghai. When I watched it, I couldn't help but think of the current Syrian refugee crisis and how my country, the US, doesn't allow many Syrian refugees to cross our borders. Like Shanghai did more than 80 years ago, the US should help those people in need, even if we do have problems of our own.

The Holocaust was one of the most horrific and notable genocides in history. It began when Adolf Hitler started to persecute Jews as a scapegoat for Germany's financial problems. That persecution became widespread in 1933 when he rose to power in Nazi Germany. Jewish homes and businesses were smashed, and synagogues were burned. Many Jewish people were put in concentration camps and were then killed in numerous ways, including starvation, gas chambers, and overwork. As a result, over 6 million Jews were killed in the Holocaust. As Jews tried to flee from Germany, they had no place to go, for not many countries wanted to rouse Germany. However, He Fengshan, a Chinese diplomat, issued Chinese visas to Jewish immigrants. The exact number of visas he issued is unknown, but he gave out 1,200 over the first three months of his position, so the number is believed to be in the tens of thousands.

One must realize during that time, China had its own hardships to deal with. The Japanese, allied with the Germans in WWII, were occupying much of China, including Shanghai. Despite their own mistreatment, the Chinese pushed their misfortunes and grievances away in order to help others. They sacrificed money and time to help refugees settle in to their new homes. The Chinese opened their arms and gave their kindness and food, even when they barely had enough food for their own families.

"What impressed me most was the welcome we received," said Jared

Cohen, one of the Holocaust survivors. " . . . they accepted us, they were happy with us, and we were respected."

Willa Sassoon, another refugee, recalled her friendly neighbors, who invited her to their home every day to play with their daughter after school. "They more or less adopted me," she said.

Today, Syria is in the middle of a civil war. Thirteen-million Syrians have lost their homes and need a safe shelter. Since 2015, 18,000 Syrians received US visas. However, in 2017, the US president, Donald Trump, imposed a travel ban on six Muslim countries, including Syria. He said terrorists may be hidden in a crowd of Muslim immigrants. That ban stopped the flow of Muslim immigrants of many ethnicities.

America, as a developed country, has more resources than most other countries and should take the responsibility to help others in need. Many Americans believe Syrians would commit crime and would be a bad addition to our society. However, that is not true. After the Syrian civil war broke out in 2011, ordinary people just like you and me lost their homes overnight. Hardworking adults and innocent kids were placed in refugee camps. Men and women who could bring benefit to our society are refused by the US government a chance to rebuild their lives. A study on Syrian immigrants by *The Washington Post* shows that Syrian immigrants have been a "highly entrepreneurial group." Eleven percent of Syrian immigrants in the US are entrepreneurs, compared to 3% of the people born in the US. Also, according to the Center for American Progress, all immigrants in the US for less than 10 years have an average annual income of $30,000, while recent Syrian immigrants earn average wages of $43,000 a year.

One of the biggest fears Americans have about Syrian immigrants is terrorism. What if a terrorist sneaks into the US by pretending to be an immigrant? According to The Nation Institute and The Center for Investigative Reporting, there have been about 90 deaths caused by Islamist terrorists in the US from 2008 to 2016. That may be a lot, but in only 2016, there have been 37,461 deaths caused by cars in the US. Does that mean we should be afraid of cars, and ban them? No, we should use precautions to make our roads safer, educate drivers, and enforce driving laws. Similarly, instead of cutting off the flow of immigrants, we should enhance border control, intelligence work, and law enforcement to minimize terrorist attacks. In fact, even with the travel ban, terrorists may still come into our country illegally, so blocking immigrants is not an effective strategy.

I live in an active Jewish community called Scarsdale, New York. At school, during the holidays, many people go around saying "Happy Hanukkah" instead of "Merry Christmas." Many of my friends are Jewish, and they are so nice, dedicated to study, and kindhearted. I hate to imagine what would have happened to them had they been living in Nazi Germany. I would have definitely helped them, even if it meant endangering myself. To put them up for mistreatment and choose not to help would have made me hate myself for the rest of my life. The Jewish people during the Holocaust and the Syrians today could be your neighbors, classmates or friends. They are just ordinary people like you and me.

In summary, Americans should allow Syrian immigrants into our borders like the people of Shanghai did for the Jews. We should look past stereotypes and fear of terrorism, and lend helping hands to less fortunate people. If the people of Shanghai were able to support Jewish immigrants on their meager resources, Americans should do so too.

Imaginary Worlds and How to Create Them
by Marco Lu, 12
Posted October 30, 2019

Detail of "Sky City" by Li Lingfei, 8. Published in *Stone Soup* March 2018.

Every story needs a setting. A world,

a universe even. And if your story doesn't take place here, you'll have to create the world. This is worldbuilding. Worldbuilding is like building an iceberg. Only a tiny bit shows, but this piece is supported by the rest of the iceberg. The purpose of worldbuilding is to make your world deeper, to make it more realized and thus more immersive.

There are two main approaches to worldbuilding: narrow and wide. Narrow worldbuilding involves building a world around only the elements shown in the story. This has the advantage of requiring very little worldbuilding. However, the world may feel shallow or unrealistic without deeper construction. This type of worldbuilding is good for when you already have a premise in mind and want to expand on it. By contrast, wide worldbuilding creates a world from the bottom up, fleshing out every aspect of the world. This can create a very realistic world and is good for when you are planning to create a new world from scratch. However, it does require much more work. It should be remembered that these are on the two ends of a spectrum and are not absolutes.

Worldbuilding can also vary when it comes to the level of detail. Typically, aspects crucial to the plot are given much more depth, while more tertiary aspects are outlined in broad strokes. More dedicated worldbuilders, though, can create a vast world in great detail, in the vein of Tolkien. Again, it should be remembered that these are on the ends of a spectrum.

There are many things to consider when creating a new world. I find it useful to start by creating a basic world map: planets, continents, cities, etc. This helps keep continuity and also can establish the interactions of political entities in the world. In our world, geography affects many aspects of life, from military engagement to voting, and thus a map is crucial to creating a new world.

You should also create multiple distinct political entities. These can create essential conflict and also shape the world around them. These can vary from local village councils to massive nations on a planetary scale. Of course, these are not completely necessary. A story with a smaller scope may not deal with higher level politics.

Another aspect shaped by the political entities is the culture of the area. Many places in our world have unique and diverse cultures, and this can be reflected in a fictional world. A place's traditions, clothing, holidays, religion, etc. are determined by things such as its history and people.

Of course, all the things I have mentioned here are only recommendations to create a world more believable in our terms. You don't need to follow them, and worldbuilding can be accomplished in many different ways. In the meantime, try building a new world.

Forts of Play
by Keshav Ravi, 7
Posted November 23, 2018

Detail of "Connected with Nature" by Antara Gangwal, 10. Published in *Stone Soup* July/August 2018.

Forts, to me, are a great place to hide away! I like to build forts because they are my little place where nobody can bother me. Forts make me feel independent; and away from all noise.

I've been building forts all my childhood, and I still do. I build my forts almost always in corners because every corner in my house has a chair, a soft thing or a window for light. One kind of fort I make is the bedsheet-supported-by-pillow fort. Other times, I find spaces and just build on them. Like the time I found a bush with an entrance and a great climbing spot. I added a trapdoor (using a branch that can bend and won't crack with weight on it), and a place to store plants (example, reeds). This spot is one of my favorites to still visit, behind a tree in the frontyard of my home. Inside the home, at my pillows-and-sheets-fort, I often make a little burrow with tunnels, and passages to small blanket-pillow rooms. I have turned even my bottom bunkbed into a fort of many rooms— a mansion palace!

Once built, I love to read in my fort. Some forts I've built have even had enough space to run around! I sometimes have a nice nap in my fort. All I can say is I'm really happy in a fort. I wish I could be there all day.

Book Reviews

Coraline by Neil Gaiman
Reviewed by Soohong Jeon, 12
Posted May 1, 2019

@stonesoupbykids

The amazing book I read this summer was *Coraline*, by Neil Gaiman. I found this book so enjoyable because there are so many surprising twists. This book starts with a curious and adventurous girl named Coraline Jones and her family moving from Pontiac, Michigan, to the Pink Palace, an extremely old building in Ashland, Oregon. Coraline keeps whining to her parents that she is so bored until one day, there is a horrible thunderstorm. With her parents busy working on a garden catalog, she finally decides to explore her new house. She keeps exploring until she tries to open the large, carved door in the drawing room. The door was locked, so she takes the iron key and unlocks the door. She expects a new room, but surprisingly, there is just a pile of bricks. That night, she quietly walks to the same door and

opens it. However, this time, instead of a pile of bricks, there was an unusual hallway. She keeps walking down, and when she opens the door, she sees her mother cooking. Or was it her mother? When her "mom" turned around, Coraline notices something weird about her. Instead of human eyes, there were black, round buttons! There, she met her button-eye dad and for the first week, they were very nice to her. However, one night her mother tries to persuade her into replacing her normal eyes with buttons. Since I do not want to spoil the book, I'll just say that throughout the story, there are many surprising and chilling twists that will make you jump out of your chair.

I think that the book *Coraline* is both dark fantasy and fairy tale. A fairy tale is a story with magical elements, and some of its common characteristics include enchanted settings (such as forests and weird castles/buildings) and clearly defined good and evil characters, a completely understandable problem, climax, and resolution. *Coraline* has all of those characteristics. Coraline and her family live in a creepy, old building, and a significant part of the book occurs in Coraline's garden. Also, clearly, the good characters are Coraline and Coraline's parents and the evil character is Coraline's fake mom. Lastly, *Coraline*'s problem, a climax, and a resolution is so clear. However, *Coraline* is not a Disney fairy tale but is more of a Grimms' fairy tale. The reason I am saying I think *Coraline* is both dark fantasy and fairy tale is this: as I said, Coraline is similar to the Grimms' fairy tales. Grimms' fairy tales are very dark, creepy, and have a lot of twists. *Coraline* has all of those traits. Dark fantasy is mainly explored in *Coraline* through the setting of both the real world and the other world. Though both settings can be very different at the start, when all the sacred truths are revealed, both settings are very similar. They have very unusual, mysterious, and chilling settings, which are definitely primary elements of dark fantasy. Even until the end, *Coraline*'s setting retains a supernatural atmosphere. Throughout the book, scary and surprising twisted parts come out, making it more of a dark fantasy. As you can see, this is why I think *Coraline* is both a dark fantasy and a fairy tale.

Coraline was a very amusing and super enjoyable novel. Though it scared me so much and sometimes gave me nightmares, this would definitely be a book I would recommend to people. In addition, I would recommend this book to people who are over 10 years old and people who are not scared of horrors. The reason is that this book can really shock someone and even terrorize someone's mental state. If you cannot bear to see, read, and imagine scary things, then please be alerted. However, if you liked *Alice in Wonderland*, you will enjoy reading this book. Those who plan to read this book, you are in for a scare!

Coraline by Neil Gaiman. HarperCollins, 2002.

Shouting at the Rain
by Lynda Mullaly Hunt
Reviewed by Vandana Ravi, 12
Posted May 5, 2019

@stonesoupbykids

"We're like tea bags. In hot water, we just get stronger and stronger." These two sentences from *Shouting at the Rain* by Lynda Mullaly Hunt echoed in my mind for days after I read them. The memorable simile seemed to sum up the essence of the book—and, ultimately, of life. I was impressed, enchanted—and when I realized that the words came from a 12 year-old kid like myself, I was under the spell of a new favorite character.

Delsie McHill dislikes surprises; that's why she loves tracking the weather, so that she can always be ready for what's coming. But one summer her life is beset with unexpected changes. She has always lived with her kindhearted grandmother in Cape Cod, but now she begins to look at her life with new eyes and wonder why her parents abandoned her. A newcomer causes her to question the game show-loving, tag sale-shopping, quiet life which she and her Grammy lead. Most painfully, her best friend is growing away from her, and she is left suddenly and starkly alone. Luckily, Delsie has plenty of friends and neighbors who—although she doesn't realize it—comprise the "normal" family she longs for. And through her experiences, Delsie finds out that people aren't just what they seem on the outside—they are made up of the layers of history within.

The thing that makes Shouting at the Rain so satisfying, yet intriguing, to read is that—unlike with many other books—the main idea is never confirmed in one climax paragraph but hinted in small ways throughout the story. Finding one of these keys to the theme is like discovering a hidden gift, giving the reader a feeling of accomplishment which isn't easily found in most middle-grade books. However, clues like the description of a boat whose top coat chips away to show a rainbow of different-colored paint layers underneath, or the main character's obsession with Strong Shoulder jars, cannot be connected to the main theme with absolute certainty because there is never any validation: novels don't have answer keys. Despite this, one of the joys of reading is the search for meaning beyond the obvious, and the author of this book is adept at providing this pleasurable literary treasure hunt.

Another thing that impressed me about Shouting at the Rain is the author's use of the "show-not-tell" writing tool; in other words, the art of showing a character's emotions through their actions. Strikingly, not once in the book did the author give away any character's feelings in a single word, but painstakingly described physical actions: staring at shoes, standing straighter, bouncing on toes. More than once, I had to stop reading and consult my knowledge of human body language—what are people feeling when they avoid someone's gaze? And do shining eyes actually entail tears? The writing style of Shouting at the Rain forced me to rethink what I took for granted about how a person's mental state correlates with their actions. In a way, it reshaped the way I look at the world. That is the power of books, and why I enjoyed this one so much.

"In hot water, we just get stronger and stronger." This is a truth that applies to everyone. Shouting at the Rain brought it to life for me, as it brought to life many other truths, skillfully woven together into a story I'll never forget. Most of all, Shouting at the Rain reminded me of how magical a good book can be, and I hope it does the same for you.

Shouting at the Rain by Lynda Mullaly Hunt. Nancy Paulsen books, 2019.

The Ramona Quimby Series
by Beverly Cleary
Reviewed by Tara Prakash, 12
Posted June 5, 2019

@stonesoupbykids

The Ramona Series are the type of books that you will just keep pulling out of your bookshelf to read, any day, any age, just because.

Maybe it's because author Beverly Cleary developed the characters so well in our minds, it's as if they are your best friend.

Maybe it's because the adventures Ramona gets into are so relatable and funny.

Or maybe it's just because these books reflect life. Messy, funny, scary at times, but always coming back stronger each time.

I think what won this book over for me was just how much of a character Ramona was. I can't even fully put it into words—it was unbelievable. This had never happened with any other book

before, just *Ramona*. She is just such a charismatic girl, filled with spunk and adventure, with such a BIG imagination, always hoping to be excited by the everyday things.

Her experiences push her forward, and throughout the books you can see her growth. During the stories, I would practically hear Ramona's voice echoing in my ears. It was as if she was alive, and words, just the sheer power of language, had never done that before.

I think what also made Ramona such a character was her family. Her sister, Beatrice, christened "Beezus," is the typical sister. Annoying, mean at times, and kind at the perfect moments. She and Ramona have the usual relationship, and you can see both girls evolve and change from their experiences with each other.

Both of them have their own problems, Beatrice with the drama that comes with junior high and Ramona with the feeling of never growing up, and throughout the book you can sense that they trust each other and support each other more, with secrets or just things both siblings want to conceal and hide.

For example, when Beezus went to the mall with her friends, she got her ears pierced but without her parents' consent. Worried about what her mom and dad would think, she told Ramona what she had done before she told her parents because she trusted her sister —that trust had been built like a wall of bricks, day after day, placing each brick on top of the other.

Ramona's father is a caring, gentle, hilarious man. He loves to draw and at home is a cartoon artist, drawing comical illustrations on her lunch bag while struggling in the first few books to get a job after he got laid off at an agency. When Ramona gets into her mayhem and accidents that don't always result well, her dad is there to hear her out, give her a hand, and help her through whatever knot she is in. Always.

Ramona's mother is more serious but has an air about her that just makes you feel comforted and happy. She is understanding, just like Ramona's father, and knows what her children need.

Aunt Beatrice, her mom's sister, is always there for Ramona. When Ramona is upset or frustrated with how something is going, whether she feels like she isn't helping her father, whether her sister has called her a pest, whether she fell off the unicycle her neighbor Howie let her ride, Aunt Beatrice is always there with a joke, or a small gift, or the perfect words or story, that make Ramona feel better instantly. She is to Ramona a one-of-a-kind ointment to the scrapes and burns that Ramona gets.

Ramona also builds friendships at her school, and throughout the series, you can see how she grows in the social arena, opening up, creating new circles, and expanding her universe.

Her neighbor and friend Howie is adventurous as well, and always open to trying new things. They get to know each other throughout the series very well, as in the earlier part of the series, Ramona went to his house every day after school until her parents got home from work. One part of the book that stands out is the part where Howie lets Ramona ride his brand-new unicycle, and he takes Ramona's bike. Ramona crashes head over heels, and she ends up being okay, but it's one of their many adventures throughout the book. They also stomp through the neighborhood one day in the pouring rain, with handmade stilts made with buckets and yarn, screaming "100 bottles of beer on the wall!"

As each book in the series ages, so does Ramona. She grows up and matures, and she has different kinds of adventures, not like the kind when she was doing a car wash on her neighbor's car (Howie's uncle), and the car rolls off the sandbag and into the shed, where over 50 buckets of paint topple onto it, causing the what was once a black Jeep to look more like an ice cream truck. These are just a few of the adventures of spunky Ramona! She meets Daisy, a kind, funny girl remarkably like her name. They grow close as Ramona nears the age of 13, which is where the book series ends.

What I loved about Ramona is that through all of her adventures, she was always trying to make the world a better place and make someone else happy. When the buckets of paint dumped on her neighbor's car, she had been doing a car wash to raise money for her family because her dad had been suddenly laid off. Everything she does is because of an outcome that she has in her mind, but more often than not, it's not what she expects, which is what makes this such a colorful, unique book that stands out on the shelves.

If you like a series in which the characters are vividly developed, have a lot of funny adventures, and are always trying to make the world a better place through them, then the *Ramona Series* is for you!

Ramona Quimby Series by Beverly Cleary. HarperCollins, 2016.

Dry by Neal and Jarrod Shusterman
Reviewed by Nina Vigil, 12
Posted August 6, 2019

@stonesoupbykids

How many of you can say that you read a book that made you thirsty? Few, to be certain; that's rarely the effect a book aims to accomplish! (And if it did, it likely wasn't intentional.) Yet now I can say that I have read a book that made me genuinely thirsty on purpose. *Dry,* by Neal and Jarrod Shusterman, is harrowing, thrilling, and feels all too real.

Dry begins in a small Southern California neighborhood. Alyssa Morrow, her younger brother, Garrett, her parents, and her dog Kingston are living a very normal life. California's drought is continuing on for longer than usual, but some laws have been put into place in an effort to conserve water. The laws are working, and California is doing fine. That is, until Arizona and Nevada cut off the Colorado River. California has become so dependent on the river, but now water is limited to what they've already got. And that's not enough for everyone. As water runs out, friends and strangers alike turn on each other in an effort to survive. When Alyssa and Garrett's parents disappear, they're forced to make an alliance with their slightly nutty survivalist neighbor Kelton McCracken. And as things get progressively worse, the trio will need to find other means of getting water, and they'll pick up some more passengers on their quest.

Dry is an addictive story. Once you pick it up, you keep thinking about doing something else, but you don't want to put it down, and pretty soon you've been reading for hours. Not only is it addictive, but it evokes real emotions. You're so worried about the main characters that it feels like you're worrying about your best friends. *Dry* is also very realistic. The symptoms of dehydration, for instance, are described in a way you can imagine, and consistent with science. The public's reaction to the "Tap-Out" (as it is called) and the following turmoil seems real, like something that could conceivably happen anywhere.

The story is told in a form I'd never seen used before. The narration switches between the main characters, but in addition to that, some "snapshots" are included that provide fresh perspectives on the situation in brief moments from different people's lives. Among those are a news reporter, a family trying to escape on a plane, and a student waiting for airlifted water. The snapshots really broaden the view of the situation as a whole, and it's nice to have a quick break from the story of the main characters.

I would recommend *Dry* for anybody 12+. I'd recommend it for everyone, but it does have some bad language in it. Nevertheless, it went above and beyond my initial expectations, and it will do the same for even those with the highest of reading standards!

Dry by Neal and Jarrod Shusterman. Simon & Schuster Books for Young Readers, 2018.

Contests

So far this year we have awarded prizes in two contests, described below, and published the winning work from 2018's Concrete Poetry and Flash Fiction contests. Congratulations to all of our winners.

As the 2019 *Annual* goes to print, we are about to close our current personal narrative contest run in partnership with the Society of Young Inklings. If you are reading this in 2019, check the Contests page at Stonesoup.com to see if there is still time to enter—and if it's 2020 or later, check it to see the winners and find out what contest is running today!

CLIMATE CHANGE STORIES FOR PODCASTING

We ran this contest in spring, in partnership with AV Education, a South African nonprofit organization that produces the By Kids For Kids—Story Time podcast. We challenged our writers to produce an original short story with a strong narrative and several characters that could be dramatized as a podcast episode. In the process of judging this contest, we realized that what works for the podcast and what works for a magazine are not quite the same thing. We published all of the top-placed stories on the *Stone Soup* website, and Olivia Park's "No Longer Blue" (first place) and Sabrina Guo's "Lilith's Quest" (honorable mention) were both recorded as podcast episodes.

First Place
"No Longer Blue" by Olivia Park, 12

Second Place
"The Dreamer" by Claire Nagle, 12

Third Place
"A Splash of Water" by Tara Prakash, 12

Honorable Mentions
"Back in the Days" by Gemma Yin, 11
"Lilith's Quest" by Sabrina Guo, 13

This contest, for long-form writing in multiple genres, topics, and forms (novels; poetry; or short story collections, memoirs, or other prose) ran from May to late August. Although we were only able to give official recognition to a handful of writers, all of us were blown away by the care and effort put into these manuscripts. Writing a book takes time, patience, and dedication, and these writers proved to us that they have these qualities in spades. Once again, as with previous contests, we were moved by how many of them dealt with climate change in one way or another. Our winning novel, by Abhimanyu Sukhdial, *Three Days Till EOC*, takes a powerful, creative approach to this topic, as does Analise Braddock in many of the poems in her collection *The Golden Elephant*. Meanwhile, in her poetry collection *Searching for Bow and Arrows*, Tatiana Rebecca Shrayer explores themes of historical and political loss alongside the enduring beauty and solace found in nature. Finally, in *Elana*, Hannah Nami Gajcowski takes us on a mad, magical adventure through an alternate universe.

First Place
Three Days Till EOC by Abhimanyu Sukhdial, 11 (Novel)

Second Place
The Golden Elephant by Analise Braddock, 8 (Poetry)
Searching for Bow and Arrows by Tatiana Rebecca Shrayer, 11 (Poetry)

Third Place
Elana by Hannah Nami Gajcowski, 9 (Novel)

Honorable Mentions
Leather Journal, Abhainn Bajus, 14 (Poetry)
The Hidden Key, Peri Gordon, 9 (Novel)
Frozen Nocturne, Sabrina Guo, 13 (Poetry)
The Demisers, Zoe Keith, 11 (Novel)
Last Birthday Boy, Olivia Ladell, 13 (Novel)
Family of Spies, Micah Lim, 10 (Novel)
Escape the War, Priyanka Nambiar, 13 (Novel)
A Brief Encounter with Chaos, Anyi Sharma, 11 (Stories)

The winners' books will be published in 2020.

Donations

Stone Soup is produced by the Children's Art Foundation, a 501(c)(3) educational nonprofit organization registered in California. While production of the magazine and website is largely funded by subscriptions, donations help us to expand our work. Our donation levels are each named for a well-known author or artist who, like our *Stone Soup* contributors, did remarkable work as children, before going on to adult greatness.

Many donors responded to our specific appeals in 2019, especially our ongoing refugee project, as well as our drive to bring *Stone Soup* to children in marginalized communities. We also received funds for the first time from Amazon Smile, as well as some corporate matched funds.

Since the production of last year's *Stone Soup Annual* in early November 2018, we have received donations from the following kind individuals (and others who wished to remain anonymous). We thank all of them sincerely for their generosity.

Charles Dickens (over $1,500)
Aileen S. Andrew Foundation
Anu Sukhdial

Jane Austen (up to $1,500)
Sabrina Guo
Spencer Guo
Marquette Bank

Edith Wharton (up to $500)
Gerry Mandel
The Bohne Foundation
Rachel Thornton

Albrecht Dürer (up to $250)
Roger Forman
Yi Lei
Cynthia Werth

Charlotte Brontë (up to $100)
Diane Aboulafia
Tara Brown
Therese Calegari
Richard Cohn
Coventry Edwards-Pitt
Barry & Denise Itzkowitz (in memoriam Lillian Perlman)
Raymond Norris

Charlotte Brontë (up to $100)
continued from previous page
Ziggy Rendler-Bregman
Doug Roberts
Brion Sprinsock & Kristine Albrecht
J. G. Stevenson

Margaret Atwood (up to $50)
E. Auberg
Gail Chesler
Joan Eisenstodt
David Harvey
Julie Minnis
Jennifer Rinterknecht
Rikke Vognsen & Bob Beaird (in memoriam Lillian Perlman)

Daisy Ashford (up to $25)
Natalie Agraz
Lisa Applegate
Annie Barentine
Anna Birman
Antoinette Benedetto
Terese Bridges
Jenhau Chen
Heather Davison
Noelle Frerichs
Debbie Gibson
Anne Githens
Alicia Jones
Laura Moran
Linda Roettger
Sharyl Ross (in memoriam Lillian Perlman)
Wes Rowe
Svetlana Rowell
Kim Sauvageot
Lucas Van Lenten
Alicia Vigil
Ekaterina de Vil
Kristina Wilson